O
VATICAN!

Also by PAUL HOFMANN

ROME: THE SWEET, TEMPESTUOUS LIFE

'O VATICAN!

A Slightly Wicked View of the Holy See

PAUL HOFMANN

CONGDON & WEED, INC.   New York

Copyright © 1984 by Paul Hofmann

Library of Congress Cataloging in Publication Data

Hofmann, Paul, 1912–
O Vatican! : a slightly wicked view of the Holy See.

Includes index.
1. Papacy.   2. Vatican.   3. Catholic Church—
Doctrinal and controversial works. I. Title.
BX955.2.H56 1983 262'.13 83-7639
ISBN 0-86553-101-3
ISBN 0-312-92597-2 (St. Martin's Press)

Published by Congdon & Weed, Inc.
298 Fifth Avenue, New York, N.Y. 10001

Distributed by St. Martin's Press
175 Fifth Avenue, New York, N.Y. 10010

Published simultaneously in Canada by Methuen Publications
2330 Midland Avenue, Agincourt, Ontario M1S 1P7

All Rights Reserved
Printed in the United States of America
Designed by Irving Perkins
First Edition

AUTHOR'S NOTE

THIS IS A book about the people who inhabit the Vatican. It is about what they do in this world center of enduring, though intangible, power and influence, and about occasional fine-spun intrigue, as observed over more than four decades.

I was born in Vienna, into the Roman Catholic Church, and served as an altar boy at mass in the Votive Church every morning before elementary-school classes. Later I became editor-in-chief of the weekly newspaper of the Catholic action movement in the Vienna archdiocese, *Katholisches Leben.* The annexation of Austria into Hitler's Third Reich in 1938 forced the suspension of that newspaper, and prompted me to emigrate to Italy. Thirty years later I became a United States citizen.

Somewhere along the way, however, I became an agnostic. Yet, I retained my interest in, and familiarity with, the Church of Rome, exasperating though I often find its corporate headquarters. I have lived in the Italian capital, off and on, for many years. I visited the Vatican hundreds of times (occasionally only to meet with tedium or frustration) when I served as Rome correspondent for the *New York Times* and as chief of its Rome Bureau. I also spoke often with cardinals, apostolic nuncios, and other high churchmen, as well as with simple priests, missionaries, and nuns of all continents.

This book, which might be considered a "sociology" of the

Vatican, is based largely on such personal contacts and private conversations. They took place under five popes—Pius XII, who reigned from 1939 to 1958; John XXIII (1958–1963); Paul VI (1963–1978); John Paul I, who was head of the church for 33 days in 1978; and John Paul II, who was elected in October of that year. I had occasion to speak to each of these pontiffs, except John Paul I, and have been in touch, in some cases over long periods of time, with close aides of all five.

Most of the sources for this book must remain anonymous or be described only vaguely. Anyone seeking facts about the Vatican, especially for publication, is struck by the personnel's general reticence. When asking straight questions, even about apparently innocuous things, one often encounters something like shocked defensiveness, as if the Holy See had guilty secrets to hide. To obtain information about the papacy and the activities carried out in its name, at times I was obliged to resort to techniques I had used when reporting for the *New York Times* from countries under dictatorial rule—extrapolation, patient weighing and correlating of seemingly unconnected details, looking for the missing pieces in a jigsaw puzzle.

When outsiders first come into contact with the Vatican they are struck by how much attention it pays to administrative, bureaucratic, legal, and political business, and how relatively little it seems to care for transcendental matters. This should explain why the reader will find plenty of mundane material in these pages rather than descriptions of the Vatican's spiritual life. It may seem as though I am reporting on one of the multinational corporations or the United Nations. But the Vatican *is* a complex business.

This book, by one who is neither a Roman Catholic faithful nor a militant anticlerical, attempts to depict everyday life in a unique enclave that, owing to papal authority and worldwide interests, has an impact of universal importance. Yet at the same time this enclave is very Italian, even parochially Roman, in its atmosphere, despite the presence of a non-Italian pope.

CONTENTS

AUTHOR'S NOTE   V

1   POWERHOUSE AT ST. PETER'S   1
A State Like No Other   ◆   *Court and Curia*

2   VICAR AND MASTER   15
A Waning Myth   ◆   *Down to Earth*   ◆   *Charisma from Poland*

3   CARDINAL POWER   49
Club of the Scarlet Hats   ◆   *Precedence and Privilege*   ◆   *The Ways of
the Holy Spirit*

4   THE CHURCH'S MANDARINS   82
The World's Oldest Bureaucracy   ◆   *Disgruntled Bishops*   ◆   *What a
Nuncio Does*   ◆   *Hard Work at the Top*   ◆   *Papal Chief of Staff*

5   PAPAL KITCHEN CABINET   127
Puissant Virgin   ◆   *Good Pope John's "Shadow"*   ◆   *Milan Mafia*   ◆
The Polish Network

6   MAMMON AT THE HOLY SEE   160
The Pope's Spending Money   ◆   *The Cardinals Ask Questions*   ◆
Pence and Properties   ◆   *Pontifical Portfolio*   ◆   *A Bulwark Bank*   ◆
The Pope's "Gorilla"   ◆   *God's Banker*

7   LOBBYING IN THE SACRED PALACES   208
The Embattled "First Legion"   ◆   *A Gentle General*   ◆   *Ignatian
Obedience*   ◆   *God's Octopus*   ◆   *Apostolate of Penetration*

8   PITFALLS OF VATICANOLOGY   243
Spies Around the Pope ◆ *Invented Secrets* ◆ *Reading Between the Lines*

9   PRINCES, SWITZERS, LABOR ACTIVISTS   271
Pomp and Circumstance ◆ *Halberds and Mace* ◆ *"Solidarity" at the Holy See*

10   THE VATICAN OF TOMORROW   294

INDEX   297

CHAPTER 1

POWERHOUSE AT ST. PETER'S

A DUTCH PRIEST, the late Reverend Cornelius Rijk, who had been secretary of a new office in the pontifical bureaucracy set up to promote better relations between Roman Catholics and Jews, once told me: "In the Vatican I hear all the time about the Holy Father. Nobody ever mentions Jesus Christ."

The pope himself, however, does speak of the Almighty, the Son of God and the Holy Spirit, of the Virgin Mary, the apostles, the martyrs, and the saints in his public utterances. He invokes them when he imparts apostolic benediction in a recurrent and overfamiliar scene: the pope, a miter on his head, standing on the central balcony of St. Peter's to bless the crowd in the piazza below. The people in one of the world's most illustrious squares cross themselves and, in Mediterranean enthusiasm that also seizes visitors from colder climes, clap their hands and cheer, *"Viva il Papa!"*

Many of them have just attended pontifical high mass in the largest church in Christendom. They have heard the Sistine Choir chant "Tu Es Petrus!" (Thou Art Peter) at the beginning of the rite, as the head of the Roman Catholic Church solemnly proceeded down the aisle to the Altar of the Confession, which rises theatrically above the presumed burial place of the Prince of the Apostles.

Those who believe that the supreme pontiff indeed "is Peter,"

1

the vicar of Jesus Christ on earth, will thus be stirred when they receive his benediction. Some will fall to their knees on the cobblestones of St. Peter's Square; pilgrims from far away will have tears in their eyes. Others in the congregation may be impressed, even stunned, by the splendor of the vestments, the music and the singing, the intricate liturgy, the fragrance of the incense, and the emotional reaction of the faithful.

One of the globe's great religious shrines, the Vatican, stages these opulent and gripping shows year-round—its canonizations, beatifications, consistories, requiems, and other sacred dramas, and every now and then even the funeral of a pope and the inauguration of his successor. No other faith produces such pageants with such frequency—which despite their venerable history seem tailor-made for video.

There is, of course, much more to the papacy and the Vatican. During pontifical mass the pontiff delivers a homily; he speaks again before the benediction from the balcony of St. Peter's; he addresses the pilgrims who flock to St. Peter's Square at noon every Sunday before he blesses them from a window in the Apostolic Palace; he delivers allocutions to the assembled cardinals or bishops; he welcomes the participants in his weekly general audience, often several thousands, and discusses some tenet of the faith for their benefit; he talks to many groups of visitors, and his remarks are published afterward; and during his travels he may give half a dozen speeches each day he is away from Rome. As if the constant barrage of pontifical oratory were not enough, a steady flow of encyclicals, apostolic letters and exhortations, messages to churchmen and world leaders, and other papal pronouncements pours out of the Vatican.

Sometimes the utterances by the head of the Roman Catholic Church are widely quoted and acclaimed, as were those of John XXIII. At other times, papal statements set off violent controversy, as did Paul VI's 1968 encyclical on birth control. All too often, lengthy documents over which the pope and teams of experts and speech writers have labored for weeks are dismissed by the world press in a few paragraphs, then quickly forgotten by the faithful. Scoffers might say that the supreme pontiff imperturbably sticks to his job—pontificating—while a distracted world hardly listens. Yet occasionally papal decisions, words, or gestures have far-reaching effects, maybe in the Middle East or Latin America or Eastern Europe.

Furthermore, the pope is one of the few authorities on earth, perhaps the only one, to proclaim ultimate moral values. Even unbelievers who put no stock in the certainties of the faith that he preaches may welcome his periodical insistence on absolute ethical standards.

The papal day is exhaustingly long, and every day is a working day. Each pontiff I've observed has been impressive in his diligence, his dogged effort to cope with the hundreds of matters, big and small, confronting the head of the church, that even follow him into his bedroom when he's sick. Much of the pope's strength and attention is absorbed by the perplexingly vast machinery that he, and only he, commands.

A STATE LIKE NO OTHER

Whoever penetrates Vatican City is at once confronted with bulky administrative mechanisms that are unconnected with the pope's function as a major voice of mankind's collective conscience, and are irrelevant to his "prophetic" mission. The fact is that the supreme pontiff of the Roman Catholic Church is also the chief of a tautly centralized and intricately structured worldwide community of more than four thousand bishops and archbishops, four hundred thousand priests, and nearly a million nuns. His word is command in tens of thousands of churches, monasteries, and convents around the globe. He is, furthermore, thoroughly enmeshed in Italian and international politics (although his spokesmen will always deny this), and maintains diplomatic liaisons with more than one hundred nations. Lastly, the pope himself is a head of state—the world's smallest state, it is true, but still one that vigorously exercises sovereignty and wields considerable financial clout, although it has lately been embarrassed by unsavory practices.

The halberds and breastplates of the pontifical Swiss Guard and the battlements of the medieval buildings near St. Peter's may suggest a Graustarkian atmosphere, but the State of Vatican City has immensely more weight internationally than such tiny principalities as Liechtenstein or Monaco, or the new dwarf republics in the Caribbean.

Today's pontifical state is a miniaturized reincarnation of the States of the Church, the vast territories in central Italy over which the popes ruled, with changing fortunes, from the early

Middle Ages until 1870. The present State of Vatican City, carved out of Rome as a 108.7-acre enclave by the Lateran Treaties of 1929, is barely seven times the area of the United Nations headquarters in New York City, and less than a sixth the size of the Principality of Monaco. About four hundred fifty persons, including several families of lay employees, live permanently in the Vatican; two hundred eighty of them hold Vatican citizenship. The pope has a white Holy See passport Number 1, and his envoys abroad also carry Vatican passports for the duration of their service. About four thousand persons, from cardinals and archbishops to broadcasters, librarians, printers, mosaic workers, tapestry knitters, drivers, and gardeners hold jobs in the pontifical enclave and its dependencies around Rome. The Vatican's automotive fleet comprises seven hundred vehicles, some of them reserved for the pope, while cardinals and distinguished visitors are entitled to ride in the dark-blue limousines of the state's motor pool; there are also buses, trucks, and fire engines with Vatican license plates.

Nobody seems to know exactly how many rooms the Vatican has, although about twelve thousand windows have been counted. There are certainly considerably more than one thousand halls, chambers, chapels, corridors, stairways, loggias, attics, passages, basements, grottoes, and modern air-conditioned offices. Through the ages the papal headquarters has grown almost uninterruptedly, with ever-new additions, towers, fortified walkways, and detached pavilions. Even today, construction work is always in progress somewhere in the pontifical state. Large cranes outside the modern buildings that house the Vatican's medical services and its telephone exchange haul material for a new wing of the Apostolic Library; elsewhere bricklayers raise a partition in a Renaissance hall; architects measure out space for a new penthouse office on top of a sixteenth-century palace. The Secret Archives have already gone underground with miles of new shelves in a fireproof, controlled-environment annex under the Courtyard of the Pigna (named after a giant bronze fir cone, a puzzling legacy from the ancients).

The oval St. Peter's Square, enclosed by Bernini's colonnades, and the Basilica of St. Peter's, are open to all comers, although both belong to the State of Vatican City. Any tourist can also glimpse the walled part of the papal enclave by taking part in one of the guided tours. Sightseers learn that about a third of the pope's domains is taken up by buildings from various

4

epochs, another third by large and small courtyards, and the last third by the gardens on the slopes of the Vatican hill. The visitors who pass through the Doorway of the Bells on the south side of St. Peter's see a huge stone trough, once used to slake the thirst of the horses that raced in the circus built by Emperor Caligula; Saint Peter is believed to have died a martyr in the circus and to have been buried nearby, on the site where the basilica named after him was to rise centuries later. A few hundred yards away, on a siding in the papal railroad station, one may watch workmen unload crates for the Vatican supermarket from a flatcar with West German markings. A spur track links the pontifical state with the Italian railroad network, but it is almost never used for passenger traffic. (The popes use it sometimes: John XXIII once traveled by rail from the Vatican to Assisi and Loreto, and John Paul II took the train to a marshaling yard on Rome's outskirts to say mass for Italian state railroad workers.)

Much more important for papal travel today is the heliport in the westernmost corner of the Vatican, wedged into a salient of its old walls. From here the pontiff takes off from time to time for his hillside residence at Castel Gandolfo, south of Rome, or for one of the city's airports, Fiumicino or Ciampino, to board a jet for one of his long-distance journeys. The Vatican state has no aircraft of its own, at least not yet; whenever the pope wants airborne transportation, the Italian air force sends a helicopter with a handpicked crew. The vicar on earth of the Prince of Peace finds nothing inappropriate in traveling courtesy of the military arm of a secular government. For papal trips to distant destinations the Vatican charters jetliners from Alitalia, the Italian national airline, or from other carriers. A sizable part of the cost is covered by the news reporters, who may fly in the papal plane as paying guests.

From the Vatican heliport, sightseers are taken to the gardens, where they see cedars from Lebanon, shrubbery from Japan, roses from Texas, and other exotic flora brought to Rome by missionaries or donated by prelates. There is also a patch of luxuriant vegetation that the papal gardeners leave alone—a miniature Vatican national park, noisy with sparrows and warblers. It is a bird sanctuary in the midst of a metropolis, although Vatican cats prowl among the trees. The pontifical enclave may hold many secrets, but the pope's kitchen garden, near the pristine sector, isn't one of them. Visitors peer through fences to note that the pontifical table this season will have a more than adequate supply of artichokes, eggplant, and lemons. (Other vegetables and dairy products are delivered to the Apostolic Palace from a model farm in the papal estate at Castel Gandolfo.)

Tourists are kept out of the Vatican's administrative sections. Anyone, however, may walk through the Gate of St. Anne, the service entrance to the papal state, north of St. Peter's Square. Through this gate, at the Pontifical Pharmacy, people may buy medicine unavailable in other Italian drugstores, or they may send registered letters or parcels to a foreign country through the papal mails. (There is also a Vatican post office in St. Peter's Square, much frequented by residents of Rome who don't trust the Italian mail service.) Also through the Gate of St. Anne— flanked, left, by the Swiss Guard barracks and, right, by the small Church of St. Anne, the parish church of Vatican City— one reaches the Apostolic Library; the Secret Archives; the Polyglot Press (which prints texts in many languages and alphabets); the Vatican's bank, supermarket, and commissary; and its technical services. The celebrated Vatican museums are a unit apart; the visitors' entrance is on the sloping Viale Vaticano on the north side of the papal state. The collections are a mixed bag of arts and antiquities, including such masterpieces as the Laocoön group, but also containing many second-rate objects that were given to the popes or otherwise acquired over the centuries. Sightseers also reach the Sistine Chapel, with Michelangelo's frescoes, through the museum entrance.

Participants in the pope's weekly general audience, whenever it is not held in the open in St. Peter's Square, are channeled through the Gate of the Holy Office, off the southern arm of Bernini's colonnades, into the Hall of Paul VI. This is a structure of reinforced concrete designed by Pier Luigi Nervi, and completed in 1972. It looks like a convention center, with a main auditorium that can accommodate up to ten thousand persons, a smaller hall, and three sets of restrooms: for men, women, and clergy.

The most impressive entrance to the Vatican is through the Bronze Doors on the right side of St. Peter's. Visitors who pass muster by the Swiss Guard sentry enter a vaulted corridor, and can walk straight ahead up the Scala Regia (Royal Stairway) to the Sistine Chapel, or the Hall of Benedictions above the portico of St. Peter's, or to other large rooms and passageways, or they can turn right and climb a few stairs to the Courtyard of St. Damasus. This is a severe rectangular square, enclosed on three sides by the Apostolic Palace, the office and home of the pope. A complex begun in the late Middle Ages, the palace also houses the pope's Secretariat of State and other key branches of church government.

The popes did not always reside in the Vatican. Until the thirteenth century they lived in the palace adjoining the Basilica of St. John Lateran, the ancient cathedral of the bishops of Rome, on the southeastern outskirts of the city. They frequently visited the Vatican, however, often harassed en route by hostile factions, or even waylaid by robbers. The Vatican, the marshy and once ill-famed area on the right bank of the Tiber, had become the center of a Christian cult in the second century, if not earlier, as the place where Saint Peter was believed to have been crucified, head downward, sometime between A.D. 64 and 67. The first St. Peter's Basilica, built over Saint Peter's burial site, was consecrated A.D. 326. During the Dark Ages pilgrims from as far away as the British Isles came to worship at the sanctuary. They found rooms and such creature comforts as the harsh epoch was able to provide in shelters that had sprung up in the neighborhood. Over the next centuries, the area became the headquarters of Christendom, and Charlemagne was crowned emperor of the West in St. Peter's by Pope Saint Leo III at Christmas, A.D. 800.

The Vatican became the seat of the papacy in the thirteenth century after Pope Nicholas III commissioned a residential building close to the basilica. It would seem he was eventually able to move into the new structure, for he ceased dating pontifical documents from the Lateran. The popes have almost continuously governed the church from the Vatican ever since they returned to Rome from Avignon, where they had been the captives of the kings of France during most of the fourteenth century. The architecture and art that today's visitor sees walking into St. Peter's or through the Bronze Doors are those of the High and Late Renaissance. In that turbulent and creative era, pontiffs with a passion for magnificence, the patrons of Bramante, Michelangelo, and Raphael, had the venerable old basilica torn down and a new, grandiose church built over its foundations. They also had new wings added to the Vatican palace to create sumptuous living and working spaces for themselves, their top officials, and a growing entourage of courtiers and clerks.

The Vatican today is a unique repository of trophies, relics,

7

documents, books, works of art, and other mementoes accumulated over many centuries. These are crammed into a walled space roughly the shape of a trapezoid, whose perimeter can be walked in about forty minutes. Ecclesiastics who have spent most of their adult lives within the Vatican walls say they know only a small part of its treasures and curiosities; even the pope can't know them all.

The Vatican is Rome, and yet it isn't. The windows of the "sacred palaces" are cleaner than those of Italian government buildings in the city; the lawns in the Vatican gardens seem lusher and greener than those in the scruffy Roman parks; sounds in the pontifical courtyards and corridors are muffled, a welcome contrast to the din elsewhere in the metropolis. But Rome and the Italian way of doing things greatly influence life in the pontifical state.

On the other hand, Rome is also, in a sense, a clerical company town with the papacy as its major industry. The profits that the city derives from the Holy See cannot be quantified, but they are huge and vital. The earnings from the pilgrimage and tourist trade, the sums spent by the Vatican and the religious bodies clustered around it, the thousands of church jobs, and the ecclesiastical money and real estate deals combine into a turnover of billions of dollars every year. The Holy See affects the lives of a large part of the 3 million Romans, even if marginally. For instance, one attends the wedding of a friend, and in the reception afterward discovers that the prelate who has been officiating at the ceremony is a high papal official; through Vatican contacts Romans may get a Filipino governess for their children, or a place for an aged relative in a nursing home run by nuns; a Vatican connection opens many doors in the city. Papal personnel and ordinary citizens share some interests and know a lot about each other. The walls encircling the Vatican may look forbidding, but there is constant osmosis between it and the ancient, mellow metropolis all around it.

COURT AND CURIA

Boccaccio in the *Decameron* has one of his seven young Florentine women, Neifile, tell of Abraam, a rich Jewish merchant in Paris, who is being urged by his Italian friend, Giannotto, to become a Christian. At first Abraam doesn't want to hear about it; but at his friend's insistence he eventually announces that before making a decision he will journey to Rome to see for himself how the pope and his cardinals live. Giannotto's spirits sink, for he realizes that if Abraam has a chance to observe the outrageous conduct of the clerics in Rome, he not only will never convert to the Christian faith, but were he already Christian he would surely embrace Judaism. Giannotto tries to dissuade Abraam from his travel plans, but in vain. In Rome, Abraam, as a guest of the Jewish community, unobtrusively observes the papal court, and sees all vices—lust, gluttony, and avarice above all—represented there. On his return to Paris Abraam reports to Giannotto he found that the pope and his hangers-on are doing everything possible to destroy the Christian religion, but since Christianity is nevertheless gaining ground continually, the Holy Spirit is manifestly at work in it. Abraam receives baptism in the Cathedral of Notre Dame, and under the Christian name of Giovanni leads a saintly life.

Neifile's mocking tale shows what kind of reputation the papal entourage had six centuries ago, and very probably not only among the sophisticates of Tuscany whom Boccaccio let speak. Distrust of the pontiff's aides has been frequent and widespread ever since. Today, too, many Roman Catholics, even priests, while professing reverence for the pope, will own up to mixed feelings about his associates in the Vatican.

The bishops of Rome have been surrounded by an official family of deacons, other auxiliary clergy, scribes, and advisers since the earliest times of Christianity. As the Roman see rose in importance, and the successors to Saint Peter asserted their primacy over a large part of the Christian church, the deacons turned into cardinals, and the clerks into powerful officials. The papal entourage became known as the *curia,* a term once denoting the court of the Roman emperors, or as the pontifical court. The words "curia" and "court" were often used interchangeably, the first stressing the bureaucratic tasks, the second the ceremonial functions of the group of church dignitaries around the pope.

The papal curia, or court, moved from the Lateran to the Vatican with the pontiffs, followed them to Avignon during their rather comfortable "Babylonian captivity" in the fourteenth century—when the papacy played the role of a pawn of French power policy—and returned with them to Rome.

For over six hundred years papal curialists and courtiers have populated the Vatican almost without interruption. The expression "pontifical court" remained in use long after World War II, but was quietly dropped in the 1960s when the papacy trimmed its ceremonial flamboyance. During the reign of Pius XII (1939–1958) no fewer than 51 categories of worthies in colorful garb still walked in the pontifical cortege as the delicate-looking head of the church, on his portable throne, was solemnly borne into St. Peter's like a precious totem, flanked by three different honor guards, each in its own uniforms.

However, Pius XII, in a gesture of austerity, had the scarlet capes of his cardinals, which required train bearers, shortened by several feet. Under John XXIII, and especially under Paul VI, papal ceremonies were streamlined, and the pageantry adapted to television. Since then the ruffs of the lay dignitaries, the bearskins of the papal gendarmerie, and the swords and comic-opera helmets of the Pontifical Noble Guard have disappeared. No chief steward is now at hand to see that the pontiff is not tossed about on his gestatorial throne; the purple-garbed *sediari* (chair carriers) do their job without supervision by a nobleman. Gone are the ostrich-feather fans on long poles that were carried on either side of the pope, looking as though they had been borrowed from an outdoor production of *Aida*. Pontifical cupbearers or "secret sweepers" no longer strut in the papal procession. (The latter title was a reminder of the time when the pope used to ride out on horseback and had a swarm of broom-wielding assistants around him to clear the roads.) Only the gaudy uniforms of the Swiss Guard, their halberds and their plumed helmets, have endured.

But although much of the old pomp has vanished, protocol and rank are still dominant in the Vatican. An American diplomat who used to confer with papal aides once or twice a week, and attend St. Peter's for all major rites officiated by the pontiff, observed: "The atmosphere is, to an astonishing degree, that of a royal court." A Renaissance court, one might add, and not only because of the Swiss Guard. (Many Italian princes during the fifteenth and sixteenth centuries relied on mercenaries from the Helvetian cantons, and the Renaissance popes followed the example of the secular rulers. These princes, dukes, counts, and condottieri and their soldiers-for-hire disappeared centuries ago, but the pontifical Swiss Guard is soldiering on.)

While many more non-Italian officials can now be encountered in the Vatican than in the 1950s and 1960s, the mood in the papal antechambers at times seems as Italianate provincial as was life in the sixteenth-century castles and palaces of Perugia, Rimini, Urbino, Ferrara, Parma, and Mantua. There the despots lorded over their sycophants, privy councillors, court painters, buffoons, and astrologers amid petty cabals and the incessant buzz of gossip in corridors and courtyards.

The Vatican no longer speaks of the papal court, although its attitudes linger on; instead, the term "curia" is very much in use. *Roman Curia,* by definition, means the complex of administrative departments, offices, and tribunals through which the pope governs the Roman Catholic Church. The main bodies within the curia are known as "Sacred Congregations," which is ecclesiastical jargon for committees. (How the Roman Curia works, how decisions are made, and how the lines of power within this bureaucratic structure run will be described in detail in chapter 4.)

In a wider sense, the expression "curia" covers the entire Vatican bureaucracy, though some of its branches—like the administration of the pontifical state or the care for St. Peter's Basilica—are legally separate from the church government.

The entire Vatican and its dependencies are pervaded by a mentality and attitude that ordinary Romans, even churchgoers, find peculiar and faintly repugnant—"curial." Its characteristics are circumspection, ceremoniousness, indirection, and secretiveness. Papal bureaucrats are usually polite, though remote, sometimes unctuous, but rarely gruff. The members of the curia, even after years of work in common, address each other as "Your Eminence" (for cardinals), "Your Excellency" (for archbishops and bishops), "Monsignor" (for lesser prelates), or "Father" (for simple priests and monks). One has many colleagues but few friends in the halls of the Vatican. Curialists often speak or write in Byzantine circumlocutions. Official Vatican documents destined for publication are customarily allusive, reticent, ambiguous, and obscure, requiring the kind of exegesis necessary for the Book of Revelation.

Many Holy See bureaucrats who were called into the Vatican as young priests at the recommendation of their bishops or other patrons spend all their ecclesiastical lives in Rome. Others are sent abroad to serve as papal diplomats for some years before being reassigned to higher curia posts. Advancement is usually slow: curial careers frequently traverse long dry patches when innumerable letters and documents have to be drafted and legal or theological texts translated in tedious back-room work, while one is being watched and evaluated by superiors and colleagues. Plodding is safer than brilliancy. Go-getters are not appreciated in the church government, and ambitions had better be disguised. Many positions of power are occupied by old men who believe themselves indispensable, and whose quirks must be humored.

Curial jokes are anemic, inviting a thin smile rather than a guffaw. The diffuse sanctimoniousness is often a cloak for cynicism, a ripe Roman quality. The hydra of intrigue has always thrived in sacred palaces. Key departments are controlled by tight little groups—typically, medium-level officials with their own network of connections in other branches of the pontifical bureaucracy. Office chiefs, who may be cardinals or archbishops, are frequently maneuvered by monsignors, who make all the decisions without seeming to do so. Churchmen at large who have had earlier experiences with the curia will, on their next visit to Rome, seek out the right insider to brief them—someone who counts, this time, in the Vatican administration.

Diplomats from secular governments who are freshly assigned to the Holy See are baffled by the insulated atmosphere in which they find themselves. When they call on a member of the pontifical foreign service, the lay envoys are led along a glass-enclosed, frescoed loggia in the Apostolic Palace to a conference room with remarkably uncomfortable chairs that seem designed to discourage small talk. The information the diplomats receive is often minimal, but every word they say, every gesture—whether they shrug or raise their eyebrows—may be recorded in the files, as scholars familiar with the Vatican archives know. These files, or dossiers, are known as "positions," and they seem to be as important to curialists as real people.

Though today's Vatican administration is equipped with electric typewriters, electronic word processors, and computers, the style of curial documents has remained bombastic. Bishops and superiors of religious orders will write that they "humbly supplicate" the pope when they ask him for a decision or a favor (which will actually be granted or denied by an obscure monsignor in an obscure curia office). Curial department chiefs who have reported directly to the pontiff on some matter note his response in a memorandum for the "position" as coming "from an audience with the Most Holy Father." The high-blown curial

12

language perpetuates the pretentiousness and insincerity of the supposedly defunct pontifical court.

The power elite in the curia is to a much greater extent male than most other large governmental and corporate bureaucracies in the contemporary world, except maybe in the Soviet Union. True, quite a number of women work in the Vatican today, but their tasks are subordinate. Members of female religious orders cook and do household chores for the pope and for high prelates. Call the Rome telephone number 6982, and a nun's voice will answer from the Vatican switchboard. Lately some laywomen have been given clerical jobs in curia offices, advise the Vatican museums as experts, or serve as linguists at Vatican Radio. But not one woman has any decision-making function in the papal administration, and none will have as long as the Roman Catholic Church reserves its priesthood for men only. There are nearly a million Roman Catholic nuns in the world, more than double the number of priests and lay brothers, but this vast female church force is represented in the Vatican by only a few mothers superior and sisters acting intermittently as consultants to curia bodies. They are officially listed as members of the papal administration, but their advice may or may not be sought; at times it is heeded, and at other times ignored.

One woman alone in modern times has exercised considerable, if unofficial, power in the Vatican—Mother Pasqualina, or Pascalina, the housekeeper of Pius XII, who was a formidable Vatican presence during the 1940s and 1950s. One has to go far back in church history to find a woman with similar influence in the papal entourage. Among the very few who had such influence was Queen Christina of Sweden when she resided for some time as an honored guest in the Vatican. In 1654–55 she abdicated her throne, forswore Lutheranism, sought out the Roman Catholic Church in Innsbruck's Hofkirche, and made a triumphant entry into Rome through the Porta del Popolo. Before her, the beautiful Lucrezia Borgia presided at the brilliant court of her father, Pope Alexander VI, during the late fifteenth century, when she was the wife of Giovanni Sforza, the first of the three husbands in her tempestuous life as a willing pawn in pontifical power plays. And in the fourteenth century, the great medieval mystic, Catherine of Siena, had a direct impact on the papacy as a one-woman pressure group. The story of "Popess Joan," a woman said fraudulently to have won the throne of Saint Peter in the Dark Ages, is dismissed as a fable by almost all scholars.

13

In our time, Paul VI and John Paul II were grateful for the support of their rigorous stand on birth control and abortion from the far-famed nun, Mother Teresa of Calcutta. Still, even including Mother Teresa, the list of women who have carried weight in the Vatican is short.

The entourage of popes has always included a few officials and aides who never took holy orders, and who were often married. However, to this day, with very few exceptions, laymen count almost as little at the Holy See as do women. The curia remains an overwhelmingly male clerical society, governed by a man who venerates the Mother of Jesus but who always speaks with the authority derived from the Son of God.

CHAPTER 2

℘VICAR ℘AND ℘MASTER

FROM THE MOMENT a man is elected to the papacy a formidable image-making campaign is launched. While the crowd outside in St. Peter's Square is still waiting to learn the identity of the new vicar of Jesus Christ on earth, the cardinals in the Sistine Chapel who have just chosen him from their midst file before the new head of the church to bend their knees and pay homage to their former peer, now their master and sovereign—a feudal rite of obeisance that they will repeat many times during his pontificate.

Until the day before, the latest successor to Saint Peter as bishop of Rome was merely one among more than a hundred cardinals, perhaps a front-runner in the pontifical sweepstakes, perhaps so obscure he was not even considered a dark-horse candidate. Now, instant hagiographers will discover proof of sanctity, flashes of genius, and portents of future greatness in hitherto unreported episodes of his life. Eastern Orthodox and Anglican churchmen will bear witness in interviews that the new pontiff has already shown himself to be an ardent ecumenist. Newspaper readers will be told that he has had close Jewish friends since his school days, and rabbis will aver that he always came out stalwartly against anti-Semitism. Television and radio reports will be full of anecdotes about the freshly elected pope chatting with Vatican gardeners, following sports events on tele-

15

vision, disconcerting his new curial entourage by flouting ceremonial, spending hours in lonely prayer in his private chapel,
ordering that truckloads of books and nothing else be shipped to
the Apostolic Palace from his former residence, and similar de-
lightful vignettes illustrating his humility, folksiness, learning,
and piety.

Whenever the new pope receives visitors in the Vatican, shows
himself to the crowds in Rome, or goes on one of the "pastoral"
journeys to faraway countries, people will try to grab his hand
and kiss it, and parents will hold up small children in the hope
he may touch them. Royalty, statesmen, and diplomats (who
may not be Roman Catholics, or even believers) will address him
as "Your Holiness."

The papacy is one of the oldest institutions on earth; only the
emperor of Japan may claim that his office predates the pope's.
To this day the pope is, at least in theory, the absolute ruler of a
worldwide spiritual reign. From the moment he accepts his election by the cardinals, he wields supreme legislative, executive,
and judiciary powers throughout the universal church. And, in
our day, the pontiff also exercises direct secular power within
the walls of Vatican City, authorizing the issuance of Vatican
mail stamps and minting of coins, commanding the Vatican police forces, and doing other things that the heads of states and
governments all over the world do.

In the past, the earthly power of the pontiff was much larger,
and at times his claims were immense. Some popes in the High
Middle Ages acted on the assumption that God had placed them
above all rulers on earth: above the Holy Roman Emperors who
held sway in Germany and journeyed to the Eternal City to be
crowned in St. Peter's, and above all the kings and princes in
Christendom. This theocratic concept of a global supermonarchy
with the vicar of Christ as its head was never fully realized, yet
it lingered on during the coronation of every pope until 1963.

In history, popes have called for crusades against the Moslem
infidel, become embroiled in the Italian wars of the Renaissance,
and (as sovereigns of the pontifical state) concluded political-
military alliances with other powers. Involved as they were in
secular politics, and quite often in wars, the pontiffs repeatedly
had trouble asserting their spiritual supremacy. For centuries
many theologians and canon lawyers contended that the ecumenical council, the gathering of all the world's bishops, was the
highest authority in the Christian church, higher even than the

16

successor of the Apostle Saint Peter. Emperors and kings would encourage conniving prelates to scheme against the head of the church, and would threaten uncooperative popes by promoting ecumenical councils, thereby curbing the popes' power. But the "conciliarists" have lost ground since the Roman Catholic Counter-Reformation of the sixteenth century. The First Vatican Council (Vatican I), 1869–70, ruled that the pope was above the ecumenical council, and that no appeal from a decision of the supreme pontiff to the assembly of all bishops was possible. Under present canon law, only the pope can convene a council. Vatican I also proclaimed, against much dissent, the dogma of the pontiff's infallibility.

In 1870 the edifice of the popes' absolute spiritual authority thus seemed completed just as the head of the church, with the unification of Italy, was losing his last shred of temporal power, the remnants of what had once been the States of the Church. In 1929 the papacy, through the Lateran Treaties, regained a token of territorial sovereignty, the 108.7-acre enclave, enough to provide it with more autonomy than any other international body enjoys, the United Nations included. Even between 1870 and 1929, when in protest against the takeover of Rome by unified Italy the popes refused to leave their walled palaces and proclaimed themselves "prisoners in the Vatican," they continued intervening in Italian and international politics in various ways. Among other things, they ignored Italian legislation that formally guaranteed the independence of the papacy, and for a long time forbade Italian Catholics to take part in Italian political elections.

Today, however, in a world where religion has become marginal in many areas, in an epoch of superpowers, nuclear arsenals, and global socioeconomic upheavals, it is questionable how far the pope's influence actually reaches. His control over the 800 million baptized persons whom the Roman Catholic Church claims as members is theoretical rather than real. How many of them, for instance, heed the papal strictures regarding contraception? Many millions of Roman Catholics are so only in name, and many churchgoers are selective in their loyalty to the pontiff, accepting some of his exhortations and ignoring the rest. Vatican influence is certainly notable in Italy, Poland, Ireland, Spain, and Latin America, but even in these areas it is by no means unchallenged. (To mention only the limitations of church power on the papacy's home grounds, the Italian Communist

17

party is the strongest Marxist movement in the West.)

Papal trips to various countries usually generate much excitement, but so do international sports competitions and outdoor concerts by famous pop groups. The law of diminishing returns also applies to the impact of pontifical spectaculars. After the fervor caused by a visit from the head of the church to a city or region, everything soon seems as it was before. Even in the pope's own diocese many more Romans, especially younger ones, flock to the Olympic Stadium, a mile north of the Vatican, Sunday after Sunday to watch the soccer championships and to cheer on the local team than gather in St. Peter's Square to listen to their bishop's weekly admonitions and receive his apostolic blessing. Pilgrims from afar regularly outnumber the Romans in the piazza.

The most absolutist of modern popes, Pius XII, described his role soon after his election in 1939 as that of a "father of the Christian family, servant of the servants of God, who verily represents the person, the word, the authority of Jesus Christ among humankind." This was a bold self-definition indeed—a bishop of Rome seeing himself as an alter ego of God's Son. With Pius XII the myth of the papacy attained a modern peak that, viewed in today's perspective, seems outright medieval.

Awe and mystery have at all times surrounded the priesthood, and in Roman Catholicism, the ancient traditions of the papal office, its spiritual and secular power, and its dogmatic underpinnings (the pontiff as the visible representative of the Redeemer) have often led believers to idolize the incumbent. In the Baroque epoch following the Counter-Reformation, the "triumphalistic" architecture of St. Peter's, the pomp of the pontifical court, and fear of the papal thought police—the Holy Inquisition—combined to create an atmosphere in which the head of the church seemed a semidivine being. (Sanctity is presumed in a supreme pontiff, although the Vatican actually acknowledges as saints only one-third of all popes in history. Even at the lowest points in the saga of the papacy, such as the reign of Alexander VI (1492–1503) with its scandals, the peccadilloes of a pope didn't seem to undermine his theological position or the prestige of his office. Many among the clergy and the faithful distinguished between the grandeur and religious significance of the office and the failings of the incumbent. "It was possible to loathe the individual and still desire his spiritual gifts," wrote Jakob Burckhardt, the historian of the Renaissance.)

Some of this exaltation of the papacy has survived into our day. Until quite recently, prelates admitted to the presence of the pope were expected to kiss the tip of one of the red slippers on his feet. This gesture, reminiscent of the homage due to oriental despots, has recently become obsolete (partly because John Paul II fancies moccasins of fine leather instead of slippers). Even today, however, some old-style churchmen still terminate letters or petitions to the pontiff with the archaic phrase "Humbly kissing the sacred slipper" before their signature.

In the era of Enlightenment and in the nineteenth century the prestige of the papacy declined. Recent popes have somehow managed to recover a bit of the old respect for their office while being stripped, or divesting themselves, of the myth. The turning point was Pius XII's long pontificate; it started a process whereby the figure of the vicar of Christ was gradually demythologized.

A WANING MYTH

The Vatican under Pius XII (1939–1958) was a place where a visitor might inadvertently walk into an office in the building of *L'Osservatore Romano* and see the deputy editor of the pontifical newspaper, Cesidio Lolli, kneeling on the floor beside his desk, alone in the room, holding a telephone receiver, and saying from time to time, "Yes, Holy Father." One might have thought he was answering a call from the Almighty rather than from the pontiff. Pius XII often picked up his white telephone to call aides, expecting them to recognize his voice instantly. The rather high-pitched voice over the Vatican's internal telephone network would upbraid aides for something they had done or failed to do, or request an urgent report or some other immediate action. It rarely explained, commented, or said "thank you"—there was just a click when Pius XII had hung up.

He allowed the cult of papal personality—always nurtured in the Vatican—to grow beyond measure during the last years of his pontificate. In Rome, veneration for Pius XII culminated after the city's liberation by the Allied forces in 1944. There was a spontaneous outpouring of popular gratitude for the pontiff, whose presence and incessant diplomatic action had helped the Italian capital to escape major destruction during the bleak nine

19

months when it was occupied by the Nazis and the tense days during which retreating German forces and advancing Allied troops streamed through its streets.

Romans, including unbelievers, praised Pius XII as *defensor civitatis,* "defender of the citizenry," a title from the Middle Ages when Rome was periodically besieged, invaded, and plundered by soldiery and raiders, a pawn in power struggles in which the hapless inhabitants were usually losers.

Today, Pius XII's role during World War II appears in a different light. From the eleven thick volumes of selected documents about the papal foreign service during the war years that the Vatican has seen fit to publish, it appears that one of Pius XII's main worries was to stave off Allied air and ground attacks on Rome. There are also ample records of how the pontiff prepared his periodical peace appeals to the belligerent powers, but there is hardly a sign that Pius XII attempted to halt the murder of millions of Jews by the Nazis. During World War II he never spoke out publicly against the genocide being perpetrated, although there is some evidence in records made available by the Vatican that the Holy See knew early on of the roundups and deportation of Jews in Nazi-occupied areas.

Toward the end of his reign, an international debate about Pius XII's wartime attitudes sprang up and became heated. The criticisms from many sides may have been the reason he increasingly isolated himself, relying on a small coterie in the Vatican, and permitting cloying sycophancy. The great prestige that the papacy had regained during World War II—greater than at any time since the Baroque age—started dwindling again.

As Pius XII grew older, he spent more and more of his time preparing long doctrinal speeches, many of them on sexual ethics or even on outright gynecological questions (for instance, should the mother or the child be saved when therapeutical abortion seemed indicated?). His phenomenal memory, which remained faithful to him until the end, enabled him to astonish his audiences by delivering, entirely by heart, addresses crammed with technical terms that he had laboriously put together with the help of consultants, or culled from specialized literature and reference works. (After his death his bookshelves were found loaded with well-thumbed encyclopedias and dictionaries.)

At the same time Pius XII permitted, even encouraged, reports that he was having mystical experiences. This hadn't happened in the first years of his pontificate. Even priests were

20

disconcerted. There was embarrassment in the Vatican one day in 1950 when *L'Osservatore Romano* quoted a high churchman, Federico Cardinal Tedeschini, as revealing that the pope had witnessed a repetition of the miracle of Fatima. While walking in the Vatican gardens, the prelate had affirmed, Pius XII had seen visions of the Virgin Mary and of the sun dancing in the sky, a replay of the famous phenomena in the fields outside the Portuguese town of Fatima in 1917, as reported by three children, and later acknowledged by church authorities. Nobody else in Rome had observed the heavenly apparition that Pius XII was said to have experienced, not even Cardinal Tedeschini.

In another account of miraculous happenings, Pius XII disclosed to some Jesuits in 1954 that Jesus had appeared at his bedside during a recent illness and said to him that his time was not yet up. When the story found its way into the press, the Vatican, after some tarrying amid suppressed snickers, had to confirm it officially.

The pontificate of Pius XII would make an excellent subject for a case study of how the lofty office transforms its incumbent: what the power, the glory, and the incessant adulation may do to human personality. It also may be recalled here that Pius XII was the first—and so far the only—pontiff to invoke papal infallibility. He did so in 1950 when he proclaimed the dogma of the Virgin Mary's bodily assumption to heaven. *Infallibility,* as dogmatically defined by the First Vatican Council in 1870, means that the pope cannot err when he makes a pronouncement ex cathedra, in the exercise of his office, on matters of faith or morals.

An old and doubtless spurious text, the so-called prophecy of Saint Malachy, that assigned a cryptic motto to a series of future popes, had described the reign destined for the former Eugenio Pacelli as that of the *pastor angelicus,* or "angelic shepherd." Flatterers pretended to take this pseudoprophecy seriously, and during Pius XII's last years used to call him the "pastor angelicus" quite often.

He lacked any pastoral experience, having spent his entire church career in the curial bureaucracy and the pontifical foreign service. During his lifetime it was fairly common knowledge in the Vatican that he was authoritarian and secretive, aloof and distrustful. He would quibble endlessly over tiny details, like a comma in a document, and he made enormous demands of himself and his assistants. Antonio Cardinal Samoré, who in 1943 had to rewrite the draft of a papal note to the Nazi government in Berlin sixteen times, recalled much later: "An audience with Pope Pius XII was like a university examination."

Pius XII was so reserved that nobody could imagine him having company at a meal. Once the United States secretary of state, John Foster Dulles, was conferring with Pius XII when Mother Pasqualina slid into the pontiff's study to tell him in German and, it seemed, rather sternly, that the soup was on the table. Pius XII excused himself and broke off the audience. He didn't ask Mr. Dulles to stay for dinner. Francis Cardinal Spellman of New York, whose friendship with the future pope began when both were curia officials, sometimes was offered a cup of tea by Pius XII during his reign. Mother Pasqualina remembers that in all her years in the pontifical quarters the pope only once asked a visitor, Michael Cardinal von Faulhaber of Munich, to remain for a meal after a long audience.

Pius XII had a strong sense of the majesty of his office. Even his elevator in the Apostolic Palace had a little pontifical throne in its old-fashioned cab. When it was time for the pope's daily constitutional in the Vatican gardens, always at the same time and for exactly an hour, the gardeners and other personnel of the pontifical state scrambled for cover; their sovereign didn't want to see any of his subjects.

To this day the Vatican is a place where journalists are not made to feel welcome, whether or not they are devout Roman Catholics or even priests. Under Pope Pius XII, the Vatican's obsession with secrecy prompted international news organizations to pay for inside information they could not otherwise obtain.

I was then reporting for the *New York Times* as a junior member of its Rome Bureau. One of my tasks was as liaison with a "Vatican informant" who had been put on our payroll in what we then thought was a great coup by an older member of our team. The colleague, an Italian-American, had attended a private school in Rome before World War II together with the nephews of Cardinal Pacelli, the future pope, and had stayed in touch with the family.

The "Vatican informant" was Pius XII's personal physician, Dr. Riccardo Galeazzi Lisi. For years he called me by phone at irregular intervals to let us have news of the pope's health and occasionally some Vatican gossip. On the phone he always introduced himself as "Dick." He was using the English abbreviation of his first name, he explained to me confidentially, because the Vatican phones were being tapped by the papal police. The pontifical doctor and I also had a code to cover a variety of Vatican developments that might have to be conveyed in a hurry. We updated the covert telephone communications system every month when I went to his private office in the Via Sistina, a fashionable street leading from the Piazza Barberini to the upper platform of the Spanish Stairway, to deliver his retainer fee in an envelope to him personally. We didn't know at the time that he was receiving more such envelopes from other clients.

Dr. Galeazzi Lisi, an eye specialist, had known the pope since the days when Pacelli was an aide in the Vatican's Secretariat of State. Shortly after his election to the papal throne in 1939, Pius XII one day slipped and fell in St. Peter's, suffering slight injuries; he asked for his friend, the eye doctor.

After that, Dr. Galeazzi Lisi became a Vatican fixture. He was addressed as "professor," although nobody knew where he had acquired that title. A half brother who was an architect, Count Enrico Galeazzi, was even closer to the pope's family than he, and served as special delegate of the pontifical commission for Vatican City, one of the highest lay jobs in the papal administration.

During all the years when Dr. Galeazzi Lisi was secretly retained by us, I had the feeling that, aside from his bulletins about Pius XII's health, he was telling us only a small part of what he must have known—that, in other words, he delivered little for the money we were paying him. Throughout the pontificate of Pius XII Dr. Galeazzi Lisi saw the pope almost daily; he had an office in Vatican City as the chief of its medical services, and attended all papal ceremonies in St. Peter's in his capacity as "pontifical archiater," or archphysician. Whenever I presented our envelope to Dr. Galeazzi Lisi and tried to worm some extra bit of inside information (to be attributed to a "Vatican source") out of him, I was amused that the mustached archiater maintained the same poker face he exhibited when, attired in black, he appeared in the pope's retinue at some canonization or pontifical mass.

I particularly remember one of our monthly meetings when I routinely asked Dr. Galeazzi Lisi how he was, and he said "just fine," and then, pressed by me, sneeringly gave me a few glimpses of what was going on in the papal apartment. The next day I read in the newspapers that the pontifical physician's wife had died earlier that week, and that a quiet funeral had already taken place. The impenetrable doctor, so recently widowed, had given no sign of being shaken by his bereavement.

From my talks with the archiater I gathered he detested and feared "the German nun," Mother Pasqualina. He resented it when, apparently at her insistence, a Swiss gerontologist, Paul Niehans, was called from his practice in Montreux to the Vatican to treat the pontiff for the complaints of advancing age.

Dr. Niehans, a Protestant, submitted Pius XII, then in his late seventies, to his controversial "living cell" therapy—injections of finely ground tissue taken from freshly slaughtered lambs. Pius XII must have been convinced that the treatment was helping him. He appointed the Swiss physician to the Pontifical Academy of Sciences when the death of Sir Alexander Fleming, the codiscoverer of penicillin, made a seat in the prestigious body available. I interviewed Dr. Niehans during one of his visits to Rome and was told by him that he had treated King George V, Sir Winston Churchill, and Konrad Adenauer, and that the pope was talking to him "like a friend," discussing scientific and cultural topics with him. (After Pius XII's death, Dr. Niehans resumed his Montreux practice full time.)

What little we knew at the time of Pius XII's "living cell" cure, we learned from the Swiss doctor and, in secret and not for attribution, from the archiater, never from the Vatican's official spokesmen. According to a sardonic saying in the curia, a pope is always in the best of health until the moment when his death is announced. In past epochs the demise of a pontiff was often kept secret for some time to permit his entourage to take the necessary precautions; Roman mobs would loot the palaces of papal nephews and other favorites as soon as it became known that their patron could no longer protect them.

As the condition of Pius XII took a turn for the worse in 1958, his archphysician was of little use to our bureau. In the palace at Castel Gandolfo where the pontiff had lived since late summer, Dr. Galeazzi Lisi felt even less free to use the telephone for personal business than in the Vatican, and he delivered his coded messages only when he briefly returned to his apartment in Rome for a change of clothes. It turned out we didn't really need his secret reports. The enterprising Jesuits who were operating Vatican Radio had prevailed upon the papal bureaucracy in what amounted to an astonishing victory over curial secretiveness, and were broadcasting live from Castel Gandolfo. In the last hours of Pius XII's death struggle, listeners could hear the voice of one of his close aides, Msgr. Domenico Tardini, reciting the prayers for the dying at his bedside. I was struck by the Roman dialectal flavor of the monsignor's Latin. Around 4:00 A.M. on October 9, 1958, Vatican Radio announced the pope's death.

In the hectic hours afterward, Dr. Galeazzi Lisi assured Vatican officials he could take care of the embalming of Pius XII's body and would call in a specialist, Oreste Nuzzi, to assist him. The duo worked for two days. In the afternoon of October 11, the body, lying in a casket of cypress wood, was taken from Castel Gandolfo to the Vatican in a hearse that had been borrowed from the funeral services department of the city of Rome. The municipal hearse was surmounted by four gilt statues of angels, holding festoons of wedding-style white damask, that seemed to nod as the vehicle was swaying; they had been added for the occasion together with an unstable wooden replica of the papal triple crown in the center of the roof. Inexperienced Vatican underlings were apparently responsible for the bafflingly tacky arrangements.

Just as the hearse stopped at the Lateran Basilica for a first funeral rite, a startling noise like a small firecracker going off was heard from inside the vehicle. A process of fermentation, favored by the temperature of one of Rome's warm autumn days, had burst open the pope's casket. The bewildered clergy of the Lateran rushed through their ceremony. The hearse continued across the center of Rome to the Vatican, the coffin was carried into St. Peter's, and the doors of the church were closed. Inside, the archiater and his assistant again labored on the pontiff's remains. The two men were busy all night in the huge, empty basilica.

At about 7:00 A.M. on October 12 the long-familiar voice called me at home and said imperturbably: "This is Dick. It's okay. I've been working on him all night, and he can be shown now."

At roughly the same time the doors of St. Peter's swung open and the first mourners and curiosity seekers started shuffling past the bier on which Pius XII was lying in state. They saw the dead pope clad in a red chasuble, a cloth-of-gold miter on his head, his face ashen. During the day, as the stream of visitors continued, the tall candles around the bier flickered, the temperature in the church rose, and the pontiff's face assumed a green hue. Also, a bad smell was spreading. The basilica was closed at dusk, and the archiater and his assistant went to work once more. The next morning Pius XII's face again looked a disconcerting gray, and soon it showed large blotches, as if decay had set in. The coffin was closed, sealed in a leaden casket, and ceremonially placed in a tomb in the grottoes underneath St. Peter's.

The dismay of Vatican dignitaries and other people who had seen the dead pontiff's body deteriorate by the hour was reflected in the newspapers. The archiater and his assistant, Dr. Nuzzi, felt compelled to hold a press conference to discuss their embalming method. Pope Pius XII's remains had been preserved in the manner the body of Jesus was treated after His crucifixion, Dr. Galeazzi Lisi explained with his habitual blandness; the dead pontiff was sprinkled with aromatic substances and wrapped into a winding sheet—"there were no injections, no surgery, no evisceration." Early Christians and such historic figures as Charlemagne had been embalmed in the same fashion, a method that might be described as "aromatic osmosis," the archiater said eruditely. Dr. Nuzzi, who claimed to have developed the technique, declared it was a rediscovery of what had been practiced many centuries ago.

While Dr. Galeazzi Lisi, flanked by his assistant, was thus defending his embalming job, various newspapers in Italy and abroad published a clinical diary under the archiater's byline, with hour-by-hour entries describing Pius XII's agony in grisly detail. The outrage it caused was deepened when picture magazines carried the photos of the stricken pope. I called Dr. Galeazzi Lisi to ask for his comments on the storm of criticism he was facing. This time he didn't use any code. He coldly said: "A physician's obligation to maintain professional secrecy ends with the patient's death. All these attacks on me only betray envy by other doctors."

The cardinals who were acting as the interim government of the church made a quick decision. In one of their daily meetings, on October 21, they stripped the archiater of his title and functions, and forbade him to set foot in the Vatican ever again. The physician's association of Rome ousted him on the grounds that he had "gravely compromised his own reputation and the dignity of the medical class" by selling professional records to the press. Still under a cloud, the former archphysician died ten years later. Why did the well-earning Vatican doctor hawk his august patient's medical secrets during Pius XII's lifetime and after his death? Had he sought the embalming assignment to earn an additional fee? Dr. Galeazzi Lisi's greed was explained to me as springing from the chronic money needs of an inveterate gambler. Whatever his motivations, the archiater contributed to demythologizing the papacy like no other individual in our time.

DOWN TO EARTH

The three pontiffs who reigned between 1958 and 1978 were very different in character and personal style, but all three contributed to humanizing the papacy—John XXIII through the warmth of his outgoing nature, Paul VI by a widely perceived lack of self-assurance, and John Paul I by his modesty and disarming smile. The following kaleidoscopic glimpses of their pontificates are intended to convey a sense of the atmosphere prevailing in each of them.

If the ascetic-looking Pius XII had embodied a high-flown, mystical mode of church leadership, his chubby successor, John XXIII, quickly brought the papacy down to earth. Within a few weeks he was immensely popular, because the Romans sensed the new pope's genuine humanity rather than feeling exposed to an orchestrated display of papal magnificence. What had happened in the Soviet Union after Stalin's death in 1953 was still vividly remembered, and there was talk about a "de-Stalinization in the Vatican." The drastic changes in papal style were jokingly compared to changes in the Kremlin under Malenkov and Khrushchev.

A few days after his election in October 1958, at the age of nearly 78 years, John XXIII remarked he had searched the sacred scriptures and had not found a single word to the effect that the pope must eat alone. He thereafter almost always had his meals in company, a Vatican revolution after Pius XII's seclusiveness.

John XXIII also had a 1,100-year-old tower in the highest part of the Vatican gardens repaired and adapted, at considerable cost, as a hideaway for himself and as a guest house. (Paul VI and John Paul II also would commission expensive construction work exclusively for their private enjoyment, the way Renaissance popes had done.) John XXIII moved into his aerie

27

whenever he felt like getting away from the Apostolic Palace and wanted quiet to read and think. His walks in the Vatican gardens did not follow rigidly fixed schedules, and nobody had to hide; he liked to chat with the gardeners. One day Mr. Lolli, the deputy editor of the pontifical newspaper who kneeled during phone conversations with Pius XII, couldn't believe his eyes. John XXIII was walking into his apartment in a building in Vatican City. The pontiff had learned that Mr. Lolli's wife had been bedridden for some time, and on an impulse went to comfort and bless her. In their emotion, the Lollis were able only to stammer to their visitor.

John XXIII moved around Rome far more often and with less formality than his predecessor had done. Soon after his elevation he visited the city's old, fetid "Queen of Heaven" jail, embracing convicts. Anecdotes about Pope John's warmth, folksiness, and sense of humor are innumerable. Whenever he addressed pilgrims and other participants in his group audiences, he rambled on and had trouble finding a conclusion. An aide and old friend, Msgr. Thomas Ryan, would provide a translation for English-speaking listeners; the towering Irishman managed to telescope a fifteen-minute speech by Pope John into three minutes. It's a good thing, too, I thought one day at an audience, because the long-winded papal oratory hadn't made much sense anyway.

Yet the same pontiff who floundered in off-the-cuff speeches issued such soaring messages to the world as the encyclicals "Mater et Magistra" (Mother and Teacher) on social problems, and "Pacem in Terris" (Peace on Earth) on human rights and individual conscience. Papal encyclicals are usually drafted and put into final shape by speech writers and experts, but the pontiff is supposed to instruct and supervise them, and John XXIII assuredly did. This likable old man full of bonhomie and peasant shrewdness put the Roman Catholic Church on a new course that he called *aggiornamento*—"adaptation to changed times."

John XXIII also struck a new posture in East-West relations. He decided early in his pontificate that it wasn't the Vatican's business to promote anti-Communist crusades the way Pius XII had done. Instead, he encouraged a new, pragmatic approach to Communist governments, which was later dubbed the Holy See's *Ostpolitik,* or "Eastern policy," a term borrowed from German journalistic shorthand for Chancellor Willy Brandt's dealings with Warsaw Pact countries.

John XXIII found one official of his Secretariat of State, Msgr. Agostino Casaroli, to be a skillful negotiator who patiently sought to reach accommodation with Communist governments in a series of agreements whereby the church hoped to gain a minimum of breathing space. The Vatican was allowed to fill some long-vacant bishoprics in Eastern Europe, and also obtained the liberation of a few ecclesiastics who had long been imprisoned. That the climate had indeed changed became evident when Pope John received Khrushchev's son-in-law, Aleksei Adzhubei, in the Vatican in 1963. Much space will be devoted to Monsignor Casaroli later in these pages.

By summoning the Second Vatican Council to support aggiornamento, John XXIII consciously unleashed liberal forces in the church. Vatican II, held from 1962 to 1965, brought about important ecclesiastical reforms, created the conditions for better relations between the Roman Catholic Church and other Christians, and started a new dialogue between the church and non-Christians. A theological, philosophical, or historical evaluation of Vatican II is not my intention, and anyway it may be too early for such an enterprise. An ultraconservative churchman, Giuseppe Cardinal Siri of Genoa, remarked more than once it would need a century to undo the damage that Pope John had wrought in the mere four and a half years of his pontificate. Small wonder that John XXIII is a hero of liberal Roman Catholics. The pontiff who seemed so much more pragmatic, compassionate, and permissive than his predecessor died like a saint.

Pope Paul VI, who succeeded John XXIII in June 1963, brought Vatican II to its end in 1965, and pledged to carry out its decisions. When he was elected to the throne of Saint Peter he was archbishop of Milan, but he had earlier served for decades in the Roman Curia. As Msgr. Giovanni Battista Montini, the frail and earnest northern Italian had been one of the closest aides to Pius XII.

A churchman, long an associate of Paul VI and who later became a cardinal, told me that when Monsignor Montini was a key official at the Vatican's Secretariat of State he kept himself available to Pius XII around the clock, day after day, year after year, "to a heroic degree." The pontiff would call Monsignor Montini at any hour, "and the phone never rang twice— Montini always had it within reach, would take it to the bathroom." Montini, the quintessential curialist, was not too glad when Pius XII sent him to Milan in 1954. Montini's elevation to the papacy meant to him a return to his world, the Vatican.

Having become interested in modern art and design during his nine years as archbishop of Milan, Paul VI had the pontifical suites and other parts of the Apostolic Palace redecorated. From the second floor, where pontiffs do some of their work and hold most of their private audiences, the heavy red damasks, the tapestries, gilt clocks, and Baroque art went out to be replaced by modern paintings and medieval statuary amid cool colors—grays, greens, pale blues, and yellows. The hall where important visitors were formally received no longer looked like a royal throne room but rather like a chapel. An austere seat of stone flanked by two early Christian sculptures was substituted for the former gilt papal armchair on a dais. On the third floor Paul VI had his private quarters decorated with teak and modern art.

The new Milan-modern look of the Apostolic Palace was not just the whim of a pope who had had many artist friends, but conveyed the message that he wanted to run the Vatican in the way of a chief executive of a large, efficient organization rather than as a feudal monarch. Like a hard-working corporation president or banker who feels he has earned the right to indulge himself a bit, Paul VI had built, at great expense, an internal staircase and a roof terrace above his apartment so that he could exercise and get fresh air—prescribed to him by his doctor—in complete privacy. In fifteen years as pope he descended into the Vatican gardens only six times.

The papal study was filled with books, conspicuous among them the works of Jacques Maritain and other French Catholic writers. Paul VI considered himself a disciple of French philosophical and theological thinking. He would analyze every issue, endlessly weigh the pros and cons of every option, and torment himself with doubts and misgivings whenever he had a decision to make. It has often been reported, but it is not quite certain, that Pope John XXIII, who never appeared to be plagued by doubt, called Montini a "Hamlet." The characterization, at any rate, captured the essence of Paul VI's anguished personality.

The agonies Paul VI habitually went through when he was confronted with a grave issue were probably never so painful as when addressing the question of birth control. A commission, set up by Pope John XXIII and enlarged by his successor, had secretly been considering whether the Roman Catholic Church's ban on physical and chemical methods of contraception might be eased. After long debates the group took a moderately liberal stand, advising Paul VI that the church's traditional teachings in the matter could, and indeed should, be changed. The recommendations were leaked, and conservatives in the curia and at large started campaigning against them. Eventually, Paul VI rejected the findings of the commission.

His 1968 encyclical, "Humanae Vitae" (Of Human Life), upheld the thesis that all "artificial" birth control was sinful. The document set off a tornado of criticism and caused great strains within the church. In the long run it became plain that many Roman Catholics, especially in the United States and other Western countries, simply disregarded Paul VI's encyclical while continuing to go to church and take the sacraments. A large part of the clergy went along in the knowledge that the overwhelming majority of their congregations was practicing contraception. Some priests explained to their parishioners that "Humanae Vitae," like all other encyclicals, expressed the supreme teaching of the church, but was not a dogma based on papal infallibility; a future pontiff might make a different pronouncement. The jarring experience of the birth-control controversy saddened the last decade of Paul VI's pontificate. His mien became increasingly mournful, his voice plaintive.

This pope, who lacked the charisma of John XXIII (and knew it), and wasn't as imperious as Pius XII, seemed to slide into frequent black moods as he grew older. Rumors cropped up that he might resign and withdraw to a monastery, the first head of the church in modern times to renounce the throne of Saint Peter. Franz Cardinal Koenig of Vienna told me: "There is no doubt, the Holy Father is thinking of stepping down." Such speculation had been touched off by Paul VI himself, as early as 1966, when he made a surprise pilgrimage to the castle on Mount Fumone, south of Rome, where Pope Saint Celestine died as a virtual prisoner in A.D. 1296, seventeen months after he had given up the papacy. Dante, in the *Divine Comedy,* contemptuously alludes to Celestine's "cowardice" in making his "great refusal." A few years after the poet's death the church canonized the former pope as a saint.

Celestine had been a hermit in the Abruzzi mountains before being chosen, almost 80 years old, to lead the church in troubled times. He is best remembered for having become an ex-pope after being pope, but he is by no means the only man in history who had that experience. In the early Middle Ages various pontiffs withdrew more or less voluntarily, or were deposed. Benedict IX was removed from the papacy three times between 1044 and 1048. The Great Schism of the church saw three rivaling popes, each with his own "obedience," or faction, of cardinals, bishops, and courtiers. The Council of Constance (1414–18) ended the three-way split by forcing the resignation of Gregory XII, deposing two antipopes, John XXIII (whose numeral Angelo Roncalli was to claim in 1958) and Benedict XIII, and naming a new pontiff, Martin V. The 1917 codification of canon law expressly stated that if a pope wanted to "renounce," he did not need the approval of the cardinals or anybody else.

There was renewed guessing about whether Paul VI would eventually renounce when, in 1970, he ruled that cardinals after their 80th year could no longer take part in a conclave to elect a new pope. Earlier, Paul VI, in keeping with a recommendation by Vatican II, had ordered that all bishops must offer their resignations on reaching their 75th year of age. Paul VI's 75th and 80th birthdays came and went and there was no hint of withdrawal. A French writer, Jean Guitton, who was a friend of the pontiff, quoted him as saying that "a father cannot resign." He didn't seem a happy father.

The happiest expression I'd ever seen on Paul VI's face appeared one morning late in 1970, in Samoa. He was as far away from the Vatican as anyone who isn't an astronaut can get—at the antipodes. The first pontiff ever to have flown in an airplane, Pope Paul was on his longest and most tiring jet journey. I was traveling, together with other reporters, on the papal aircraft, and on our arrival in Manila we had witnessed a man, later identified as a Bolivian, lunging at the pontiff and trying, unsuccessfully, to attack him with a knife. As our jet touched down in Pago Pago, American Samoa, the Vatican dignitaries in first class and the journalists in economy-class compartments crammed with television gear and the other paraphernalia of our trade looked rather wilted after the long flight from the Philippines. Pope Paul, however, had a fresh and joyful countenance. Having spent most of his adult life in the confines of the Vatican, he must have discovered he really liked traveling, the wide world, the cheers of un-Roman crowds, and the exotic sounds and sights.

He had inaugurated the era of papal jet travel with a visit to the Holy Land—Jordan and Israel—soon after his election in 1964. During the last years of his life arthritic pains kept him from journeying farther than to Castel Gandolfo, where he died after a brief illness in August 1978.

Albino Luciani, patriarch of Venice, who succeeded Paul VI as Pope John Paul I for only 33 days, would be a dim figure in the rich tapestry of church chronicles. He is better remembered for his startling death than for what he did during his life, except for two decisions: he was the first pontiff in history to style himself with a double name, and he repudiated the age-old rite of coronation, thereby in effect abolishing it.

Since the early Middle Ages, popes had been crowned in a solemn ceremony. The papal triple crown, or tiara, was placed on the pope's head, implying that he wielded temporal, or political, power as well as spiritual authority.

The last pope on whose head the tiara was ceremonially placed was Paul VI, nine days after his election in 1963. At the beginning of the long, elaborate rite, an ecclesiastical master of ceremonies reminded the new pontiff in a form that went back to the Middle Ages that fame and power are fleeting and that death awaits everyone. As Paul VI approached the high altar, the master of ceremonies, holding a burning tuft of flax on a metal rod before him, chanted: "Sancte Patre, sic transit gloria mundi!" (Holy Father, thus passes away the glory of the world!). While the flame flickered and went out, the doleful warning was repeated two times. The remainder of the coronation ceremony was full of the traditional pageantry. The pope was formally enthroned, on either side an attendant with an ostrich-feather fan. The ranking cardinal deacon recited: "Receive the tiara, adorned with three crowns, and know that thou art the father of princes and ruler of kings, the vicar on earth of our Savior, Jesus Christ."

Pope Paul VI later donated the gem-studded triple crown, a gift from the city of Milan, to the archdiocese of New York during a drive to raise funds for poor people. The pope confirmed the validity of the archaic coronation ceremony in a church law issued in 1975. After a papal election, the text read, ". . . finally, the pontiff will be crowned by the senior cardinal deacon."

For the Roman Catholic Church, the pope is the supreme and sovereign lawgiver; each pontiff may revoke or change the edicts of his predecessors. Pope John Paul I, whose official motto had long been *Humilitas* (humility), simply ignored the crowning rite mentioned in Paul VI's legislation. Instead, he marked what he called the beginning of his "ministry as supreme shepherd" by a solemn outdoor mass in St. Peter's Square with a bishop's chair of authority instead of a throne, no tiara, no baldachin, and no ostrich feathers. During the inauguration liturgy, Pericle Cardinal Felici, a conservative curialist who had also been in the running for succession to Paul VI, acting in his role as the senior cardinal deacon, put the pallium, a band of white wool with black crosses, around the new pontiff's shoulders. The pallium symbolizes fullness of the episcopal office; receiving it, the new pope considered himself formally installed as the 263rd bishop of Rome.

Traditionalists in the Vatican, like Cardinal Felici, weren't too happy about John Paul I spurning the tiara. (As patriarch of Venice, the future pope had sold a golden chain and a pectoral cross that had once belonged to Pius XII to help finance an institution for handicapped children, and had urged his parish priests to get rid of unnecessary church plate and other valuables to raise more money for the same purpose.) The curia didn't like the discarding of the coronation rite by the newcomer from northern Italy because Rome's ecclesiastical bureaucracy, deriving its worldwide influence from the pontiff, frowns on anything that seems to diminish his stature, power, and glory. The proverbial attitude of being more papal than the pope lives above all in the offices of the Vatican.

John Paul I tried also to abolish the *sedia gestatoria,* the portable throne on which pontiffs are borne into St. Peter's or into audience halls by a squadron of seat carriers. However, when pilgrims who hadn't been able to conquer a vantage point in the throng complained they could hardly get a glimpse of the pope while he was making his appearance on foot, the practice of bringing him in aloft on the swaying chair was quickly restored, to the relief of the sediari, who had been worrying about their jobs.

The "smiling pontiff" devoted much time to preparing the addresses he delivered at his general audience every Wednesday. His speeches sounded homely and improvised, but were in fact carefully researched and rehearsed. In one of them, John Paul I delighted Romans by quoting Trilussa, a well-remembered and beloved vernacular poet whose oeuvre included many bawdy verses that the pontiff, an avid reader, must have known. During one of his general audiences, John Paul I called a little boy to his throne and before the crowd engaged in a question-and-answer session with him the way he may have done as a young curate in an Alpine village. Some Vatican aides rolled their eyes over this simplicity, but the throng in the audience hall was captivated. There is no doubt that if the pope with the winning smile had lived longer he would have developed a new, unpretentious manner of being head of the church.

However, less than four weeks after his inauguration, John Paul I was found dead in his bedroom in the Apostolic Palace. Rome was at once as thick with rumors of foul play as its air is with sand from the Libyan deserts when the autumn sirocco winds blow from the south.

Romans have reveled in spicy gossip about mighty figures in their city since antiquity, as Suetonius, Tacitus, and other Latin authors have shown. The metropolis has seen about everything in its 2,500 years of history, and I have again and again been told the most outrageous stories about popes, kings, presidents, and leading politicians. For scandal-loving Italians, prominent personages are forever cuckolds, sodomites, lechers lusting for young blood, and whores; they are impotent, feebleminded, corrupt, and above all, *jettatori*—persons endowed with the evil eye. The heads of the church are not immune to such slander. The deaths of the powerful in the Eternal City are usually surrounded by much curiosity, often of a malevolent kind. The end of Pope Pius XII, as has been recalled earlier, bared the unsavory affair of his doctor; a poison plot was suspected when Pius XI died in 1939, just before he was to deliver an address critical of the Fascist regime; there was talk of poison after the deaths of Saint Pius X at the outbreak of World War I in August 1914, of Leo XIII (at the age of 93 years in 1903), and of Pius VIII in 1830. Farther back in the annals of the papacy, chroniclers have recorded assassinations and mayhem; a lethal "white powder" was a notorious technique of pontifical policy under the Borgia pope, Alexander VI.

So, in 1978, Romans delighted in the "plot theory" of John Paul I's death that sprang up overnight. It seemed to corroborate their worst assumptions about Vatican cabals, and to fit in with the terroristic and Mafia-style conspiracies that at the time had become a pattern of life in Italy and its capital.

Hadn't the Metropolitan Nikodim, the visiting representative of the Russian Orthodox Church in the Soviet Union, died in John Paul I's arms during an audience? Yes, they said it was described as heart failure, but hadn't it actually been the effect of poison ("white powder"?) in a cup of tea—or was it coffee?— really destined for the pope? Nothing new there, of course, for Alexander VI had died in a similar mix-up in 1503: only the poison then had been supplied by himself or his son, Cesare Borgia, and was meant for the pontiff's guests, the cardinals.

Why should anyone have wanted to dispatch the "smiling pope" so soon after his elevation? Roman gossip had a scandalous reply to that question too. The story told gleefully around the city was that the Vatican power brokers who had chosen the little-known Cardinal Luciani had soon realized, to their dismay, that he was obviously incapable of governing the church and was squandering its money in freewheeling donations; they decided to eliminate him at once before he could do major harm.

Actually, in the conclave of August 1978, a majority of the cardinals who had assembled in Rome, most of them from outside Italy, had picked their colleague from Venice as the new pontiff because he had never served in the Vatican and was expected to guard his independence of its bureaucracy. Nobody can say how Pope John Paul I eventually would have dealt with the curia. Usually, however, there is a "curial party," and Luciani certainly was not its candidate in 1978.

In the days after the pope's death, four Vatican officials told me separately, in almost identical terms and with similar tones of condescension, that "poor Cardinal Luciani" who had spent his life in the mountains of his native Dolomites region and on the calm Venetian lagoon before he was suddenly transplanted to the Apostolic Palace, had simply been overwhelmed by his new powers and responsibilities. All those dignitaries to see day after day, those secret reports to read and documents to sign, those decisions to make had caused his weak heart to yield to the unaccustomed strain.

Rome learned incredulously from official accounts that the entourage of the "smiling pope" had let him die alone, like a traveler whose cold body is found in a hotel bed by the maid. To make matters worse, the curia dealt ineptly with the inevitable questions.

Traditionally, the death of a pope is a vast and somber tableau. Cardinals and other high churchmen are summoned to his bedchamber and glumly look on as doctors hover over the sinking patient. The pontiff's chaplain or sacristan administers communion and the sacrament that in a stern past was known as extreme unction and is now called the "anointment of the sick." Friars murmur litanies. The nuns who were in charge of the papal household huddle in a corner in tearful prayer. Until modern clinical practices took over, a dignitary would hold a feather or a burning candle before the dying pope's mouth to see whether he was still breathing.

When all signs of ebbing life seemed to have ceased, the cardinal camerlengo tapped the pontiff's head with a silver hammer three times, calling him by the name he had been given in baptism and had heard from his mother. If there was no response and it was certain that the head of the church was dead, the camerlengo, or chamberlain, broke the fisherman's ring, the heavy golden band bearing the emblem of Saint Peter with which the dead pope had sealed his most solemn documents.

When Pope John Paul I died, at the age of 65 years, nobody was aware of it. His end came suddenly, the Vatican stated, while he was reading in bed; the lamp on his night table was still burning in the morning.

According to the official statement, a Vatican doctor had "certified that the unexpected death [of John Paul I] occurred at 11:00 P.M. on September 28 owing to myocardiac arrest," a form of heart failure.

According to the terse announcement, one of the pontiff's two secretaries, the Reverend John Magee, entered his bedroom toward 5:30 A.M., having in vain awaited the pope in his private chapel for the usual morning mass, and found him dead. Actually, a nun had been the first person to sense that something was wrong when she noticed that a cup of coffee that she had put on a table outside the papal bedroom had remained untouched. The nun alerted Father Magee (an Irishman who had also served as an English interpreter and secretary to Pope Paul VI).

That first official account didn't say that the pope had apparently felt ill and tried to summon help by pressing a button on the night table. The secretary who was supposed to have been on duty in the pontifical suite apparently hadn't heard him, and neither had the nuns from Venice who were assigned to the papal quarters, or the Swiss Guard who were posted outside. Even if the pope had been attended promptly in what may have been a coronary occlusion, no defibrillator or any other intensive-care equipment would have been quickly available. (The Vatican medical services have since been modernized.)

And what had John Paul I been reading when he was stricken? A Vatican spokesman at first stated the pontiff was found holding an edition of the *Imitation of Christ* by Thomas a Kempis. The edifying story that the last lines the bookish pope had been perusing were devotional was later dropped. The substitute version was that John Paul I had been reading a document, but its nature was never disclosed; whence a spate of rumors. It was suggested, among other things, that the pontiff, already under strain, had been mortally shocked by a confidential report on the Vatican's finances or by secret charges against a prominent prelate. Another rumor said John Paul I had been struck down while revising a severe address that he was to deliver in front of the leadership of the troubled Jesuit order. A text of such a proposed speech was in fact published after his death.

Why was no postmortem performed to determine the causes and nature of John Paul's last illness? Vatican officials explained lamely that the apostolic constitution "On the Vacancy of the Holy See," issued by Pope Paul VI in 1975, lacked any provision regarding an autopsy after a pontiff's death. Actually, Pope Paul's 1975 legislation was highly detailed in some points (including a rule on which vestments the cardinals should wear when they meet), vague in others. It said that "no one is permitted to take photographs of the supreme pontiff, whether on his sickbed or after his death, or to record his words on tape," an overt allusion to the abuses during Pius XII's agony, but didn't mention embalming or prohibit an autopsy. The impression remains that the Vatican was not eager to investigate the sudden death of the "smiling pope."

Despite the shortness of his pontificate (he would have objected to the word "reign"), John Paul I left a vivid memory in the Roman populace, who loved him. His portraits continued selling briskly in souvenir stores long after a new, forceful pontiff had acceded to the throne of Saint Peter.

CHARISMA FROM POLAND

When the cardinals reassembled in Rome in October 1978 to elect a successor to John Paul I, many of them were again searching for one of their rank who was not identified with the Vatican curia. This time, in a bold and imaginative vote, for the first time since 1522, they chose a pontiff from outside Italy.

The archbishop of Krakow, Poland, Karol Cardinal Wojtyla, who became Pope John Paul II, must have reread the story of his remote predecessor from Utrecht, Adrian VI. The Romans had made fun of the earnest, well-meaning churchman, who had been Archduke Charles's (Emperor Charles V) tutor; the curia had lustily indulged in its habitual intrigues while, far away in the north the defiant Augustinian monk, Martin Luther, was translating the Bible into German. When the Dutch pope, a deeply frustrated man, died nineteen months after his election, the Romans mockingly adorned his doctor's house with flowers. The inevitable rumors of a poison plot swept Europe. His brief, unhappy pontificate seemed to prove once and for all that a "foreigner" had no chance on the slippery marble floors in the Vatican. There has never been a Pope Adrian VII.

The first non-Italian pontiff since then, and the first Slav in history to sit on Saint Peter's throne appeared to have realized from the beginning that he needed the goodwill of the Romans, and had to be careful in handling the curia. In his first public speech, an hour after his election, he wooed the crowd in St. Peter's Square by apologizing for any slip he might make "in your—our Italian," adding: "If I make a mistake you will correct me."

The day after his election, John Paul II made what was to be the first of his many sorties from the Vatican. He slipped out of the pontifical state, to the dismay of aides and the security services, to visit an old Polish friend, Bishop Andrzej Maria Deskur, in hospital. Bishop Deskur, who was chief of the curia's office for communications media, had suffered a stroke and was under treatment in Gemelli Hospital on Mount Mario, about two miles from Vatican City. John Paul II stayed for a long time in his stricken friend's sickroom, and then briefly addressed a crowd of doctors, nurses, and patients who had gathered in the corridor outside. When the new pontiff turned to leave, one of the few men who had accompanied him to the hospital, Archbishop Giuseppe Caprio, whispered something into his ear. "Ah, yes," John Paul II said aloud. "He told me I should give you my blessing. And he is right. You see, I still have to learn how to be a pope." And then he made the sign of the cross with his hand and said the Latin benediction formula. Archbishop Caprio, a southerner who forever seems to be fighting five-o'clock shadow, later became a cardinal.

Actually, John Paul II appeared to be totally sure of himself from the very start of his pontificate, as if he had trained for it all his life. He brought instant charisma to his office, coupled with an unfailing sense of its dignity. From his first moment as pope he spoke in the way his predecessor, John Paul I, had done during 33 days in the Vatican—he used the word "I." The majestic "we" of earlier pontiffs would henceforth be banned even from encyclicals.

John XXIII and Paul VI had referred to themselves in first person plural in documents and addresses, but usually said "I" on less formal occasions. John XXIII had also done away with the pompous style in which *L'Osservatore Romano* had until then published the text of papal remarks. Under Pius XII the standard presentation had been: "Following is the allocution by His Holiness as we have gathered His words from His august lips." John XXIII had told the editors of the pontifical newspaper: "Just write, 'the pope said' or 'the pope did.' "

The Polish pope also followed the example of his self-effacing predecessor, John Paul I, in the ritual of his investiture; he had himself installed as bishop of Rome with the pallium, and refrained from having the tiara put on his head. It is a moot question whether John Paul II would have renounced the coronation if John Paul I had not done so such a short time before him. The concept of a papal superroyalty, a universal kingdom of faith above all secular rulers, might have held a strong appeal to the patriotic Pole, whose nation once was a monarchy before it was carved up by Russia, Prussia, and Austria. The Polish church, which even today doesn't disdain the pageantry of clerical power, promotes the cult of Our Lady of Jasna Gora, the dark Madonna icon in the national shrine on the Mountain of Light, as "Queen of Poland." One could imagine the first Polish pope being attracted by the triple crown, hadn't his predecessor forestalled the display of the ancient emblem. Later in his pontificate, Pope John Paul II did show remarkable flair for the sartorial splendor of his office—the cut, coloring, and adornments of pontifical robes, and their effectiveness on television.

Five days after his election, John Paul II broke new ground by improvising what was in effect the first papal press conference ever held. The setting was the Hall of Benedictions above the portico of St. Peter's, filled with hundreds of news reporters, photographers, and television crews for what had been scheduled as a special audience for the press. The three previous pontiffs had had a few similar encounters with journalists, and on those occasions had given predictable speeches urging the press to report "the truth" and to shun rumors and sensationalism. John Paul II's prepared address didn't depart from the pattern. But then something new happened. The Polish pope stepped down from his dais, followed by flustered Vatican dignitaries, and informally spoke to the reporters thronging behind the wooden barriers on either side of the central passageway like a politician working the crowd.

In the give-and-take, the new pontiff genially answered questions, switching from Italian to Polish, from English to French, German, and even Russian. One newsman, alluding to the Polish pope's well-known love of the outdoors and of winter sports, asked: "Holy Father, will you go skiing again?" John Paul II glanced over his shoulder at his new Vatican aides and said ruefully: "I don't think they'll permit me to do that."

John Paul II wouldn't get on skis again, but he would work out physically. His early decision to have a covered swimming pool built in the Castel Gandolfo estate shocked conservative churchmen, caused Romans to gossip endlessly about the "athlete of Christ," delighted cartoonists, and contributed like few other innovations to impressing on devout Roman Catholics that the charismatic head of their church was just a man like others.

No pope has ever been known to go swimming, although Saint Peter, the fisherman, might have practiced in the Tiber River what he had probably learned in the Sea of Galilee. Quite a number of pontiffs in history fancied strenuous physical exertion. Pope Pius II, the fifteenth-century humanist from Siena, was an outdoorsman; the warrior pope, Julius II, braved hardship as leader of his own troops; and Leo X, the Augustan son of the magnificent Lorenzo de' Medici, not only patronized Raphael but also liked to hunt in the surroundings of Rome—not bothering to get out of his muddy boots when someone wanted to perform obeisance and kiss the "sacred slipper." But that was the Renaissance.

More recently, popes have gotten most of their exercise from strolls in the Vatican gardens. Pius XI often sighed, alas, he would never again be able to climb his beloved Alpine slopes. His successor, Pius XII, delicate though he looked, pedaled and rowed on training machines installed in a gymnastics room in his private apartment. Paul VI had his promenade on top of the Apostolic Palace.

The Castel Gandolfo swimming pool with the pope in it represented an irresistible challenge to the Roman paparazzi, and that aggressive tribe lived up to its reputation for cunning and perseverance. Several free-lance photographers uncharacteristically

41

banded together and, eventually, from a hollowed-out tree near the papal bathhouse, shot the series of pictures that were sold throughout the world.

When the mass-circulation magazines published the photos, an Italian writer, Ferdinando Camon, observed: "These pictures would have been sacrilegious with Pope Pius XII, unthinkable with John XXIII, incredible with Paul VI; they are normal for John Paul II." The comment illustrated how demythologized the person of the pontiff had become.

The photos of the muscular Pole, then nearly 60 years old, crossing himself before entering the water, and swimming with a forceful breaststroke, were felt to be much less scandalous than those of Pius XII on his deathbed. There were also rumors that a picture of John Paul II, naked while changing into or out of his swimming trunks, was in existence somewhere.

From the beginning of his pontificate, the vigorous Polish pope caused speculation about the physical side of his personality. Romans noted that in his doctrinal addresses during the weekly general audiences the pontiff seemed to concentrate on themes that had to do with sex—even with sex, or rather the absence of it, in heaven. Couples who had been married on earth would meet again in paradise, the pope told his listeners one day, but there would be no physical relationship. *Il Messaggero* of Rome carried a cartoon picturing an evidently frustrated man and woman in Eden, the legend in the little balloon reading: "Let's go back to earth!"

There were also stories in Rome about the young Karol Wojtyla—the worker in the Solvay chemical plant in Krakow, poet, and amateur actor—having been briefly married, or at least engaged to marry, a young woman who had died. Similar tales were told in Poland shortly after John Paul II's elevation.

In Warsaw, a Communist government official, Religious Affairs Minister Kazimierz Kakol, confided to me piously: "Don't be surprised if one day some impostor were to claim he or she is a child of the pope. That's precisely the kind of rumor that may be set afloat to discredit the pope and Poland." The minister kept a straight face, but I sensed he didn't really mind the suggestion that the Holy Father might also be a biological parent. Shortly after I returned from Poland to Rome, an Italian magazine, *Oggi,* published photos—"world exclusive"—showing Cardinal Wojtyla, the future pope, relaxing during what was said to have been an outing in the countryside near

Krakow in 1975. The archbishop and cardinal, in a T-shirt and shorts, had been photographed in the company of younger men and women in hiking attire. A few pictures showed him near an attractive blond woman, playing with a little boy, apparently hers. Such snapshots were "truly unusual to us Italians," a tongue-in-cheek caption said. "One has never before seen a cardinal in shorts, sitting on the grass." However, the magazine explained soothingly, the Polish pope had always been noted for his informality and his desire to communicate with his fellow beings.

On the day *Oggi* with its startling pictures went on sale, at least half a dozen Romans, including a couple of priests, winking and smirking, asked me, didn't I agree that the little boy shown climbing all over the future pope was the spitting image of a child-sized John Paul II, surely his offspring? A Polish nun, who had been living in Rome for many years, said tearfully: "It's a trick photo—those Italians will do anything to slander our pope—nothing is sacred."

The pope who, as a cardinal, had enjoyed leaving his fortress-like palace in Krakow to go hiking and skiing, showed from the start of his pontificate that he didn't feel comfortable within the narrow confines of the Vatican. He managed to get out far more often than any of his predecessors of the last century. Almost every Sunday he visited one of Rome's churches, often on the city's outskirts, or some ecclesiastical institution. Every now and then he retreated to Castel Gandolfo for quiet work and exercise in his swimming pool. When he was in the Vatican he occasionally stole out of the Apostolic Palace, accompanied only by his Polish secretary, incognito—or so he seemed to think (an Italian police detail would discreetly tail him). He would usually visit the Polish ecclesiastical hospice in the heart of Rome for a few evening hours of chatting and relaxation. Added piquancy was provided by the circumstance that the Polish institution and its Church of St. Stanislas is next door to the massive pseudo-Renaissance palace that houses the national headquarters of the Italian Communist party.

Above all, the restless pontiff enthusiastically engaged in the pattern of pontifical jet travel that Paul VI had developed. For months, preparations, including language coaching, for each of his trips abroad absorbed much of John Paul II's time and energy, and kept many Vatican aides busy. In almost all of the countries the pope visited he was cheered by immense crowds—

Turkey was the exception—and everywhere he was deferentially welcomed by the civil authorities.

The papal journeys were international media events, prompted postal administrations to issue commemorative stamps, and brought the head of the Roman Catholic Church in touch with local officials and representatives of other faiths. The travels also showed up the extent and limits of papal power in the present world. The apotheosis of the Polish pope in his homeland only seven months after his election and again in 1983 proved to be a stirring emotional experience for millions of his countrymen, releasing religious and patriotic forces that were to be felt for years to come. John Paul II's sojourn in Ireland also was a triumph, but his plea for an end to the violence in Ulster fell on deaf ears. In the United States, the pontiff, who revealed a genius for public relations, received more television time and newspaper space than any other visitor—but was there any lasting impact? For instance, the majority of Roman Catholics in America went on ignoring the Vatican ban on contraception as they had done before, although the pontiff had sternly restated the church's rigorous stand.

In the curia, many prelates became increasingly vocal in airing their misgivings about John Paul II's wanderlust. "All this journeying is harmful to the papal mystique," a cardinal who had once been a pontifical diplomat told me. "As long as he stays in the Vatican, the Holy Father is surrounded by mystery and awe. He really ought to show himself only on rare occasions— every one of his public appearances would thus be an important event. People will listen to what he has to say if he doesn't speak too often."

The cardinal went on: "Papal travels, if they must take place at all, should serve important purposes—Poland, perhaps, was such a case—and become historical milestones, to be remembered for centuries. But the supreme pontiff mustn't become a competitor of the United Nations secretary general. The pope's job is to govern the church from the Vatican, to act as the highest moral authority on earth, not to seek acclaim all over the globe. Let papal legates do the traveling. Besides, in a world full of nuts and terrorists all those trips are dangerous. Mark my word, sooner or later something terrible is going to happen."

A couple of months after the cardinal's worried remarks something did happen, but it happened in St. Peter's Square.

The attack on the pontiff by a Turkish gunman on May 13,

1981, when John Paul II was grievously wounded, may also be viewed as a violent episode in the process of the papacy becoming demythologized. Through the centuries, popes have been slain, poisoned, physically abused, and taken prisoner. Pius IX, the nineteenth-century pontiff, had to flee from the Vatican when his subjects in the pontifical state proclaimed the Roman Republic (which was to have a brief life), and even after his death ran the risk of ending up in the Tiber. Pius IX's successors were spared brushes with violence until 1970, when Paul VI was assaulted in Manila.

John Paul II became the first pontiff in history to be taken to a public hospital. Only minutes after Mehmet Ali Agça, the assailant, had fired shots at the pope, the ambulance that stood by during his public audiences rushed him to the Gemelli clinic. There the pontiff, who was in critical condition, underwent surgery that saved his life.

As recently as 1967 clinical equipment had to be moved into the Apostolic Palace, and a team of doctors and nurses had to work in the unfamiliar and possibly unsanitary surroundings of a Renaissance building when Pope Paul VI required a prostatic operation. The surgery was successful, but it was understood at the time that the patient would have remained in the Vatican for further treatment if complications had occurred.

The Polish pope was in shock and was rapidly losing blood as he was put in the ambulance, but his aides knew they were acting according to his wishes when they ordered the driver to race to the Gemelli. It was the same medical complex that John Paul II had visited the day after his election. He must have been favorably impressed by the institution, which serves as the teaching hospital for the Rome medical school of the Sacred Heart University in Milan. (Located on Mount Mario, the heights on Rome's northern outskirts that aren't part of the historic Seven Hills, the hospital is named after the Reverend Agostino Gemelli, a Franciscan friar and scientist who was president of the Roman Catholic University in Milan.) The pontiff had given instructions that if he ever needed emergency treatment he wanted to undergo it at the Gemelli.

After John Paul II's six-hour operation and during his days in the hospital's intensive-care unit, his doctors reported publicly on his condition as they would have done with regard to any other prominent patient. The outside world was told about the pope's temporary colostomy, a procedure whereby a bowel is cut and an artificial opening in the patient's tissues and skin is made to give a portion of wounded large intestine time to heal without body wastes passing through. The public was also informed of the pontiff's temperature readings and other clinical data. This too was an innovation, because the medical bulletins that were sometimes issued when previous popes were seriously ill used to be in bland and general terms. John Paul II himself, in weekly messages that were taped in his sickroom, told the faithful of his "sufferings," obviously meaning physical pain. Such candor was apt to bring home even to mystically inclined Roman Catholics that the "vicar of Christ" was a clinical case who, though in the care of an elite team of physicians and nursing personnel, had to endure his share of discomfort.

As John Paul II's life hung by a thread, and in the many weeks afterward when his progress was slower than his doctors had hoped, the curia seemed close to being confronted with a problem that has never been solved: how to govern the church when the pope is incapacitated. In theory, the supreme pontiff exercises his vast powers until the moment of his death, and some of them cannot be delegated. Only the pope can name cardinals and bishops, only he can summon a general assembly of the church hierarchy (the ecumenical council), and only he can infallibly define a new dogma. His decision, or at least his formal consent, is also needed for a great number of other matters, like the release of priests from clerical vows or the proclamation of new saints.

When a pope is seriously ill, major church business just stops, although the Vatican machinery keeps clanking on with routine matters. Visitors to the pontifical enclave the day after the attack on John Paul II noted that curial committees were holding their scheduled meetings, dignitaries were receiving bishops from distant sees who had come to Rome to discuss the affairs of their dioceses, and documents were being sent back and forth between the departments of the church's central administration as they always have been.

Yet at the same time various cardinals were quietly consulting with one another—some by long-distance telephone—about what should be done if John Paul II were unable to carry out his functions for a long time. In the thicket of canon law, as it has evolved since the Middle Ages, there is no provision for emergency procedures in case a pontiff lapses into a long coma or becomes certifiably insane. True, such occurrences seem remote, but they are not totally improbable. Toward the end of his long life, Leo XIII was said to have had only a few lucid intervals every day. Paul VI was plagued by gaps in his memory in his last few years. When an aide reminded him one day that President Nicolae Ceauşescu of Rumania would appear for an audience, the pope was upset and asked why he hadn't been told earlier about such an important visit; actually, his staff had briefed him at length, and memos on what he should bring up in the talks had been on his desk for weeks.

The attack in St. Peter's Square also raised another unsettling question: what if a terrorist gang were to kidnap the head of the church and hold him incommunicado? After all, the ultraleftist Red Brigades had managed to abduct a former Italian prime minister, Aldo Moro, in Rome in 1978, while killing five of his bodyguards. They had subjected the politician to a mock trial in a secret "people's prison," and had eventually assassinated him. All the police forces of Italy had proved unable to free the prisoner, and the terrorists had also ignored Paul VI's plea "on my knees," to spare the life of his friend, Mr. Moro.

Pope John Paul II recovered, but the muted discussion on how to cope with a hypothetical situation in which the supreme pontiff is incapacitated continued among the cardinals. They are the pope's electors, and each of them has what might be called a vested interest in the pontifical throne, each being a potential successor to the incumbent head of the church. The cardinals would be eager to fill the vacuum if the pope were not able to function. However, the unofficial consultations among key prelates reached no consensus; the potential problem of how to rule the church when a pontiff is alive but is for a prolonged period unable to do so remained unsolved. When the Vatican issued a new codification of canon law in 1983, it again lacked any provision concerning procedures to be followed if the supreme pontiff were incapacitated.

Early in 1983 there had been new fears for John Paul's physical safety when he visited Costa Rica, El Salvador, Nicaragua, Panama, Guatemala, Honduras, Belize, and Haiti. Leftists heckled the pontiff during mass in Nicaragua, but no violence occurred throughout the fatiguing trip. High churchmen in Rome nevertheless shook their heads, and privately questioned the wisdom of Pope John Paul's "pastoral visits" to such unstable countries.

The Polish pope showed himself aware of such curial criticism when he returned to Rome, and shrugged it off. "With that pope," he told a small crowd in Castel Gandolfo with mock exasperation, "one never knows where he is—in the Vatican or abroad." John Paul II appeared to enjoy the image of an itinerant head of the church, always on the move, unfazed by danger.

CHAPTER 3

CARDINAL POWER

NOBODY SPEAKS TO the pope like a cardinal: whenever the head of the church receives a member of the sacred college in private audience he may expect a show of reverence, but he may also be in for some straight talk. There are often overtones of uneasiness in the dealings between the pontiff and individual members of the college of cardinals, and sometimes such hidden strains are also felt in the halls of the Vatican. The pope is aware that his visitor in scarlet might one day become his successor; the odds may seem formidable, but church history records many instances when a long-shot candidate gained the throne of Saint Peter. Unless the reigning pontiff himself has given the red hat to the man standing before him, he probably won't know whether the cardinal voted for or against him in the conclave that led to his own elevation. Popes expect special loyalty and support from members of the sacred college whom they themselves have named, and naturally resent it if such members prove to be their own men. Besides, gratitude is no more a universal trait among prelates than it is among other people. All this makes for a certain subterranean awkwardness in the relationship between the supreme pontiff and the cardinals.

The office of the cardinals lacks any foundation whatsoever in Christian theology. The appointive aristocracy of the Roman Catholic Church developed in the Middle Ages, and since 1059 the cardinals have elected the popes. For many centuries dominated by Italians, only after World War II did the sacred college become more representative of the Roman Catholic orbit by the inclusion of a larger number of non-Italian members. And since 1978, when a majority of cardinals in two consecutive papal elections bypassed the favorites of the Roman Curia, the sacred college seems to have asserted a more corporate role. At the same time the archbishops and bishops throughout the world, who are much more numerous than the select circle of cardinals, have insisted on sharing responsibility with the pontiff in the government of the church, although he, at least in principle, remains its absolute ruler. In practice, the new tendencies toward power among cardinals on the one hand and bishops and archbishops on the other may eventually lead to a watering down of papal power and, especially, downgrading of the Roman Curia.

In Roman Catholic doctrine the pope is the successor of Saint Peter, and the archbishops and bishops are the successors of the other apostles. An Italian prelate who had just been consecrated archbishop and was soon to become a cardinal once remarked to me: "Being archbishop means having attained the fullness of the priesthood. Becoming a cardinal means nothing under divine law. Jesus spoke of shepherds; He never spoke of cardinals. The pope might as well name me a knight commander of some order of chivalry instead of giving me the scarlet." The churchman who professed such disdain for the cardinalate failed to mention the actual power that goes with it, divine law or not. But, in theory, some future pope could abolish the sacred college altogether without infringing on the basic tenets of Roman Catholic faith.

Throughout history ambitious churchmen have striven and schemed to win the red hat. When I once visited the late Archbishop-Bishop Fulton J. Sheen, the "television bishop" of the 1950s, in Rochester, New York, where he had become the head of the diocese, he said: "I could have gone higher and higher in the church if I had paid the price." He obviously meant he might have become a cardinal, but he didn't tell me what the price was —full submission to Cardinal Spellman? more money for the Vatican? less concern for minority groups than Sheen was able to show in Rochester?

Whatever the hitch in Sheen's case, a good way of getting the red hat is to have the right connections in Rome.

CLUB OF THE SCARLET HATS

The first act of pontifical mass and the other liturgical spectacles that are periodically enacted in St. Peter's, or in the piazza outside the huge church, is the obeisance of the cardinals. At times there is a pontifical ceremony every week—a canonization, a beatification, or a papal requiem for some deceased prelate—and at other times months may pass before the pope again receives the parade of the cardinals.

One by one the men in rustling scarlet silk and brocade file past the pontiff who, miter on his head, is seated on his throne, and each bends and kisses his hand. The pontiff will then get up to embrace one or another, or even each one, of the prelates who are paying homage to him. Such marks of special favor will be keenly noted and commented upon. Some twenty of the cardinals who live in Rome and perhaps one or two other ones from outside the city may participate in the rite, or—on special occasions —most of the 120 or 130 men who today make up the sacred college.

The men in front of the pope are the princes of the church, although the title is no longer in official use. Their ritual to honor their sovereign symbolizes the self-perpetuating nature of the papacy, a kind of institutional immortality that is one of the strengths of the Roman Catholic Church. The system, peculiar to the Church of Rome, whereby its head names the cardinals and they in turn choose the pope, has on the whole been successful. There have been no antipopes or major schisms implicating members of the sacred college since the fifteenth century.

The cardinals who bend their knees before the enthroned pontiff are his "creatures"—or those of one of his recent predecessors—handpicked lords who have been coopted into the aristocracy of the church. Each of them may be the next pope, and many of them, maybe all, will be electors of a successor to the man before whom they are humbly parading.

The sacred college of cardinals is the oldest club in the world and, despite recent broadening of its membership, still one of the most exclusive. To be a cardinal is at least as prestigious as being a Nobel laureate; a prince of the church radiates a sense of power as does a United States senator, and never has to worry about reelection.

When they enter Vatican City, the members of the sacred col-

51

lege instinctively strike proprietary attitudes. They don't own the place, but they will run it and the entire church government, collectively, in the interregnum between the death of the current pontiff and the election of the next.

Watch Their Eminences when they attend one of the many diplomatic receptions in Rome. More than fifty governments maintain permanent embassies to the Holy See in the Italian capital, and most of them throw open their doors for formal parties to mark their national holidays or some other event. No such diplomatic affair is a success unless at least a brace of cardinals are present; sometimes half a dozen or more turn up. On such occasions the princes of the church tend to talk mainly to one another, like the members of the Soviet politburo at Moscow receptions, though the cardinals often haughtily stay away from the buffet, which the Kremlin rulers generally do not.

What do the princes of the church talk about when they meet? Mostly about their sovereign, the supreme pontiff. What the pope does or doesn't do, his public pronouncements and private remarks, the conduct of his entourage, and, most important, the state of his health, are constantly under the cardinals' scrutiny. Court gossip. It is all done very respectfully, at least on the surface; the barbs are underneath. Some of the cardinals who live permanently in Rome have only to look at each other on certain days to know what they are all thinking about—maybe a newspaper report that the Holy Father seems fatigued, or what sounded like a theological blunder in his latest address.

The cardinals of the Roman Curia at times gaze at one another with the proverbial enigmatic smiles of the augurs, the official soothsayers of ancient Rome.

They will never say so quite openly, but the men in scarlet are forever thinking of the day when the good Lord will call his servant of servants, the pope, to heaven, and they will all be governing the church for a few heady weeks until one of them becomes the new vicar of Jesus Christ on earth.

With the exciting prospect of the next conclave in mind—it may be held in a month or in ten years—the cardinals patiently build alliances, acquire newcomers to their number and initiate them into the club, maybe work at burnishing their own images if they think of themselves as *papabiles,* men of papal timber. But ecclesiastical Rome can be an excruciatingly slow-moving world. Some of the cardinals who reside in the Vatican or elsewhere in the city go to the diplomatic parties because they have little else to do and like to meet their peers to exchange sardonic jokes in language so cryptic that an eavesdropper wouldn't know what it is all about.

Those princes of the church who have plenty of time on their hands are generally very old. As a group, the sacred college boasts an enviable record for longevity. "The red hat automatically adds fifteen years to a prelate's life expectancy," the secretary of a "young" cardinal in his fifties told me with a smile that could have been a clerical sneer. It is also said that "all sick cardinals miraculously get well the moment the pope dies."

Other members of the sacred college attend the embassy receptions because they must do so for reasons of protocol. They are the chiefs of the pope's Secretariat of State and of other Vatican departments. They briefly talk to their hosts, chat a little with the other cardinals present, and depart early; some of them are very busy.

Other cardinals come to Rome only occasionally, and their visits may mean important developments in church affairs or even in their home countries' or international politics. They are the archbishops of the big Italian cities—Milan, Florence, Naples, and others—and the incumbents of important sees around the world, from Paris to New York, from Warsaw to Manila. On their arrival they report to the pope, and they need his consent, though it is now usually a mere formality, when they plan to leave Rome again.

During their stay in the city they attend meetings of the Sacred Congregations, or curia departments, to which they are permanently assigned; confer with Vatican officials and superiors of religious orders on matters concerning their own area; perhaps meet with the ambassador of their home country; and have confidential exchanges with their peers in the sacred college about the latest high-level gossip. A visiting cardinal from an important archbishopric somewhere in the world always has a crowded schedule in Rome—luncheons and dinners, diplomatic parties, audiences, consultations in various Vatican offices, maybe a lecture in an ecclesiastical college or university, and the obligatory religious ceremonies.

In the Vatican, old hands note perceptible shades in the way individual cardinals are received. The Swiss Guard at the gate present their halberds in the same snappy manner to each one of Their Eminences, but from then on there are nuances. Toward the cardinals who are archbishops of New York or Chicago, Cologne, or Mechelen-Brussels and represent great wealth in addition to political and ecclesiastical influence, the doorkeepers and domestic prelates of the pontifical antechamber will be more deferential than to members of the sacred college from Africa or Asia. Some cardinals from rich archdioceses who are known to take care of Vatican subalterns and leave generous gratuities are fawned upon. Some princes of the church manage to get a papal audience within hours; others have to wait a few days. Third World cardinals who come to Rome for financial help may feel ever so slightly patronized.

During my time in Rome, the visitor with probably the strongest clout in the Vatican was Cardinal Spellman of New York. He was thoroughly familiar with the ambiance and methods of the curia because he had worked for years in its Secretariat of State; his friendship with Pope Pius XII went back to those days. He brought fat checks, in dollars, for the pontiff and various church projects, and didn't forget to tip the Vatican flunkies. He was chummy with Pius XII's three nephews and other members of the papal entourage, and it was said that some of his friends were awarded Vatican City dealerships for an American automobile firm or gained some other lucrative sideline through the good offices of the well-connected cardinal from New York. Mother Pasqualina also liked Cardinal Spellman, and he was eventually to become her protector when powerful Vatican figures turned against her.

While other visiting members of the sacred college were, according to an old custom, staying in some convent or ecclesiastical college where they were honored guests, Cardinal Spellman almost always stayed at the Grand Hotel. He preferred the amenities of the establishment—which still breathes the traditions of the fabled César Ritz—to the often indifferent plumbing, food, and service of church institutions around town. Clerical Rome chuckled when during one of Cardinal Spellman's visits thieves raided his hotel suite and carried off his golden pectoral cross together with other valuables.

Like every other member of the sacred college, the archbishop of New York had what is known as a titular church in Rome—in Cardinal Spellman's case it was the church of Saints John and Paul—with an adjoining monastery where he might have stayed (and once actually did). Cardinal Spellman used to joke he couldn't afford to live near his titular church because the good fathers of the Passionist order to whom the 1,500-year-old com-

54

plex is entrusted would present him with new plans for costly repair and restoration work every time he visited. Much money from the archdiocese of New York did go into the church and monastery of Saints John and Paul. The buildings on the Caelian hill south of the Colosseum are today one of the best-preserved landmarks in the Eternal City.

The assumption that each cardinal, whether he lives in the Vatican, in New York, or in Karachi, is in charge of one of the hundreds of churches in Rome, permits him to represent the sacred college as a part, and indeed the cream, of the city's clergy. Such participation in the pastoral care for the population, though only symbolic today, is an important prop for the church historians who have to explain why the pope, as bishop of Rome, is elected by the cardinals. In early Christianity, as it happens, the Roman clergy and people chose their own spiritual leaders. As the presumed successor to Saint Peter, the bishop of Rome also enjoyed special authority among Christians in faraway places. A large part of this prestige was due to the fact that the city of Rome itself inspired awe all over the known world.

The pope thus based his claim to a paramount role, or primacy, in the world-wide Christian church on his function as bishop of Rome. By the eleventh century, however, the democratic procedure of election by the clergy and people of Rome had broken down, and a group of grand electors, the cardinals, began to choose the pontiff. To justify their role, they maintained the historical-legal fiction that they were (or at least represented) the clergy of Rome. This fiction is still alive today. The cardinals elect the pope, who in turn appoints new cardinals on the pretense that he is appointing senior members of the Roman priesthood.

Any prelate whom the pope appoints as bishop or archbishop of certain sees may expect, in due course—rather sooner than later—to be raised to the cardinalate. A red hat almost automatically goes to the archbishops of the big Italian cities—Milan, Turin, Genoa, Bologna, Florence, Naples, Palermo, and Cagliari and to the patriarch (the historic title with little present-day meaning) of Venice. "Cardinalitial" sees are also Paris, Toledo, Lisbon (a patriarchate), Mechelen-Brussels, Cologne, Munich, Vienna, Esztergom-Budapest, Zagreb, Gniezno-Warsaw, Krakow, New York, Chicago, Los Angeles, Rio de Janeiro, Buenos Aires, and others.

In addition, modern popes have ranged far and wide in their

selection of outstanding churchmen for the sacred college. Paul VI made the bishop of Samoa and the Tokelau Islands in the South Pacific a cardinal, probably because he was enchanted by the islands when he visited them in 1970. John Paul II showed his esteem for an 87-year-old French Jesuit theologian, the Reverend Henri de Lubac, by giving him, to his immense surprise, the red hat in 1983.

Leading officials of the curia and Vatican diplomats often receive the red hat as a fringe benefit, sometimes as a retirement bonus. There is now an age limit for service in the curia, and all bishops around the world must offer their resignation to the pope when they are 75, but there is no age limit for becoming a cardinal.

The pontiff may, if he so chooses, give the scarlet to a simple priest, as John Paul II did to honor Henri de Lubac. Until the nineteenth century, even men who had not been ordained to the priesthood were eligible for the cardinalate provided they were unmarried. In earlier centuries popes often gave the red hat to their own nephews (or illegitimate sons), or to the younger sons of princes or dukes whom they needed as political allies. Some of these cardinals, who were laymen or at most had received the lower orders without attaining the priesthood, were teen-agers. At least one of them became pope later.

At present, as a rule, a cardinal has slowly risen in the church ranks—from simple priest on duty in a parish or, more likely, serving as an aide in some diocesan office, up to monsignor, then to bishop, maybe to archbishop with an assignment to an important see or a powerful position in the Roman Curia. The Italianate title of monsignor comprises various ranks of clerical dignitaries. All churchmen from the level of monsignor upward are bunched together by the term "prelate."

Although a prelate who has been named to such a see as, for instance, Milan or Paris, may count on eventually becoming a cardinal, he can be kept waiting for years. The pope holds consistory to appoint new cardinals whenever he likes; nobody can force him to do so, although his closest aides—who may or may not be princes of the church themselves—might discreetly suggest to the head of the church that the sacred college is depleted and needs to be filled up again.

Watching the impressive ceremonies in St. Peter's when the pope "creates" the new princes of the church, I have always thought of the cardinals of past eras who were powerful political figures, like Richelieu or Wolsey ("Had I but served my God with half the zeal as I have served my King, He would not at my age have left me naked to my enemies."). In our time, Cardinal Spellman of New York; the primates of Poland, Spain, and Ireland; and some cardinals in Latin American countries have wielded great political influence.

Up to recently the pope in consistory would present each new prince of the church with the badge of his dignity, the broad-rimmed tasseled red hat that is never worn but would be pictured in his coat-of-arms and put on his coffin. The pontiff would tell the freshly created cardinal that he must defend the Christian faith even at the cost of his life. (The Latin formula said painstakingly, and a trifle bureaucratically in its precision, ". . . usque ad sanguinis effusionem inclusive"—"to the point, inclusively, of shedding your blood.")

Lately the ceremonies of the consistory for the creation of new cardinals have been streamlined. The pope puts the scarlet skull-caps and birettas (stiff caps) on the heads of the newcomers to the sacred college, but no longer gives them the broad red hat. However, in an address, he still reminds the new princes of the church of their obligation, if necessary, to shed their own blood for the faith. That this is not anachronistic rhetoric has been shown in our times by the imprisonment of cardinals like Mindszenty in Hungary and Wyszynski in Poland, and the violence that other members of the sacred college and lower prelates suffered.

Among such heroic figures was Josyf Cardinal Slipyj, the Ukrainian who had spent eighteen years in Soviet imprisonment. His liberation and expulsion from the Soviet Union in 1963 was a by-product of John XXIII's Ostpolitik. The Ukrainian religious leader, who bore the historic title of archbishop major of Lwow, was 75 years old when Paul VI included him in the sacred college. The bearded Slav cardinal always looked immensely decorative and was usually seen frowning.

He had been assigned an apartment in the Vatican, but had been given nothing to do and was dissatisfied. He would mutter that a Russian detention camp was preferable to what they were calling freedom in Rome. Revered by Americans of Ukrainian origin and by Ukrainian exiles all over the world, the scowling and long-lived cardinal from Lwow was for many years a walking reminder to the Vatican that it had, for reasons of expedi-

57

ency, acquiesced in the extermination of the once-flourishing
Ukrainian Catholicism, with the state-dominated Russian Orthodox Church snapping up the poor spoils.

Cardinal Mindszenty, too, was a study in bitterness after he
had come out of fifteen years' isolation in the United States embassy in Budapest. During the uprising of 1956, the Hungarian
primate was freed from house arrest and enjoyed a few days of
hectic liberty. But when the Soviet tanks crushed the Hungarian rebellion, he found refuge in the United States mission,
then a mere legation, and he stayed on. Over the years I visited
the cramped building on Budapest's Freedom Square, a former
bank, several times, but was never allowed to see the cardinal.
From diplomats in the embassy I learned that he had settled into
a daily routine of saying early mass in his quarters, studying
the newspapers, listening to broadcasts, reading historical and
religious books, keeping a journal, and taking a walk in the narrow courtyard after office hours when most of the personnel had
gone home. Outside, Hungarian police in a booth were watching
day and night and photographing all visitors to the American
mission.

When East-West relations were thawing and the Vatican
inaugurated its Ostpolitik, the first suggestions were conveyed
to Cardinal Mindszenty that he might be able to leave the United
States embassy if he agreed to abandon Hungary. He refused.
Cardinal Koenig, the archbishop of Vienna who visited the Hungarian primate in an attempt to persuade him to leave, told me
afterward: "Cardinal Mindszenty is quite prepared to stay to his
death in the American embassy. He has a vocation for martyrdom." It required an order from Pope Paul VI to induce the
primate to come out of his refuge and board a Rome-bound airplane. In the Vatican, Cardinal Mindszenty was put up in the
tower apartment that Pope John XXIII had had built. But unlike the leader of the Ukrainian Catholics, Mindszenty wouldn't
stay in Rome.

The primate established his residence in a Hungarian church
institution, the Pazmaneum, in Vienna; he regarded the moody
building, which happens to be close to the United States embassy
in Austria, as a piece of his homeland. There I visited Mindszenty several times. He had harsh words for Paul VI's aides in
the curia who, he growled, had capitulated to communism, and
he didn't appear to think highly of the political acumen of the
pontiff himself. But an ultimate disappointment was still in

store for the cardinal. The indomitable old prelate had become an embarrassment to the Vatican diplomats who were negotiating an accord with the Communist government in Budapest whereby vacant bishoprics were to be filled with mutually acceptable churchmen. Early in 1974 the Vatican announced that Mindszenty had "renounced" his see of Esztergom-Budapest. Actually, Paul VI had ordered him to withdraw and thus give up his, purely theoretical, function as primate of Hungary. The cardinal died fifteen months later.

One of Mindszenty's former secretaries, Laszlo Lekai, became the new archbishop of Esztergom-Budapest and primate. Even before his appointment was official, Cardinal Mindszenty glumly told me that Lekai was collaborating with the Communists. An American diplomat in Budapest gave me the following appraisal of the prelate who, in the wake of Ostpolitik, had been placed at the top of the church hierarchy in Hungary: "Lekai is the ultimate realist. He has an uncanny instinct for how far he can go in dealing with the Communist authorities; he knows the limits of his possibilities, one way or the other, to a fraction of an inch."

Later, the new Hungarian primate visited the Soviet Union and, exceptionally, was authorized by Moscow to visit Lithuania, where Roman Catholicism is still a force. Afterward Cardinal Lekai turned up in Rome, relaying his impressions of the Soviet Union with bland, if not rosy, reports on the conditions in which Roman Catholics were living there. He may have given the pope a different account, but conservative churchmen and Western embassies found that Cardinal Mindszenty's successor as primate of Hungary was "soft on communism."

That the loyalty of a cardinal to the Holy See is, rightly or wrongly, questioned, is by no means a new twist. Throughout church history, various members of the sacred college have been suspected agents for the emperor, the king of France, the Republic of Venice, the House of Medici, the king of Naples, or some other temporal power. In the conclave of 1903, the archbishop of Krakow, Jan Cardinal Puzyna, acting on behalf of Emperor Francis Joseph of Austria-Hungary, blocked the election of Mariano Cardinal Rampolla del Tindaro when the Sicilian prelate seemed ahead in the race for succession to Pope Leo XIII. The assembled cardinals bowed to the Austrian emperor's ancient right of veto, and elected the patriarch of Venice, Giuseppe Sarto, who became Pope Pius X and, after his death, a saint. Soon after his elevation, Pius X formally declared null and void any privileges that had entitled certain secular powers to exclude candidates to the papacy. Since then, cardinals have not ceased serving as conduits for political influences and pressures.

PRECEDENCE AND PRIVILEGE

When the princes of the church file past the pontiff in the rite of the obeisance, the primate of Hungary will step up after cardinals from the Philippines, the United States, and Brazil and before colleagues from Britain, the Malagasy Republic, and Czechoslovakia as long as they are alive and whenever they take part in the stately parade. Thus are the rigid rules of seniority and precedence. Every cardinal knows his place.

First come the six cardinal bishops. All six reside permanently in Rome and are nominally in charge of episcopal sees in the surroundings of the city that go back to primitive Christianity. Most of the six ranking cardinals, if not all, are usually Italians, and at least some of them hold high posts in the curia until they get too old. They are often condescending to other cardinals—a little club within the club—and sometimes even sour toward the man who happens to be pope at the moment; they may have been in the sacred college when he was a mere bishop. The six cardinal bishops, quite often intensely jealous of one another, elect one among them as the dean of the sacred college. He doesn't have to be the oldest of the six, and there are usually much older men among the cardinals outside their tight little group.

The cardinal dean has precedence over all his colleagues and speaks on their behalf when the sacred college presents its collective good wishes to the pontiff on his birthday, on the day of his patron saint, and at Christmas. The cardinals may also send their dean to see the pope with requests or complaints, but nowadays this happens rarely. During the declining years of Pius XII, when the state of his health was causing many rumors, the dean of the sacred college—who was then a Frenchman, Eugène Cardinal Tisserant—demanded a private audience with the pontiff to see for himself. When it wasn't granted right away, Cardinal Tisserant angrily told some of his colleagues he was being denied access by Mother Pasqualina. Eventually he was admitted to the presence, and could inform the other cardinals that Pius XII was lucid, but plagued by fits of hiccuping. How Cardinal Tisserant took revenge on the pope's housekeeper will be told later.

After Pope John Paul II was shot in St. Peter's Square in 1981, the 87-year-old dean of the sacred college, Carlo Cardinal Confalonieri, was one of the first visitors to be allowed to the bedside of the critically wounded pontiff. Although there is no written rule, the dean of cardinals cannot easily be barred from the person of the pope. If the church ever were to work out a procedure whereby a pontiff could be declared incapacitated, the cardinal dean would play an important part in it.

In order of precedence, the dean and the other five cardinal bishops are at present followed by the patriarchs of Eastern rites who happen to have received the red hat from the pope. (The word *rite* has a special meaning—a Christian community that has certain traditions and ceremonies.) The Eastern rites are small, old communities—Armenians, Copts, Maronites, and a few others—who cling to their own liturgies and usages, and sometimes allow their priests to marry. In early Christianity married men could be priests, although bishops and patriarchs usually had to be celibate. This tradition continues in the Middle East. The Eastern rites are proud of their ethnic-religious identity and separateness, but recognize the pope in Rome as the supreme head of the faith. In the curial phrase, they are "in communion with the Holy See," meaning they acknowledge the pontiff as their highest spiritual authority, although they may have little use for the edicts from the Roman Curia. Their own spiritual leaders bear the ancient Christian title of patriarch, and at times also play political roles. They reside in Beirut, Cairo, Damascus, Jerusalem, or other places in the region, but fairly often turn up in Rome, where some of their communities own real estate.

Compared with the Latin (or Western) rite, the mainstream of Roman Catholicism, Eastern-rite Catholics are insignificant with nominally a few million, actually hardly more than some hundred thousand active communicants. However, their leaders enjoy considerable leverage in the Vatican because of the papacy's interests in the Middle East in general and in the Holy Land particularly. Israel's intelligence agents are always anxious to find out what the patriarchs from predominantly Moslem countries are up to in Rome.

61

For many years the Eastern patriarchs have been pressing claims that they not only have the same rank as cardinals, but they have a higher—and certainly older—dignity than that office. In an attempt to appease the Eastern rites, the pope's masters of ceremonies, who are clever at such things, created a special category of precedence in the sacred college for patriarchs who are also cardinals. Since most patriarchs are not, the proposed compromise didn't really satisfy them, and wrangling over the exact rank of the Eastern patriarchs continues.

As if to complicate the issue, a few prelates of the dominant Latin rite also are patriarchs—namely the incumbents of the ancient sees of Lisbon and Venice, who are usually cardinals; and the spiritual leader of the Western-style Roman Catholics in Jerusalem, the rest of the Holy Land (Israel and Jordan), and Cyprus, who is not. The Latin-rite patriarchates are historical oddities that aren't entitled to any special precedence in the sacred college; however, patriarchs who are not cardinals outrank archbishops.

Outsiders may regard such distinctions as trifling, but they would be surprised to observe how seriously prelates take their real or presumed prerogative of walking a few steps ahead of or behind others, or being seated on a higher chair, in church ceremonies.

The cardinal priests, ranking below the cardinal bishops and the Eastern-rite patriarchs who are cardinals, make up the bulk of the sacred college. Within their group, or "order," precedence is regulated by seniority in the cardinalate: anyone who has received the red hat earlier than a colleague outranks him. All cardinal priests have precedence over cardinal deacons. This junior order in the sacred college until the nineteenth century included members who were not full priests. Giacomo Cardinal Antonelli, the secretary of state of Pope Pius IX, had received only the lower orders, as had Ercole Cardinal Consalvi, the brilliant chief of Vatican diplomacy in the Napoleonic era. Antonelli and Consalvi thus were less than priests. Today only a priest can become a cardinal, and if he isn't already a bishop, he is consecrated to the episcopacy before receiving the red hat.

A cardinal may renounce his dignity, reverting to the status he had attained in the church before becoming a member of the sacred college; or the pope may depose a cardinal for good reasons. No instance of either case has occurred since before World War II. A prince of the church who is in trouble at home can always count on finding a dignified refuge in Rome. The archbishop of Kinshasa, Joseph Cardinal Malula, sought asylum in Rome when the president of Zaire, Mobutu Sese Seko, expelled him in 1972 in a church-state conflict over "Africanization." Mobutu later made peace with the Vatican, Cardinal Malula returned to his see, and Pope John Paul II visited Zaire in 1980. Cardinal Mindszenty, as has been recalled, didn't care for Vatican hospitality.

At times the pope gives an assignment in the Roman Curia to a cardinal in a faraway see because the prelate may be useful in Rome, or because he has difficulties locally. It is hard to say no to such a call from Rome. Agnelo Cardinal Rossi, archbishop of São Paulo, Brazil, appeared surprised, and would have preferred to stay where he was, when Pope Paul VI named him head of the Vatican's missionary department in 1970. In 1954, Samuel Cardinal Stritch would have liked to have remained archbishop of Chicago rather than obey Pope Pius XII and become the first United States cardinal ever to be nominated to a post at the top of a curia department, the missionary agency that later went to Cardinal Rossi.

Cardinal Stritch never took office because he arrived in Rome with a bloodclot in his arm, and after surgery died without having seen Pius XII (who was himself to die five months later). A guest house not far from the Vatican, where churchmen from Chicago and other American dioceses usually stay during visits to Rome, is named after the cardinal to whom the transfer to Rome meant suffering and death, Villa Stritch. The building also serves as a residence for United States ecclesiastics who hold curia posts.

Every now and then a member of the sacred college finds himself embroiled in scandal, but his rank may ensure special treatment by church and state authorities. After Jean Cardinal Daniélou was found lifeless in the home of a nightclub stripper in Paris in May 1974, it appeared that he had been shadowed by French detectives for some time, and that his private activities had been recorded in a dossier at police headquarters. Cardinal Daniélou, a Jesuit who was among the 40 "immortal ones" of the French Academy, had been a simple priest before receiving the red hat. The author of 40 books and uncounted articles on religious topics, Daniélou had been a consultant to Vatican II. He was a staunch defender of papal primacy in the church, and was rewarded by Paul VI with the cardinalate in 1969. As a prince of the church, Daniélou continued doing what he had done before—he remained in Paris, habitually wore civilian clothes, mingled with intellectuals, and worked on his literary projects. Learning of Daniélou's sudden death, Paul VI said in a message to the archbishop of Paris that "special bonds of esteem and affection" had existed between him and the cardinal.

The first reports said that the 69-year-old prince of the church had collapsed "after complaining of illness while he was visiting friends." Later it was revealed that it had been just one friend he had been seeing, Mimi Santoni (the Italian name means "great saints"), 24 years old. The police had been at the scene remarkably fast and had found a large sum in cash on the dead churchman who appeared to have suffered a ruptured blood vessel. Neither the police nor the church authorities would disclose any details. Friends of Cardinal Daniélou suggested that he had been seeking to induce the young woman to mend her ways for some time, and had been aiding her financially. Only God, who sees into the hearts of men, knew the secret motives of the cardinal's conduct, was the gist of such posthumous explanations. The French Jesuit magazine *Études,* for which the dead cardinal had once worked as an editor, said in a note: "The Daniélou Affair. Despite the requests it has received, *Études* keeps silent in the present state of affairs. Who can bring out the truth, and how could one do so under such circumstances, in justice to a dead man?"

Another affair that embarrassed the Vatican and the church had John Patrick Cardinal Cody, archbishop of Chicago, as its central figure. For years the Roman Curia had unhappily been receiving protests against the cardinal's alleged high-handedness from priests and lay people in his archdiocese. Then Rome learned of more serious and circumstantial charges of financial mismanagement.

In 1981 the *Chicago Sun-Times* reported that a United States grand jury was investigating allegations that Cody, then 73 years old, had for years been channeling tax-exempt church money to a woman friend. She was Helen Dolan Wilson, a 74-year-old divorcée whom the cardinal had at various occasions described as his sister, his cousin, or his niece, but who actually was related to him only by the marriage of an aunt. The news that a member of the sacred college was under a federal probe shocked many Roman Catholics. The Apostolic Delegation in Washington sent voluminous reports to the Secretariat of State in Rome, where Cody had worked as a young priest before starting out on his remarkable ecclesiastical career in the United States.

The archdiocese of Chicago is one of the largest and richest in the Roman Catholic world, traditionally a generous source of funds for the Vatican. Cardinal Cody had not only kept the source flowing but—knowing the ropes—had also shown himself to be generous with gratuities for Vatican personnel whenever he visited Rome. The fact that the cardinal had been cultivating Chicago's large Polish-American community had endeared him to the Polish pope who, during his 1979 journey to the United States, was enthusiastically welcomed in the city. (John Paul II bypassed Detroit, although it too has a strong Polish-descended population. The city's Roman Catholic archbishop, John Francis Cardinal Dearden, had a reputation as a moderate liberal, unlike the authoritarian and conservative Cody. This prompted much speculation about why the pope had visited Chicago but not Motor City.)

Confronted with the Chicago unpleasantness, the Vatican reacted as it had, more or less successfully, in many similar situations—it withheld any public comment. Privately, friends of Cody's spread the word that enemies of the cardinal and the church were waging a slanderous campaign in Chicago. The cardinal himself said he was ready to forgive those who had brought unjust accusations against him, "but God will not forgive them." He also announced through his vicar general that he intended to retire on his 75th birthday. The federal investigation was still continuing when Cody, who had been suffering from diabetes and heart trouble, died in April 1982, at the age of 74. There was a faint but unmistakable note of relief in the Vatican's official mourning for the cardinal from Chicago.

Many churchmen in Rome and Chicago were expecting that Pope John Paul II, in an ethnically motivated appointment, might choose a Polish-descended prelate for the see. However, the pontiff picked Joseph L. Bernardin, the 54-year-old archbishop of Cincinnati, who was of northern Italian stock, as Cody's successor. Bernardin had long been regarded as a rising star in the Roman Catholic hierarchy of the United States. He was a moderate in theology, and had attracted international attention because of his opposition to Washington's nuclear policy. Bernardin's promotion to Chicago, and the red hat he received on February 2, 1983, led churchmen to predict that he would play an increasingly important role as a spokesman for American Roman Catholicism, a forceful figure such as had not been seen since Spellman.

The questions of precedence and seniority within the sacred college may be of stupendous importance to its members, but to lesser clerics and to the faithful laity, a cardinal is a cardinal. Each prelate may, if the Holy Spirit so wills, be the next pope. If such a possibility seems in some cases remote, a cardinal nevertheless has a lofty position that commands reverence even outside the Roman Catholic Church.

Within the church, cardinals enjoy a great number of privileges that are enumerated in canon law. They may say mass in every church or chapel all over the world, may hear confessions anywhere, impart blessings similar to those given by the pontiff himself, and carry out other religious acts from which lower clerics are barred. On a worldly level, cardinals may freely dispose of their income and, in their will, may leave their properties to whomever they choose.

Under old rules that have never been formally voided, cardinals possess the same dignity as princes of the Blood. Once the members of the sacred college were supposed to reside in stately buildings with a special doorway for carriages, a private chapel, and a hall with a throne under a baldachin where they would receive lesser people. They were to be attended by a secretary, a chaplain, a majordomo, and other ecclesiastical and lay staff, and until some time ago were expected to travel in reserved railroad compartments and avoid public transport in cities. But the jet age has done away with much of such princely exclusiveness.

Still, quite a few of Their Eminences have a throne room in their sumptuous apartments, although they may use it only rarely. Others don't care for the anachronistic splendor. Paul Emile Cardinal Léger, archbishop of Montreal, gave up his see and went to work in a leper colony in Africa. Michele Cardinal Pellegrino of Turin used to wear a priest's simple cassock and told the people in his archdiocese to call him "Father" instead of "Your Eminence."

The advances of secular and anticlerical forces in the world have long eroded the power and prestige of the cardinals, which were immense in the Renaissance and Baroque ages. And lately the influence of the individual members of the sacred college has been diluted by their increase in number. Since the sixteenth century there were never more than seventy princes of the church at one time, until Pope John XXIII abolished this numerical ceiling. He and his successors designated additional titular churches in Rome and named new cardinals for them, bringing the membership of the sacred college to well over one hundred. The senior cardinals weren't too happy about the new trend; in their time, receiving the red hat was somewhat more exceptional than it is now.

Until after World War II, Italians were the majority in the sacred college. Pius XII changed this in the consistory of 1946 when he created 32 new cardinals, the highest number of red hats ever handed out by a pontiff in one ceremony. One of the recipients was Cardinal Spellman. The archbishop of New York, who arrived in Rome with a large party of churchmen, lay friends, and hangers-on, saw to it that his elevation received thorough coverage in the American press.

At the beginning of Pius XII's pontificate, in 1939, there were 36 Italian cardinals and 29 non-Italian ones. After the 1946 consistory, the number of the Italians in the sacred college had shrunk to 28 and that of the cardinals from outside Italy had risen to 42. Italian prelates in the Vatican and Romans in general spoke at the time, with overtones of chauvinistic resentment, of the new preponderance of "foreign" cardinals, although in a religious community that claims to be universal nobody should be regarded as a stranger. Pius XII knew, as his aides have attested, that his historic decision in 1946 to "internationalize" the college of cardinals would pave the way toward breaking the 400-year-old Italian monopoly of church rule. Nevertheless, it would take another 32 years before a non-Italian pope could be elected.

The increased number of cardinals and the fact that many of them lived far away from Rome made it hard for the members of the sacred college to know one another well. When the "plenum," or maximum number, of the body was 70 cardinals, most of them Italians, they had less trouble establishing contacts among themselves and laying the groundwork for alliances.

The cardinals—whether Italians or non-Italian ones—who hold posts in the Roman Curia and those who are in charge of archbishoprics or bishoprics at large have different, and sometimes divergent, interests. The curialists want to run the church by papal edict and administrative circular from the Vatican; the cardinals in dioceses around the world often bridle at such centralism. Together with the church hierarchies in their own areas, cardinals outside Rome often press for more autonomy to adapt religious practices to local conditions and to work out their relationship with the political systems under which they and their flocks live.

A few of the cardinals at large have more muscle in dealing with the Vatican than others, either because they themselves have a curia background, or because of the money they send to Rome, or because of great personal prestige in their own country. They usually have little trouble getting what they want from Rome—whether special papal messages of public support, the appointment of clerical friends to bishoprics, Vatican honors for important members of their clergy or laity, or curial policy decisions that will facilitate their dealings with their home governments. In some areas of church government the Vatican can give a free hand to a cardinal abroad who has the good sense regularly to transfer substantial money contributions to Rome.

Cardinal Spellman, who knew the ins and outs of the Vatican firsthand from his years of service in the Secretariat of State, and gave a great deal of financial aid to the pontifical treasury, wielded such influence as no American cardinal since has been able to match. The West German cardinals usually receive special curia treatment in deference to their financial power. Stefan Cardinal Wyszynski got what he wanted from the Vatican most of the time because he was a great national figure, especially before a younger colleague became the first Polish pope.

Despite outstanding personalities among the cardinals at large, the Roman Catholic Church's permanent power structure centers around the pope in the Vatican. There are a group of a dozen to twenty princes of the church who hold key posts and see the pontiff often. Some live within the walls of Vatican City, others nearby.

A modern Vatican-owned apartment house in the Piazza della Città Leonina, just north of St. Peter's Square, across the street from one of the main entrances to the papal enclave, counts among its illustrious tenants the cardinals heading the curia's departments of orthodoxy, of bishops, and of education, as well as the cardinal camerlengo, who becomes chief of the church's interim government when the throne of Saint Peter becomes vacant. (The dean of the sacred college, Cardinal Tisserant, acted in this capacity after Pius XII's death because that pontiff had failed to fill the post of cardinal camerlengo.)

Too bad that some of the well-appointed suites of Their Emi-

nences look out on the often-crowded terminal of the number 64
bus and on the unseemly entrances to the underground public
toilets that always prove inadequate when large crowds gather in
St. Peter's Square. Behind the subterranean facility—such jux-
tapositions are frequent in the Eternal City—is the covered
walkway through which Clement VII and his cardinals escaped
to safety in the Castel Sant'Angelo when the ragtag soldiery of
Emperor Charles V was sacking Rome and invading the Vatican
in 1527.

Of the nearly forty cardinals who reside permanently in
Rome, at least eight have apartments in the Apostolic Palace,
under one roof with the pontiff, or elsewhere in the Vatican. Another fifteen or so live in buildings close to Vatican City, five are
housed in a massive structure that was built under Pius XI in
the teeming, earthy Trastevere district on the right bank of the
Tiber downstream from the Vatican, and the remainder are installed in other ecclesiastical real estate scattered around the
city.

In past centuries, cardinals, who were often related to
princely families, maintained dazzling Roman establishments—
palaces erected expressly for them by famous architects—scores
of retainers, gilt coaches, lavish entertainments. Today, cardinals who have just received the red hat or have been freshly assigned to some curia post often wait for years in unsatisfactory
living quarters before the desirable apartment of an older colleague becomes available through death or retirement.

Some high offices in the curia—like that of cardinal secretary
of state—come with handsome apartments in the Vatican. Other
accommodations within the walls of the papal enclave may become vacant, and may be offered to a well-connected cardinal at
nominal rent. Many princes of the church who reside in Rome
prefer living outside the Vatican to retain a measure of independence. They can receive visitors without having them cleared—
and probably reported to higher-ups—by the Swiss Guard and
pontifical security officers at the Vatican's gates. A cardinal who
is not entitled to an apartment in the Apostolic Palaces and cannot, or doesn't want to, find accommodation in one of the Vatican-owned buildings around Rome will canvass religious orders
and colleges in the city for low-rent or no-rent living quarters,
necessitated by his small salary.

As in real estate markets everywhere, a house-hunting prince
of the church needs the right connections or a windfall to get

what he wants. When His Eminence at last has the key to the suite he has coveted, he will think about redecorating it, which may cost $100,000 or more. The Vatican may help out, or perhaps the archdiocese from which the cardinal came. Then there is the problem of a housekeeper and other domestic help. A widowed sister or a maiden niece may come in handy. Franjo Cardinal Seper, the Croat who, as prefect of the Sacred Congregation for the Doctrine of the Faith, was the Vatican's chief guardian of orthodoxy for nearly thirteen years, 1968–81, was envied by his colleagues because his household on the Piazza della Città Leonina was kept running smoothly and economically by female relatives who also saw to it that a steady supply of sausages from home dangled from the cardinalitial kitchen ceiling.

Usually a cardinal in Rome can count on being provided with two or three nuns as household staff by a religious order for which he acts officially as "protector." The role doesn't entail much trouble—attendance at an occasional ceremony, saying mass in the general house now and then, assisting the mother superior in getting things done through church authorities, and other small favors. But religious orders have womanpower problems nowadays, and the gastronomic skills of nuns, often questionable, seem to be falling off. The secretary of a cardinal who was a newcomer to the curia complained to me that when his patron had at last obtained the temporary help of a nun, they were served, as a disheartening starter, frozen frankfurters, not quite thawed—"Frozen franks for lunch!"

Many cardinals insist on having an ecclesiastical assistant, a priest or a monsignor, on constant call. A cardinal's secretary serves at morning mass in the private chapel or in a nearby church, shares breakfast with his chief, opens the mail, answers the telephone, participates in ceremonies in which his patron officiates, and makes himself useful in other ways at the residence and at the office. Such symbiosis may become frustrating to the younger man, particularly when His Eminence, with advancing years, gets cranky or ailing. On the other hand, the secretary of a cardinal moves in high church circles, picks up useful information, and makes contacts that will be valuable for his career. Many a churchman who, in his early years after ordination to the priesthood, was secretary to some cardinal and followed his patron as "conclavist" into the seclusion of a papal election (secretaries no longer do so nowadays) emerged as the closest aide to the new pope and eventually became a cardinal himself.

Carlo Cardinal Confalonieri, long-time secretary to Pope Pius XI and much later dean of the sacred college, was an example of such a rise in the church.

The secretary of a cardinal who heads a curia department once told me: "We are going out little these days; we have had the flu." The secretary, a sturdy monsignor, didn't make clear whether both he and his scholarly patron had been ill or whether the "we" meant just the cardinal. A good clerical secretary identifies completely with his chief. At the same time, the secretaries of the ranking cardinals in Rome form one of the tightest networks in the Vatican grapevine, and always have much to tell one another when they meet in a curial anteroom or in the side chapel of St. Peter's where the princes of the church get ready for the big pontifical ceremonies.

Every cardinal who resides anywhere in Rome automatically enjoys Vatican citizenship and is entitled to a State of Vatican City passport. He is exempt from Italian taxes and, like all other Vatican dependents, may buy duty-free food items and other merchandise at the papal state's commissary. The Vatican car pool provides free transportation in limousines with SCV— State of Vatican City—license plates, although it discourages clerical joyrides. Rent in a church-owned building is low or is completely waived. All these fringe benefits permit a prince of the church to live on his Vatican salary, quaintly called *piatto cardinalizio,* a "cardinal's dish." His Eminence finds the lira equivalent of about $1,500 in his figurative dish every month, but with this paycheck must take care of his secretary, other staff, and the utilities in his apartment. Heating the fifteen-foot-high halls in a Renaissance palace may alone gobble up a sizable portion of the cardinal's dish. One suspects that the reason why some of the older members of the sacred college hardly ever miss a diplomatic reception in winter is that most embassies are nice and warm.

The $1,500-a-month salary is that of a senior judge or an army general in Italy; it's not princely pay. From time to time the Holy See adjusts the salaries of cardinals to make up for Italian inflation. However, the members of the sacred college in Rome, unlike the Vatican employees, don't get periodic raises. Cardinals in curia posts may be granted expense allowances, and may occasionally receive bonuses for attendance at committee meetings. Older princes of the church who have had to give up their Vatican jobs and continue to live in Rome must make do with their "cardinal's dish."

Cardinals in Italian cities outside Rome and in countries outside Italy usually have incomes from their archdioceses or other local church organizations that are sometimes considerably higher than the Vatican's salary. The cardinals of New York, Chicago, Cologne, or Munich surely don't need the Holy See's $1,500 a month, and don't get it. Members of the sacred college in poor Third World countries benefit from the money that the Vatican or, more frequently, rich church bodies in the industrialized nations send them.

THE WAYS OF THE HOLY SPIRIT

The oldest men among the long-lived cardinals in Rome have been in ecclesiastical limbo since 1970. A few days before Pope Paul VI was to leave on his journey to the Philippines and the antipodes in November of that year, he issued a decree curtailing gerontocracy in the church. Cardinals occupying posts in the curia, he ruled, were henceforth to offer the pontiff their resignation on completing their 75th year of age; those who might be asked by him to stay in office must at any rate withdraw at 80. Earlier, a general retirement age of 75 years for all bishops and archbishops had been set, following a recommendation by Vatican II. Paul VI's decree of November 1970 also contained an even more startling innovation: cardinals who had reached their 80th year could no longer take part in a conclave to choose a new pontiff. The measure, the first substantial change in the rules of papal election in seven centuries, stunned the elderly members of the sacred college.

For an octogenarian cardinal (there have been quite a number of nonagenarian ones too in recent times), the prospect of playing a role in the making of the next head of the church has always been an exhilarating and invigorating thought. To be barred from any future conclave with its excitement, possible religious fervor, and probable web of intrigue apparently dealt many overage princes of the church a blow as hard as if Saint Peter personally had locked them out of the gates to paradise.

For once, there was something of a rebellion in the senior ranks of the sacred college. Pope Paul VI's edict "is an act committed in contempt of a tradition that is centuries old," snarled

Alfredo Cardinal Ottaviani, who as prefect of the Sacred Congregation for the Doctrine of the Faith had long been the implacable nemesis of alleged heretics. Nearly blind, but as pugnacious as ever, the 80-year-old cardinal, who was of Roman lower-class origin and proud of it, told an interviewer in an angry voice flavored with the vernacular of the Trastevere district: "Over the centuries, in fact, it has been immutably held that it is precisely advancing age that guarantees to the church councillors who are rich in experience, prudence and doctrine." Paul VI evidently had failed to ask such councillors for their advice. His decree was at once applicable to 25 of the 127 cardinals who then made up the sacred college.

One of the humbled octogenarians was the dean of the cardinals, Tisserant, then 86 years old. Once a French army officer in Syria, the bearded, erudite cardinal, who had acted forcefully as head of the caretaker administration in the church interregnum between Pius XII and Paul VI, made no effort to hide his irritation. With Gallic adroitness he had a reporter ask him on television whether Pope Paul himself would resign on reaching the age of 80, and gave at once the following reply: "This hypothesis has been mentioned more than once. Certainly, his [Paul VI's] health is such that it is possible he may not even have to make a decision on this point."

A superstitious Italian would automatically have crossed his fingers or performed a cruder gesture to ward off such malevolence. Paul VI probably didn't, and the suggestion by the dean of the sacred college that he might not live long enough to become an octogenarian eventually proved wrong. Cardinal Tisserant was a conservative like Cardinal Ottaviani and most of the other 25 members of the sacred college who were then over 80. Pope Paul VI excluded the oldest cardinals from conclave doubtless on the assumption that they would always be opposed to change and favor a candidate to the papacy who seemed to guarantee the status quo.

It may be recalled, however, that there was no age limit in the conclave of 1958 in which an aged cardinal was chosen pontiff. That was John XXIII, who was anything but a defender of the status quo. If a man 77 years and 11 months of age can become head of the church, why not an octogenarian? Paul VI's decree in fact did not rule out the eligibility to the throne of Saint Peter of a cardinal who, because of his age, is denied lesser Vatican posts and access to conclave. What a defeat for ageism, what a posthumous triumph for Cardinal Ottaviani it would be if an octogenarian were one day to be chosen as supreme pontiff, like the saintly hermit Pietro di Murrone who was 80 when he became Celestine V in 1294! Only, Celestine resigned five months later.

Since the thirteenth century the college of cardinals has always chosen the head of the church from its own ranks, although nowhere does canon law say that it must do so. Theoretically, the cardinals may elect to the papacy any baptized male; he doesn't even have to be a priest, and he could be a teenager. (This isn't spelled out in precise terms, but interpretation of the legal texts implies such minimal conditions for eligibility.)

The notion that a candidate for the papacy mustn't necessarily be a cardinal is not entirely abstract. In 1958 there was some speculation that the archbishop of Milan, Montini, might be chosen as successor to Pope Pius XII. Four years earlier, as the reader will recall, Pius XII had suddenly plucked Montini out of the curia and appointed him to the see of Milan. At the time there was much guessing why the pope had deprived himself of such a devoted aide. A benevolent interpretation was that Pius XII wanted to give Montini an opportunity for gathering what is known as pastoral experience, and thus add to his qualifications for eventually succeeding himself on the throne of Saint Peter. To have headed a large archdiocese is considered a vantage point in the race for the papacy (although Pius XII himself had never been a diocesan bishop or archbishop). Archbishop Montini was expected to receive the red hat in the first consistory that Pius XII would hold after his aide's transfer to Milan. However, the pontiff unaccountably let the years pass without scheduling such a ceremony for the naming of new princes of the church, and eventually died, leaving Montini outside the sacred college.

If the cardinals in their 1958 conclave really considered reaching outside their own group to make the archbishop of Milan the new pope, they quickly rejected such a possibility and turned to the patriarch of Venice, Cardinal Roncalli. Pope John XXIII soon held the overdue consistory and put Montini at the top of his list of new cardinals as, in the curial parlance, his "first creature." After John XXIII's death the archbishop of Milan, at last a cardinal, entered the 1963 conclave as a favorite and came out of it as the new head of the church, Paul VI.

In the first conclave of 1978, after Paul VI's death, some of the cardinals who arrived at the Vatican from all continents had to be introduced to one another. When they reassembled in Rome a few weeks later, after the unexpected end of John Paul I's pontificate, the members of the sacred college were already well acquainted. The non-Italian cardinals and a few Italian ones quickly reached a consensus that the power of the curia must be curbed, and that none of the Italian candidates for the papacy could be expected to do the job. The hour of Karol Wojtyla of Krakow had struck.

Cardinals may not admit it even to their secretaries, but there are plenty of clues that many of them are always thinking about the next conclave. A slight papal cold is enough to cause Their Eminences to put their heads together or call each other long-distance to exchange guarded reports and prudent speculation. Potential candidates are mentioned and possible lineups in a hypothetical conclave explored.

The outside world had no inkling that the archbishop of Krakow might be an aspirant, a papabilis, but his peers had been watching Cardinal Wojtyla for years: what he was doing in his own archdiocese and his nation, his travels and lectures in many parts of the world, how he was cultivating key members of the United States and West German hierarchies, the learned articles and books he wrote, his role at church gatherings in Rome, and Paul VI's surprising decision to select him as a Lenten preacher when the pontifical household went into its customary pre-Easter retreat in 1976.

Electioneering for the papacy that may have been going on covertly for years surfaces when the supreme pontiff dies. The cardinal camerlengo of the Holy Roman Church automatically becomes the head of a stopgap administration and, jointly with all the other members of the sacred college who are already in Rome and those who day after day arrive in the city, prepares the deceased pope's funeral and makes arrangements for the election of a successor.

All the cardinals meet daily in "general congregation," sessions to consider current affairs. They are forbidden by canon law to make decisions about matters pertaining exclusively to the head of the church, like the proclamation of a new dogma; the next pope will deal with such things. While the members of the sacred college are thus exercising their functions as the interim government of the church during daily meetings behind closed doors, they make a great number of informal, secret contacts to launch candidacies or firm up coalitions supporting papal hopefuls. When conclave at last starts—at the latest, twenty days after the pope's death—the field of favorites in the race for succession has usually been narrowed down to a few papabiles (qualified candidates).

Pope Paul VI, reconfirming earlier church laws in his 1975 apostolic constitution on the vacancy of the Holy See, forbade "anyone, even though he be a cardinal, during the lifetime of the pontiff and without having consulted him, to deliberate on the election of his successor, promise votes, or make decisions in this regard in private meetings." The wording, by implication, permits a pope to recommend someone as the next head of the church, and even to seek support for his eventual election. Pope Pius XI, for instance, told several cardinals at various times he would like his secretary of state, Cardinal Pacelli, to be chosen as his successor. There was little competition anyway and Pius XI's closest aide was elected pontiff in March 1939 in one of the shortest conclaves in history, lasting just a day.

Since any pope may change church law at will, some future pontiff might name his own successor, to follow him either after his death or upon resignation. "It is unlikely that any pope in our time would institute a hereditary monarchy in the Vatican, found a dynasty, so to speak," a high prelate told me, "but it's theoretically possible. The present method of papal election, old though it is, is not founded on divine law; there is nothing in the Scriptures that says how the head of the church must be chosen. As the church's supreme legislator, any pope may introduce new procedures."

A radical change would nevertheless meet with strong opposition from the sacred college of cardinals and from many bishops, and might even lead to a split within the church, a schism. For the foreseeable future, the only procedural reform for choosing a pope that may be reasonably considered is the inclusion of a few handpicked bishops, priests, or lay people in the electoral college, now exclusively made up of the cardinals. Such an innovation has been advocated by liberal theologians and other churchmen, and was for some time contemplated—but eventually rejected—by Paul VI.

Paul VI's new rules prohibited "any pact, agreement, promise or other commitment of whatever kind" that might oblige cardinals to give their vote to a certain person in the papal election, and pronounced any such deal null and void, with anyone violating the ban automatically incurring excommunication. "We do not, however, have the intention of forbidding the exchange of views concerning the election during the period in which the [pontifical] see is vacant," Paul VI's text continued. The fine distinction between commitments and exchanges of views, and the fact that the excommunication threatened by Paul VI isn't pronounced by anybody, but is a matter of the transgressor's individual conscience and need never be known to anybody but him (and God), leaves room for any number of maneuvers, of soundings during discreet lunches or casual encounters in Vatican corridors during the giddy days preceding the papal election, and of undertakings by cardinals that eventually may or may not be honored.

Over the centuries curial wisdom has warned that "whoever enters the conclave as pope comes out a cardinal," meaning that favorites are often dumped by their foxy supporters or blocked by last-minute cabals. Paul VI's legislation exhorted the cardinals that in electing the head of the church they "should not let themselves be guided by friendship or aversion, or be influenced by favor or respect toward anyone, or be forced by the intervention of persons in authority or by pressure groups, by the suggestion of the mass media, or by force, fear, or the seeking of popularity," but should solely have in mind "the glory of God and the welfare of the church." The admonitions to the cardinals are permeated, as is much of canon law, by deep pessimism regarding human nature.

In Roman Catholic doctrine it is the Holy Spirit who designates a pope through the cardinal electors. The princes of the church intone the "Veni Creator Spiritus," the ancient invocation to the third person of the Trinity, when they enter the walled-up, secluded section of the Vatican where they will live together until the new pontiff is chosen. They are assigned "cells," which may be partitions of a twenty-foot-high Renaissance hall with a brass bed, an old-fashioned washstand, and the toilet down the corridor, or the comfortable living quarters of the Vatican librarian who has been temporarily dislodged from his apartment and found a refuge in some convent. The cardinals take their meals together and solemnly meet twice daily in the cramped Sistine Chapel to cast their votes.

The Paraclete, or Holy Spirit, usually works by indirection (and there is really no theological reason why He shouldn't descend on octogenarians). In modern times there has been no in-

77

stance of a new head of the church emerging by acclamation, as canon law says, "when the cardinal electors, as it were, through the inspiration of the Holy Spirit, freely and spontaneously, unanimously and aloud, proclaim one individual as supreme pontiff." The normal way, instead, is by balloting until one man wins two-thirds plus one of all the votes cast. In a prolonged deadlock some other electoral system may be tried if the cardinals in conclave unanimously agree.

In centuries past some popes won the throne of Saint Peter through bribery. The great powers of the time, the Holy Roman Emperor, the kings of France and Spain, and other rulers, usually tried to have one of their favorites elected to the papacy, and often succeeded.

The last recorded instance of a secular power directly intervening in a papal election was Emperor Francis Joseph's veto against Cardinal Rampolla, mentioned earlier. Indirect pressures from governments and other political forces will probably accompany papal elections as long as the heads of the church are chosen the way they have been until now.

That secret contacts, deals, caucuses, and other techniques of electioneering can be theologically justified was shown by Cardinal Siri, the ultraconservative from Genoa, in a sermon in St. Peter's after the death of Paul VI. A candidate for the throne of Saint Peter himself, Cardinal Siri said: "Divine omnipotence, though it can do anything, leaves to every creature its share of freedom. . . . Human responsibility remains. From this viewpoint, I think, I have a duty to remind my venerable brethren of the sacred college of the task before them, which they cannot evade by saying 'This is what the Holy Spirit thinks.' " In other words, the cardinal electors ought to get busy lining up a majority for some candidate (for example, Siri) rather than wait for the Paraclete to manifest His choice.

Whenever a pope dies, there are always a few cardinals who don't want, or say they don't want, to become his successor but instead try to rally voters behind a colleague, exercising the responsibility of which Cardinal Siri spoke, and helping the Holy Spirit a little. Such power brokers and self-appointed grand electors may act for factions in the Roman Curia or in other church bodies, or they may conceivably promote the interests of political forces or even business groups. If successful, the power brokers may later be rewarded with posts in the curia or at least with more influence in the church. Their role has become more important since the number of participants in the papal election has risen. Pope Paul VI set a new ceiling of 120 members of the sacred college under 80 years of age and therefore qualified for entering conclave; John Paul II declared in 1983 he would abide by this maximum figure. However, the rules may be changed again at any time.

Some future pope may bring the number of cardinals under 80 years to more than 120. Commissions of theologians and experts in Rome and elsewhere have recommended that a few selected bishops, simple priests and laymen, even some women, be permitted to join the sacred college in choosing the head of the church. Whether these reform proposals are eventually accepted or not, the conclave will always need leadership if its task of giving an orphaned church a new Holy Father is to be carried out effectively and speedily.

In the election of the church's first Polish pope, cardinals from West Germany, Austria, Spain, Brazil, and the United States were believed to have acted as grand electors. Cardinals are not supposed to reveal what has gone on in conclave; however, it is known through various hints and clues that John Cardinal Krol of Philadelphia, whose roots were Polish, Cardinal Koenig of Vienna, and Joseph Cardinal Ratzinger of Munich were the prime backers of the archbishop of Krakow.

In every papal election of this century there was a curial party of cardinals who were, or had been, holding posts in the Vatican and favored candidates whom they expected to strengthen the church's central government. Pius XII and Paul VI were typical curialists. John XXIII had, as a pontifical diplomat, been an agent of the Roman Curia, but he had also managed to maintain a measure of independence. As an apostolic nuncio in Paris he had won the sympathy of the French hierarchy, which over the centuries has been anticuria. French cardinals persuaded other members of the sacred college who were seeking a "transition pope" after the long, authoritarian pontificate of Pius XII, that Cardinal Roncalli, the patriarch of Venice, had the qualities for such a role. John Paul I and John Paul II were both the choices of an anticuria bloc that included most European and many Third World cardinals.

The election of the first non-Italian pontiff in modern times became possible when the curialist party, in which Italians were dominant as usual, split into various factions, each with a candidate of its own: they canceled one another out in the voting. It took eight ballots in two days before white smoke rising from the makeshift flue over the Sistine Chapel announced that the church had a new head.

The bizarre method of sending smoke signals through a rather tacky stovepipe to communicate with the outside world is an egregious example of how the Vatican clings to archaic practices, however inane. During the two conclaves of 1978 there was, in fact a telephone line between the secluded sacred college and Vatican officials outside. It was used, at the particular urging of the media-conscious Jesuits of Vatican Radio, to find out whether the whiffs of smoke that could be seen curling into the sky were black, meaning inconclusive balloting, or white. In the Roman dusk and with the roof of the Sistine Chapel floodlit, the crowd in St. Peter's Square and the news reporters weren't sure about the color of the smoke.

While the Roman stovepipe charade was being played out, the Polish candidate for the papacy promised backers and sympathizers in the conclave that, if elected, he would see to it that the cardinals would participate in church government to a much greater extent than they had recently done. The fact of such a statement by John Paul II to his electors can be inferred from remarks by him and by various cardinals at the beginning of his pontificate.

Popes may or may not keep promises they have made before their election—in the same way a United States president may honor or forget his usual campaign pledges. Canon law establishes that the cardinals "form the senate of the Roman pontiff," but modern popes before John Paul II have summoned them as a body only for ceremonial purposes. The ritual meeting of the pope with the cardinals, sometimes with certain bishops joining them, is called "consistory." Such formal gatherings are held in the Vatican from time to time to prepare the canonization of new saints and acknowledge papal appointments of bishops or cardinals. There is no debate or vote. The pontiff makes his announcements and asks in Latin: "What is your opinion?" The cardinals and bishops gathered in the Apostolic Palace's Consistorial Hall briefly bare their heads in sign of assent.

When John Paul II asked all cardinals to come to Rome in November 1979 to discuss church business with him, their session was the first of its kind in more than a century. One hundred twenty members of the sacred college attended the gathering, officially called a "consultation," behind closed doors in the Synodal Hall of the modern audience building south of St. Peter's. The cardinals who were older than 80 years were, to their delight, invited to participate. It turned out that most of the debates dealt with Vatican finances. John Paul II also promised the cardinals he would consult them regularly and fully on important church matters. A first step toward what might become a functioning "senate" of the church had been made.

Three years later, in November 1982, John Paul II again summoned all cardinals, regardless of their age, to Rome. Again, their discussions focused on Vatican money matters. At the end of the four-day session, the pontiff told its nearly one hundred participants they had furnished convincing proofs "of the vitality and of the tasks that belong to the ancient institution of the college of cardinals as the senate that assists the pope in fulfilling his worldwide duties in the service of the church and of the brethren."

CHAPTER 4

THE CHURCH'S MANDARINS

JOHN XXIII, IN an often repeated and quoted aside, liked to tell old friends who were visiting him in the Vatican that "I am only the pope here." He meant to say, only half in jest, that things were really being run by the curia machinery. Shortly after the start of his pontificate, he gently suggested to an old and reactionary cardinal who was filling a key slot in the church's central government that maybe the time had come for the prelate to think about retirement. "He said no!" John XXIII afterward reported to a member of his entourage. "Would you believe it? He said no to me—the pope!"

Two decades later, John Paul II, when he was discussing the attitudes of the curia with Polish associates or visitors from other countries, would refer to it as "they," slightly jerking his chin toward his left shoulder. "They" were opposed to some project, such as another papal journey, or were dragging their feet in carrying out his instructions.

Theoretically, the pontiff is, as has been set forth in the chapter on the papacy, the absolute ruler of the church, equipped with the redoubtable instrument of dogmatic inerrancy, and unhampered by any constitutional system of checks and balances. In practice, however, his power is considerably tempered by the administrative mechanisms of the Roman Curia—the ecclesiastical officials who draft the documents that he signs, write many of the speeches he delivers, lay down the ceremonial of the rites in which he officiates, regulate access to him, choose many of the prelates he will promote to high church posts, manage his and the Vatican's money affairs, and make many decisions in his name without even consulting him.

Throughout history long-lasting empires have been based on dedicated, efficient civil service systems. The Roman Catholic Church, an empire if ever there was one, is no exception. Its worldwide hierarchy of archbishops and bishops handles many administrative tasks; the Roman Curia and the pontifical envoys in various countries (who are part of it, though on temporary duty abroad) are the elite of the church's civil service, its mandarins. Civil servants, even competent and incorruptible ones, usually cling to the status quo, are jealous of their jurisdictional fields, and are annoyed by outside interference. A strong leader will know how to get the most out of his mandarins; a weak one will become the captive of his civil service. This is true of the popes and their relations with the curia, which comprises most of the persons working in the Vatican.

A new factor in this relationship was introduced in 1978 when the cardinals broke the nearly five-hundred-year-old Italian grip on the papacy, electing a Polish pope. Although "internationalized" to some degree during the preceding decades, the Roman Curia had remained under the dominance of Italians, as it had been from its origins in the Middle Ages. The durability of the Italian-controlled papal administration over the centuries is somewhat of a paradox in a nation that—aside from the admirable ambassadors and other officials of the long-defunct Venetian Republic—lacks outstanding civil service traditions. The government bureaucracy of unified Italy from the second half of the nineteenth century to this day has failed to gain much prestige among the population. The competence, dedication, and occasional brilliance of papal officials through the ages would suggest that the church has drained Italy of top administrative talent.

What are the motivations for becoming a curialist? Faith may be one, although one would imagine that an ardent believer who enters the priesthood would rather choose to serve as a pastor or missionary. In many talks with high Vatican officials over the years I have gained the impression that some of them were obtaining personal fulfillment from being members of an institution they deemed useful for humankind. Status in the church and in the world, the satisfaction and challenge of working for a universal organization, the prestige of being associated with the papacy, and, surely, the joys of exercising power are other incentives for devoting much of one's life to the esoteric world of the Roman Curia.

THE WORLD'S OLDEST BUREAUCRACY

No one person could possibly get the full picture of what is going on any weekday morning in the buildings that cluster around St. Peter's, not even the pope. Yet it is in his name that everything is being said and done in the one thousand rooms of the Vatican.

At the Bronze Doors on the north side of St. Peter's Square a Swiss Guard presents his halberd to a cardinal who walks to the weekly meeting of the Sacred Congregation of the Sacraments and Divine Worship, the liturgical department of the central church government.

In a sober cubicle nearly one hundred feet up, a Carmelite scholar from Wisconsin is translating a papal encyclical from Italian into Latin. The document was originally written in Polish and was translated into Italian to be circulated among experts who couldn't read the papal draft in its original language. Other linguists and theologians will later check the official Latin against Polish, and against versions in English, French, German, Spanish, and Portuguese before the sheets, in folders marked SECRET, are sent to the Polyglot Vatican Printing Press a few hundred yards to the north.

In the Palace of the Congregations, a solid structure in bright brick and porous travertine stone just outside St. Peter's Square, half a dozen black bishops from Tanzania wander from office to office, trying to find someone who can tell them how to get funds for their schools and new churches. The Africans are on their "visit to the tombs of the Apostles," the journey to Rome that every bishop in Europe is supposed to undertake every five years, and each bishop in an overseas country every ten years, to report to the pontiff (really, to the curia) on the state of his diocese. They will eventually see the pope in a fifteen-minute collective audience.

The African bishops brush against a Jesuit with a bulging briefcase. He is calling at the Sacred Congregation for the Causes of Saints to push the sluggish proceedings to have Pope Pius XII proclaimed "blessed," a step on the road to sainthood in the Church of Rome. The Jesuit is the postulator of the cause of Pius XII; in his briefcase he carries testimonials purporting to prove that a woman in Mannheim, West Germany, was miraculously cured of stomach cancer after praying for help to the "pope who loved the Germans."

A Dutch priest with a black necktie and a white shirt instead of a Roman collar (one of his many mistakes in the Vatican) is climbing the gloomy staircase of the Palace of the Holy Office, the severe Renaissance building south of St. Peter's Square. In a room lined with writings by church fathers and Saint Thomas Aquinas, he will have to convince a thin-lipped monsignor that he is not teaching heresy in his seminary back home.

In his office in the Apostolic Palace, the pope's secretary of state, who is a cardinal, is reading a long telex message from the Holy See's permanent observer to the United Nations. The message contains an analysis of the previous night's vote in the world organization's Security Council on the Middle East, and excerpts from New York and Washington newspaper comments. Later the cardinal secretary of state will see the French ambassador, who has a message from his president to the pontiff.

In a nearby room, two floors below the window from which the pope blesses the crowd in St. Peter's Square at noon on Sundays, a lay official of the Administration of the Patrimony of the Apostolic See is on the phone instructing a bank in Zurich to subscribe to a new Eurodollar bond issue of Norway, which has a good rating because of that country's offshore oil wealth. And later in the day, in the fifteenth-century Bastion of Nicholas V, a squat tower near the east facade of the Apostolic Palace, the Vatican bank dispatches over its telex line 610030 a sell order to a brokerage house on Wall Street following a report from the pope's own investment analysts that a high-technology stock is performing poorly.

At the same time, in a new building in the Via dell'Erba between St. Peter's Square and the Tiber embankment, a group of rabbis from Israel and the United States are paying a courtesy visit to an Argentinian monsignor who is running the Vatican's office for religious relations with Judaism.

And beyond the river, in a Renaissance palace that legally is an appendage to the Vatican, a Roman lawyer who charges high fees submits a brief replete with gynecological technicalities to prove that the marriage of a well-to-do Filipino couple was never consummated and should therefore be annulled by the church tribunal of the Sacred Rota.

These are just a few glimpses of what happens in and around the Vatican from, say, 8:00 A.M. to 1:00 P.M. every business day. Priests are early risers; when they report for work in the curia long before other offices around the city come to life they have already said morning mass and maybe even done most of the day's breviary readings. But in the afternoon the universal church's central government drops into lethargy. The Roman Curia, despite its recent internationalization, has remained very Roman in its observance of the siesta. True, the Polish pope startled the Vatican by working right through the hallowed hours after lunch, from 2:00 to 4:00 or even 5:00 P.M., but his barbarian habits disrupted the biorhythms of only his closest entourage. After a few futile attempts at raising other curialists during siesta time, he gave up. He realized he was, after all, bishop of Rome, and eventually he, too, found that a twenty-minute nap after lunch was a good thing.

Not much is done in the Vatican after siesta time either. Work in most branches of the curia is not exactly hectic, and never has been. Until Pope Paul VI's 1970 decree setting 80 years as compulsory retirement age for cardinals of the curia, some Vatican departments were headed by very old men, and their geriatric pace slowed down the tempo of the entire machinery. Over the centuries, the Roman Curia has always been notorious for its majestic lack of haste. It usually could afford to dawdle in the knowledge that it would have the last word, the ultimate power of decision: *Roma locuta, causa finita* (Rome has spoken, the case is closed). Today, ecclesiastical and lay employees in the Vatican punch the time clock when they arrive in the morning and leave for lunch, but many of the archbishops, monsignors, nuns, accountants, and secretaries seem far from hurried during working hours. The only exception is the Secretariat of State.

Most of the doorkeepers, subalterns, and almost all of the uniformed and plainclothesmen of the Vatican police—now called the Office of Vigilance—are Italians, mostly Romans. Many of them treat outsiders, whether they are prelates from distant countries or shy nuns who for once have ventured out of their convents, with a condescension that is centuries old.

The cardinals, other prelates, simple priests, monks, friars, nuns, and members of the laity who work full time or part time in the Vatican and its dependencies in other Roman neighborhoods are formally employed by diverse juridical entities—the Roman Curia, the Holy See, the State of Vatican City, the Vicariate of Rome, and others—sometimes by more than one of them. Many of these people are listed in the *Annuario Pontificio,* the fat red-bound pontifical yearbook (the pope's own copy comes in fine white leather binding). It is published every February in Italian, but it now acknowledges the principle of a universal church at least to the extent of listing the first names of non-Italian officials as Walter and Joseph instead of—until recently—Gualtiero and Giuseppe, and giving preference to New York and Paris over Nuova York and Parigi. Nearly one-tenth of the more than two thousand pages of the yearbook are devoted to the Roman Curia in its various legal and bureaucratic costumes. The headings suggest a baffling maze of Sacred Congregations, tribunals, secretariats, commissions, councils, committees, offices, archives, directorates, special funds, and other bodies.

Anyone who takes the trouble to analyze the listings finds quickly that the curial apparatus is an interlocking system in which some officials belong to various units at the same time, and sit on each other's committees. For instance, the Substitute and Secretary of Encipherment in the pope's Secretariat of State, a titular archbishop, is also a member of the Pontifical Commission for Russia, a consultant to the Sacred Congregation for the Doctrine of the Faith and for the Bishops, a consultant to the Pontifical Commission for Latin America, and a member of the Pontifical Commission for Ecclesiastical Archives in Italy. The "substitute"—an Italian title meaning deputy—furthermore belongs to the select group of dignitaries who attend major papal ceremonies, and to the consultive council of the Pius XII Foundation for the Apostolate of the Laity. Continually snowed under by curial papers in his main job, the official would have to work around the clock if all the agencies of which he is nominally a part were in action all the time. However, some commissions meet only every now and then, and other departments call on his services only irregularly. Many officials in the curia, wearing different bureaucratic hats in addition to their clerical biretta, don't seem particularly busy.

A further examination of the listings in the pontifical year-book confirms what any visitor to a Vatican office will notice at once: Italians still occupy many of the full-time key positions. The non-Italian names often belong to prelates who head archbishoprics and bishoprics in various parts of the world and who only come to Rome from time to time. What's more, Italian is the Vatican's working language, although its official documents and solemn papal addresses are often in Latin. (But even the church's Latin is, as a rule, "macaronic," the Italianate idiom of the seminaries and sacristies that is a far cry from Ciceronian classicism.)

Many of the non-Italian officials in the Vatican are actually interpreters who translate Italian material into their various languages and vice versa. Papal pronouncements nowadays are often issued simultaneously in all the languages that are spoken by the largest number of Roman Catholics—English, French, German, Italian, Polish, Portuguese, and Spanish. Other Vatican documents and messages, addressed to particular countries, are also issued in other languages.

Priests and nuns from outside Italy who are assigned to Vatican posts usually learn the working language quickly, a task made easier by their familiarity with ecclesiastical Latin. Giuseppe Cardinal Mezzofanti in the early nineteenth century spoke at least fifty languages and dialects, but the majority of today's Italians aren't great linguists. Lately Italy has had many prime ministers and foreign ministers who have needed interpreters for all their international talks. In the Vatican, Italians don't have to know any tongue but their own and a little Latin because everyone else is familiar with the two. But if a prelate were secretly to entertain pontifical hopes, he would do well to become polyglot: in the era of satellite television and papal jet travel, linguistic skills are an important qualification for an aspirant to the throne of Saint Peter. Pope Pius XII spoke German fluently, French and Spanish well, and English haltingly. John XXIII knew only French besides his native Italian. Paul VI was fluent in French and Spanish, but his English was poor. John Paul I spoke French and German. John Paul II's proficiency in Italian, English, French, German, Spanish, Russian, and other Slavic idioms in addition to his native Polish will be hard to top by any successor. He was already pontiff when he learned Portuguese and Dutch.

There are many other features of life in the curia that are

Italian, though not the early start of the working day. Strong coffee is brewed in many offices, and the espresso machines hiss in the cavernous sacristy of St. Peter's and the barracks of the Swiss Guard. Newcomers to Rome soon discover that they too need the stimulant, caffeine, because of the local climate, which is hardly invigorating and is blamed for the general lassitude. In true Roman fashion, relatives, friends, friends of friends, and even chance acquaintances around the city want favors from curialists all the time. The nuns at the Vatican switchboard are kept busy with incoming calls that have nothing to do with the government of the church—somebody wants the clerical uncle of a cousin to pick up a few cartons of imported cigarettes in the Vatican City supermarket; a Roman matron asks an archbishop to write a letter of introduction to an Italian cabinet minister for her grandson who needs a job; a Communist party bigwig calls a monsignor with whom he went to school to inquire whether he knows of a vacant apartment in one of the Vatican-owned residential buildings as a new home for his daughter who is getting married ("they'll have a church wedding, of course").

Then, there is the all-pervasive gusto for gossip that is probably as old as Rome; it certainly is as old as the curia. Elegant young monsignors and gray-haired cardinals, sacristans and nuns, they all enjoy exchanging tidbits and anecdotes about what is going on in the "sacred palaces," the relations of the pope with his entourage, who is in and who out, or forthcoming staff changes.

During a visit to the Vatican, William Cardinal Baum, archbishop of Washington, D.C., first learned of the pope's intention to assign him to the Roman Curia as chief of its education department when a Swiss Guard told his secretary "you will be back soon." The cardinal and his secretary dismissed this as just another piece of unfounded gossip and returned to Washington. Weeks later the official call to Rome came.

The penchant for indulging in stories of a personal nature, trivia, and rumor is the reverse side of the Vatican's obsession with secrecy. Curia personnel must swear not to divulge anything that comes to their knowledge in the fulfillment of their duties. Various departments, like the Secretariat of State or the Sacred Congregation for the Doctrine of the Faith, request all members of their staffs to take special, complicated oaths pledging to observe strictest secrecy under pain of automatic excommunication. If this were to apply—as it does theoretically—to the foibles of a Vatican bureaucrat's colleagues and superiors, I know quite a number of churchmen who, maybe over a cup of coffee, have voluntarily separated themselves from the community of the faithful by telling me about their office life. But such excommunication needn't have any outward consequences, because in addition to being self-triggering, it is confined to the "inner forum," the conscience of the person concerned, who may not even be aware of the grave church punishment he has incurred. This type of excommunication is not inflicted by the pope or some other church authority, but is exclusively a matter between the sinner and God. (For believers, this is a deterrent or punishment; for unbelievers, it is not.)

The perennial grapevine in the curia might seem to justify the often heard view that "there are no secrets in Rome." In truth, the real secrets of the Vatican, such as its money matters, are often well kept. Only a few high-level ecclesiastics share certain information, and the pope sometimes doesn't tell even close aides what heads of state, political leaders, and other prominent or obscure visitors confide to him in private audience.

Even high churchmen at large find the labyrinth of papal bureaucracy baffling. Letters from bishops or bishops' conferences somewhere in the world asking for a ruling on specific questions often remain unanswered for a long time while Vatican departments keep sending memos back and forth between one another. "It seems our communications to the curia are regarded as postcards with greetings when they arrive in Rome," a Canadian bishop remarked. "The curia may deign to acknowledge receipt, but it doesn't give precise replies to precise requests."

The principal administrative divisions of the Roman Curia, the Sacred Congregations, have existed since the sixteenth century, and their working methods are still ponderously baroque despite their modern office equipment. In theory, the congregations are committees of cardinals and, since Vatican II, a few coopted bishops, who meet once a week to consider pending matters. In practice, most of the committee members stay in their sees, which are often far away, and the weekly "plenary meeting" of the congregation is a cozy get-together of a handful of cardinals of the curia, presided over by one of their number who is the prefect, or department chief. If the cardinal prefect is pliable, routine decisions are taken by the secretary of the Sacred Congregation, who is a titular archbishop—he has the rank but no actual see and archbishopric to go with it—or a mere monsignor. The many consultants listed in the pontifical yearbook may or may not be heard.

The curia department with the greatest authority, the real nerve center of the Vatican, is the Secretariat of State. Next to it in importance is the Sacred Congregation for the Doctrine of the Faith. Before 1967 it was known as the Supreme Sacred Congregation of the Holy Office, and before 1908 as the Holy Inquisition. Something of the awe and terror evoked by that name still clings to the Palace of the Holy Office on the left side of St. Peter's Square. Despite its new, soothing name, the Roman Curia's high court of orthodoxy is still in the business of ferreting out heretics. However, it can no longer turn them over to the "secular arm" of some complaisant government with the ritual, hollow plea for mercy that would not save its victim from death at the stake. Neither does the doctrinal congregation deal with Jews, Protestants, alleged witches, or alchemists any longer. The Holy Office (as the body is still generally called in Rome) can, and does, reprimand, silence, unfrock, or excommunicate priests and nuns; it examines books and investigates members of the clergy and the laity on charges of offending the faith or Christian morals. The procedures are shrouded in mystery and obfuscation.

Modern theologians and thinkers such as Pierre Teilhard de Chardin, Ivan Illich, Hans Küng, Edward Schillebeeckx, and many others have been under investigation by the Holy Office. The Reverend Dr. Küng for years ignored summonses to appear before his judges in Rome, and continued his work at the University of Tübingen, West Germany, even after the doctrinal agency, fourteen months after Pope John Paul II's election, stripped him of his qualification as a "Catholic theologian." The Swiss scholar told me in Tübingen: "Whatever the name, it is still the old Inquisition. There is no due process in Rome."

After the redoubtable Cardinal Ottaviani, the post of grand inquisitor, or chief of the doctrinal congregation, was held for nearly thirteen years by Cardinal Seper. He was succeeded in 1982 by one of the "grand electors" of John Paul II in the conclave of 1978, Josef Cardinal Ratzinger, the son of a Bavarian policeman and professor of theology before he became archbishop of Munich.

The Holy Office has been assisted, since 1969, by an International Theological Commission of up to thirty members, to be chosen, as Paul VI directed, from various currents of modern

Roman Catholic thought. In practice, conservatives and moderates quickly became predominant in the body, which is presided over by the cardinal prefect of the Holy Office, and is therefore hardly independent.

The heresy hunters of the Holy Office aren't too happy with interferences by the Secretariat of State that have become frequent lately, and seem unafraid of interdepartmental squabbles with that superagency. The other Sacred Congregations, on the whole, yield more meekly to the Secretariat of State. They are the departments for the bishops, the clergy, the religious orders, missionary activities, the Eastern churches, liturgy, education, and "for the causes of saints." Each of these bulwarks of curial bureaucrats has its own outworks and auxiliaries of committees, special secretariats, and consultants.

Common to all these departments and subdivisions of church government is a legalistic approach to human problems. Canon law and service regulations prompt more curial decisions than does charity. In 1981 the Sacred Congregation for Catholic Education provided an example of the prevailing attitude when it fired a file clerk because she had gotten married in a civil ceremony to a Yugoslav who had abandoned the priesthood without proper authorization from his church superiors. The former clergyman had as yet been unable to find a civilian job in Rome, and the couple had been living with their baby daughter on the woman's Vatican salary. The congregation cited a provision in the rules for curia employees that threatened dismissal in case of "grave dereliction of their ecclesiastical and Christian duties," implying that the file clerk had been guilty of such an offense.

The bewildering organizational chart of central church government has been expanded since Vatican II by a cluster of additional agencies that are unofficially known as the "new curia." Personnel of the older departments snipe at the newcomers for three reasons: the new curia tends to hire more members of the laity than the old one; it costs money and is clamoring for more funds; and it has a more modern and open-minded outlook than the traditional Vatican apparatus.

The first, and still the most important, of the new units is the Secretariat for the Union of Christians. This ecumenical agency was set up by Pope John XXIII in 1960 to promote dialogue and collaboration with Christian churches and communities outside the Roman fold in view of the forthcoming Vatican Council. Under the leadership of Augustin Cardinal Bea, the brilliant

German Jesuit who was one of the giants of Vatican II, the secretariat became an interfaith center and a rallying point for council liberals.

The ecumenical secretariat also started Catholic-Jewish conversations through an appendage, the Commission for Religious Relations with Judaism. After Cardinal Bea's death in 1968 the Vatican's interfaith arm was guided by a Dutchman, Johannes Cardinal Willebrands, a conciliator who also served as archbishop of Utrecht and primate of the Netherlands.

Other new curia units with small permanent staffs are the secretariats for non-Christians and for nonbelievers; the Pontifical Council for the Laity; the Pontifical Commission "Justitia et Pax" (Justice and Peace), the Vatican's human rights and antiwar agency; and the Pontifical Council "Cor Unum" (One Heart), which administers Vatican welfare efforts. The last two bodies were for years headed by the curia's first black leader, Bernardin Cardinal Gantin, a strapping prelate from Benin, formerly Dahomey (who accompanied John Paul II on the pontiff's 1982 visit to that professedly Marxist country). Gantin, who is so informal that he opens his apartment door himself when a visitor arrives, proved that a black African can quickly become acclimatized in ecclesiastical Rome.

Of all the curia departments beside the Secretariat of State and the Holy Office, the Sacred Congregation for the Evangelization of the Peoples, the Vatican's missionary arm, has the most autonomy. Its headquarters is in an old palace on the Spanish Square in Rome's center, far from the Vatican, and its modern training center for future missionaries is on the Janiculum Hill overlooking St. Peter's Square. The missionary department has revenues of its own—sizable funds periodically collected all over the world for the spreading of the faith. Lately the other Sacred Congregations have become more and more dependent on the superagency at the summit of the Vatican bureaucracy, the Secretariat of State.

According to canon law, the Sacred Congregations, tribunals, and offices of the Roman Curia must not take any action in "grave or extraordinary" matters unless their heads have previously reported these matters to the supreme pontiff. The curialists nevertheless handle much business that they choose to consider neither grave nor extraordinary without bothering to inform the pope. Every so often during a papal audience, an outraged bishop will whip out a letter from some Vatican department and show it to the pontiff, who is surprised or even startled by its content. The Sacred Congregation for the Doctrine of the Faith may have disciplined a priestly author for his writings, or the liturgical congregation may have banned a local form of worship, such as African music at mass—all in the name of the pope, who has not been told about the issue.

The relationship between the head of the church and the curia is one of the basic and permanent problems of the papacy. Since the Middle Ages, the Vatican clerks, instead of serving as the pontiff's assistants, have again and again tended to dominate and manipulate him. How the pope uses the Vatican bureaucracy—if it is not using him—is different in every pontificate. The curialists have always insisted on pontifical power and centralized government in the church; forever attempting to strengthen the papacy, they seek to enhance their own importance. If papal authority is strong, Vatican bureaucrats who act on its behalf are all too easily tempted to impose their will on churchmen at large, even on cardinals and archbishops of important sees. A forceful pope may be able to check this tendency, but even he is unable to control the Holy See's entire machinery, and he may lose his grip with advancing years.

DISGRUNTLED BISHOPS

One of the surprises of Vatican II was the widespread resentment of the Roman Curia revealed by the cardinals, archbishops, and bishops from around the world who had attended the historic church gathering. They complained about the Vatican's administrative arm during the plenary sessions in St. Peter's and even more so during commission debates and in well-publicized private remarks.

These critics charged that the ordained bureaucrats who were supposed to help the supreme pontiff govern the universal church were legalistic quibblers, high-handed, slow, insolent, uncharitable, devoid of pastoral experience, and provincially insensitive to the diversity of local conditions around the world. In fact, a classic story about the lack of understanding of human problems and the Italian chauvinism in the Roman Curia has Cardinal Ottaviani, the long-time watchdog of orthodox faith and morals, attend a meeting with prelates from different countries and listen to their worried reports about the sexual tribulations of their young seminarians. "Pasta e fagioli, pasta e fagioli!" the old cardinal muttered, convinced that a diet of macaroni and beans will abate the fleshly yearnings of the troubled students of the priesthood in, say, Nigeria or Sri Lanka.

Many of the 2,500 participants in Vatican II, the "council fathers," had had frustrating experiences with the curialists during previous visits to the Vatican. It may have taken days, even weeks, for an archbishop from the Philippines or Canada to get an appointment with a simple monsignor who happened to occupy a key spot in one of the curia departments. The meeting, when it eventually took place, may have been unsatisfactory, the papal bureaucrat turning down the prelate's plea for special appreciation of the difficulties in his area. An effort to seek a review of the case by the monsignor's superior, an elderly cardinal, may have proved futile, a desperate attempt to appeal directly to the pope utterly unsuccessful. The Vatican protocol officers who managed to fit a lengthy audience for members of the left-wing Roman city government into the pontiff's tight schedule—important because the Vatican needs City Hall and vice versa—would tell the prelate there was no time for him except a few minutes at next Wednesday's general audience when the pope would briefly welcome all members of the episcopate who happened to be present. "The pope isn't a supermarket where you can walk in any time you like," a prelate may have observed.

Doormen in the curia department may have snarled at the visiting prelate with the characteristic gruffness that subaltern laymen in the pope's service—their cushy jobs often go from father to son—reserve for ecclesiastics from outside the Vatican who aren't known as good tippers.

The archbishop, returning to the convent or ecclesiastical college where he was staying while in Rome, may have felt like a colonel commanding a field brigade who is slighted by mere captains and pushed around by master sergeants during an attempt to tell army headquarters about his logistical and tactical problems. Such bitterness about the Vatican bureaucrats, accumulated over many years, flavored the debates of Vatican II when it got around to considering a reform of the central mechanisms of church government.

As has been recalled earlier, Pope John XXIII summoned Vatican II with the avowed aim of bringing the Roman Catholic

Church up to date. Realizing that the self-perpetuating Vatican bureaucracy was standing in the way of aggiornamento, he counted on the assembled hierarchy from all parts of the world to weaken the curial conservatives' resistance to change. The introduction of the locally spoken languages (the vernacular) to replace Latin in worship, the emphasis on individual conscience in religious belief, the overtures for interfaith collaboration, and other reforms adopted by Vatican II were indeed victories of a liberal-moderate majority among the council fathers over a conservative minority backed by the curia. Eventually, Vatican II also considered reforms in the curia itself.

A decree on the pastoral office of bishops in the church, voted by the council shortly before its end in 1965, noted that "in exercising his supreme, full, and immediate authority over the universal church, the Roman pontiff employs the various departments of the Roman Curia, which act in his name and by his authority for the good of the churches and in the service of the sacred pastors." The decree went on to outline a plan for thoroughly revamping the Vatican administration: "It is the earnest desire of the fathers of the sacred council that these [curia] departments . . . should be reorganized and modernized, should be more in keeping with different regions and rites, especially in regard to their numbers, their names, their competence, their procedures and methods of coordination." The text also suggested that curia personnel be chosen "on a more representative basis so that the offices of the central agencies of the church may have a truly universal spirit," that bishops with a pastoral background be coopted by the curia, and that the advice of "laymen of virtue, knowledge, and experience" be sought more often than had been done thus far.

The emphasis of the council fathers on the need for more international and pastoral know-how in the Roman Curia was a slap at the Vatican bureaucrats. There have always been plenty of bishops and archbishops in the offices of the curia, but the vast majority of them were, and still are, titular. A monsignor who for ten years or so has been shuffling papers in some Vatican agency and hasn't rocked the boat may count on being eventually, and almost automatically, promoted to some bishopric in North Africa that once existed but no longer does, or to some other long-extinct see, and will go on shuffling papers as a titular bishop.

Graduates of the Ecclesiastical Academy, the training school for Vatican diplomats near the Pantheon in Rome's historical core, may find themselves titular archbishops in their forties—ordinarily a very early age for that rank—when they are given their first major foreign assignment. Eventually they may become nuncios, or papal ambassadors in some important capital, such as Paris, Bonn, or Madrid, and may expect to get the red hat at the end of their tour of duty. As new cardinals they may be called into the Vatican to take up a high curia post. They will have spent twenty or thirty years in various countries, but always will have moved among diplomats and high churchmen, and will lack any firsthand knowledge of the problems the local pastors face every day. On the other hand, the residential bishops and archbishops—usually natives of the country where they work and who deal directly with the churches and pastors there —as a rule have been active in the field for long years and know what a parish priest is dealing with.

The curial remoteness from the way other people—and ordinary priests—live and from their everyday worries is almost always coupled with a special cant of ostensible nostalgia for pastoral work. Over the years, whenever I have spoken in a more than perfunctory manner to an ecclesiastic in a Vatican job, he would inevitably, sooner or later, confide: "That time when I was a humble curate in a faraway parish—those were the happiest years of my life," or perhaps: "Of course, it's a great thing for me to be of some use in the central government of the church, but I badly miss being out there doing something for the spiritual needs of the people."

Such longing for fieldwork may sometimes be genuine. Nevertheless, it is a fact that, with thousands of clerics in the Vatican and in church institutions around Rome, the city has a shortage of clergy. The vicariate, which is in charge of church affairs in Rome on the pope's behalf, has had to import priests from Spain, Poland, Belgium, and other nations. The cardinal vicar, the pope's lieutenant for his own diocese, would be delighted if ecclesiastics holding curia posts volunteered to help out, part time, in the Roman parishes. Very few do. A papal diplomat, an Italian monsignor in his early fifties who had been reassigned to the Vatican after several years in nunciatures abroad, told me how he enjoyed being able to do pastoral work in Rome at last. I asked him for specifics. It turned out that the monsignor said mass for the good nuns who were offering him a temporary, and presumably comfortable, home in their convent; "and I hear their confessions too."

An innovation in the curia that would surely be applauded by priests at large might be a papal order to all Vatican bureaucrats to get out of their offices periodically to make house visits in the shantytowns that ring Rome, or help operate day-care centers for slum children, or try rehabilitation of drug addicts, or counsel jobless youths. A group of sari-clad nuns whom Mother Teresa of Calcutta sent to Rome are doing just that; by joining them, the priests in the Vatican administration would get some useful pastoral experience, and learn about the social problems of their time.

Following Vatican II's call for curia reform, Pope Paul VI introduced some new features for Vatican service. An apostolic constitution (a name for a major piece of papal legislation) in 1967 reorganized the central church government, defining and coordinating the tasks of its main bodies. New rules for recruitment, promotion, transfers, holidays, and other job conditions for curia personnel were issued in 1968. Two years later Paul VI angered the older members of the sacred college with his apostolic letter setting retirement ages for cardinals. Bishops from far-flung sees around the world and other staff from outside Italy joined the Roman Curia. Nevertheless, the atmosphere in the citadels of Vatican bureaucracy remained remarkably unchanged.

Paul VI also set up something like a papal cabinet by having his cardinal secretary of state and the chief of the other curia departments meet periodically to discuss current business. Pope John Paul II himself occasionally presided at such high-level sessions. One result of the new cabinet system was that the cardinals heading the Sacred Congregations lost their right to regular private audiences with the pontiff—usually twice a month—to submit important matters concerning their departments to his ultimate decision. Now everything goes through the secretary of state, the "prime minister" of the papal government, and the volume of paper work has swollen. Since the cardinal secretary of state cannot handle everything, let alone report to the pope on everything, many matters are delegated to senior aides in the Secretariat of State. Decisions that are handed down on behalf of the supreme pontiff all too often have been made by some titular archbishop or monsignor who is an assistant to the cardinal secretary of state.

The curia department that prepares the appointment of new bishops, receiving the comments of the Secretariat of State on a list of candidates for vacant sees around the world, may find that one or the other of the proposed nominees has been vetoed. Who set up the roadblock in the career of the unwitting churchman in, say, Bolivia or Cameroon? Was it the pope, the cardinal secretary of state, or an anonymous curialist who had seen a report by the apostolic nuncio in La Paz or Yaoundé that gave poor marks to the hapless candidate?

Vatican II stressed the "principle of collegiality," meaning that the church was not to be governed by the supreme pontiff alone, but by him jointly with the world's bishops as the successors of the twelve apostles. Since Vatican II, the term *collegial* has become a Roman Catholic code word for currents in the church that oppose the monarchic absolutism of the papacy and de facto rule by the Roman Curia as its executive arm. Shortly before Vatican II ended, Pope Paul VI responded to the almost general demands for more "collegial" church government by creating a new body, the Bishops' Synod. This is essentially a consultative assembly, made up of delegates elected by all bishops' conferences throughout the world, plus representatives of religious orders and cardinals of the Roman Curia. It meets in plenary session every three years when about two hundred prelates from many countries gather in the Vatican to advise the pope on matters selected by him.

The synod is much less than a church parliament. It cannot convene without being summoned by the pope; cannot take up business outside the official agenda that the pontiff, its president, has chosen for any given sessions; and cannot override his decisions. It may only make recommendations. Topics before the synod so far included "Justice in the World," "The Priestly Ministry," "The Christian Family," and others. Although the themes were broad enough to permit diverse views on present-day problems to be aired, so far there hasn't been any real opposition to the pope. Even on such a controversial issue as birth control, the synod in its 1980 session endorsed the rigorous stand of Paul VI and John Paul II.

With all its limitations the synod is nevertheless a new forum for periodic dialogue between the pope and the world's bishops, and may eventually lead to a more representative church government. However, the Roman Catholic Church is not, by definition, a democratic society but a hierarchical theocracy. It would therefore be rash to view the Bishops' Synod as the fledgling stage of a future lower house of a legislature in tandem with an upper house—

the college of cardinals, revived by John Paul II as "senate of the church." Doctrinally, the synod can be much better justified as an advisory body, because its members are regarded as the successors to the apostles; the sacred college is a group without any basis in the Scriptures—as is the Roman Curia.

The determination of the Vatican's administrative apparatus to defend its power monopoly, synod or no synod, was graphically expressed in a mot by Cardinal Felici, the curia's ranking expert on canon law who was secretary-general of Vatican II. A traditionalist with more than the usual dose of Roman cynicism, Felici said: "The world's bishops want the keys to the church government? Well, of course, we shall give them those keys— only, we'll change the locks."

Unloved by the curialists, the synod, which has a permanent secretariat in the Vatican, at any rate provides new opportunities to churchmen at large for visiting Rome and getting to know one another. One of those who seized on the chance and made the most of it was the archbishop of Krakow, Cardinal Wojtyla, whom the Polish bishops' conference had elected and reelected as a delegate to the synod sessions in the 1970s. His speeches at the Rome gatherings and the contacts he established on these occasions brought him to the attention of influential cardinals, and such exposure helped him prepare the basis for his eventual elevation to the papacy.

As head of the church, John Paul II undertook to revamp the Roman Curia by thoroughly amending Paul VI's halfhearted reform legislation of 1967. In 1982 the pontiff told the assembled cardinals in Rome he intended to see to it that the central machinery of the Holy See cooperated more efficiently and closely with church hierarchies all over the world, and that curial work be "more and more pastorally oriented." Implicit was an acknowledgment that many churchmen at large were strongly critical of the Roman Curia, and that their state of mind was justified.

WHAT A NUNCIO DOES

During Vatican II it became clear that the strong feelings among the world's bishops against the Roman Curia seemed to include the Holy See's representatives abroad—the apostolic nuncios and apostolic delegates. Many of the council fathers made no secret of their dislike of these papal ambassadors in their nations' capitals. Officially, the tasks of the nuncios are twofold: to represent the pope in dealings with the governments in various countries, and to serve as middlemen between him and the local church apparatus.

However, quite a number of participants in Vatican II let it be known that they regarded those ecclesiastical diplomats as curial spies who did things behind their backs and fomented intrigues. Why not abolish the network of Vatican envoys altogether, saving the Holy See millions of dollars every year? Why maintain their sumptuous nunciature buildings and their limousines with diplomatic license plates? Why should they go on holding receptions and giving state dinners? The critics of the papal foreign service contended that relationships between the Vatican and national governments might be ensured by the bishops' conferences. Such bodies, grouping the Roman Catholic hierarchy of a country or a larger area, have been established lately in most parts of the world. They have permanent secretariats and could well take over the substantive tasks of the nunciatures and apostolic delegations, disregarding the diplomatic frills. (Nuncios, as papal representatives, are formally recognized as ambassadors by civil governments; apostolic delegates are papal envoys, lacking full diplomatic status. Nevertheless, in Washington and in some other capitals apostolic delegates enjoy quasi-diplomatic privileges, and in effect function like ambassadors.)

Bishops arriving in Rome for synod meetings or their regular five- or ten-year visits continue to grumble about the papal envoys in their countries. When the Canadian bishops' conference wanted to issue a statement condemning violence in El Salvador, the apostolic nuncio, Archbishop Angelo Palmas (a titular archbishop without a real diocese), told the group they should avoid meddling in international politics because it was a field reserved for the Holy See.

Third World bishops have repeatedly been warned by the papal representatives in their areas not to try to link up directly with church groups in Western countries and solicit funds from them, bypassing the Vatican. An archbishop in South Africa and a bishop in Yugoslavia both told me, separately and in almost the same words, that the pope's diplomats often were in touch with civil governments, and made deals with them, over the heads of the local episcopate. In the United States some influential prelates with rich dioceses behind them aren't afraid of the apostolic delegate in Washington; other churchmen defer to the pope's envoy because they know he can make or break a career, inducing the Vatican to grant or withhold favors and promotions.

Despite the resentment of cardinals and bishops in many countries, it is most unlikely that the Vatican will voluntarily give up the system of permanent papal envoys in the world's capitals that has served it so well for four-hundred years. The network of nunciatures and apostolic delegations has in fact been expanded since Vatican II. It helps the Roman Curia keep the church organization throughout the world under control, and, equally important, formal diplomatic ties with many governments strengthen the papacy's claim to sovereignty.

In Roman Catholic theory, this papal sovereignty is not vested in the present State of Vatican City but in a superior spiritual entity, the Holy See, which now happens to wield territorial jurisdiction over the 10.78-acre enclave in Rome. When the pope lacked an actual territory of his own during the period between Italy's unification in 1870 and the Lateran Treaties of 1929, apostolic nuncios still acted as his diplomatic envoys in various capitals. The dainty distinctions between the Vatican (the walled complex of buildings and gardens around St. Peter's), the State of Vatican City (the area of the pope's territorial jurisdiction including St. Peter's Square and detached dependencies, as defined in 1929), and the Holy See (an imaginary authority claiming independence of any worldly power) lend themselves to nice legal and semantic jugglery by the pontiff's jurists and diplomats.

When the system of resident ambassadors and permanent embassies developed in Europe during the Renaissance, Italians—especially Florentines—occasionally acted as envoys for foreign potentates because they had a reputation for adroitness and were masters of Latin rhetoric, then an important skill in diplomacy. Today, Italians still dominate the pope's diplomatic service, although quite a few ecclesiastics from other nations have joined them since World War II. Bishops everywhere are under standing instructions to recommend the best and brightest among their young priests for diplomatic training in Rome. As fluency in Italian is one of the requisites, most of the non-Italian personnel chosen have already studied for the priesthood or done postgraduate work in Rome.

Candidates for the Vatican's foreign service are priests with outstanding qualifications who have been admitted to the Ecclesiastical Academy. About thirty students attend the two-year course of the institution at any time. The academy, founded in 1701 and long reserved exclusively for ecclesiastics who were also noblemen, lately has been headed by Archbishop Cesare Zacchi, a former papal envoy to Cuba and friend of Prime Minister Fidel Castro.

As the Vatican's man in Havana, Archbishop Zacchi was the only pontifical diplomat stationed in any Communist-governed country until Yugoslavia established formal relations with the Holy See. The music-loving churchman from Tuscany, who had formerly served at the nunciature in Vienna, and the Cuban dictator took a liking to each other that brought some benefits to the church on the island, but scandalized old-time ecclesiastics. Spanish-descended clergy whom the Castro regime considered undesirable were replaced with Canadians and others. Archbishop Zacchi even obtained import licenses for cars, no mean feat in Communist Cuba at the time, to make the island's bishops and priests more mobile. Occasionally, Castro would turn up at a diplomatic reception at the apostolic nunciature in Havana's smart Marianao section and stay until long after midnight, playfully taking Archbishop Zacchi's skullcap and putting it on his own hirsute head. When the archbishop was at last called to Rome, the Cuban strongman continued to send him Havana cigars through his embassy to the Holy See.

In Havana, as in many other capitals of the Third World, the pope's envoy is officially a pro-nuncio. The title nuncio is reserved for the representatives of the Holy See in countries that recognize them as deans of the diplomatic corps in their capitals. This privilege was sanctioned by the Congress of Vienna (1814–15), which not only redrew the map of Europe after Napoleon's downfall, but also laid ground rules for the diplomatic service.

The Vatican's Secretariat of State attaches the utmost importance to its diplomatic network, its eyes and ears in the world. Special attention is paid to the United States. The apostolic delegate in Washington, as has been mentioned, runs what amounts to a full-fledged Vatican embassy and is in frequent touch with the White House, the Department of State, and diplomats from Third World powers; he also has almost daily contacts with the National Conference of Catholic Bishops and with individual American prelates. The permanent observer mission of the Holy

See to the United Nations, in a town house on Manhattan's East Seventy-second Street that was bequeathed to the church by its former owner, monitors all activities of the world organization and keeps an eye on what other diplomats in New York do.

As a foreign correspondent for the *New York Times* in various capitals I always visited the papal representatives because they were usually well informed. Their knowledge of local conditions, political and social forces, and the motivations of influential personages sprang from many sources: what prelates, priests, and well-connected members of the local laity were telling them, their contacts with public figures and officials, shrewd evaluation of the news media, and personal research. Nuncios and their aides are interested in much more than just church affairs and official matters. I remember a papal diplomat (he later became a cardinal) who, with obvious gusto, filled me in on the racy details of a dalliance between the wife of a Latin American head of state and the chief pilot of her husband's presidential aircraft. I felt sure at the time that a similar report, though maybe devoid of some graphic particulars, was sent, in code, to the Vatican.

Thousands of bundles and folders containing reports from nunciatures since the sixteenth century are stored in the Vatican's Secret Archives, together with innumerable other records, many of them much older. The illicit love affairs of emperors and kings and the cabals of courtiers and churchmen are buried in the archives together with analyses of important events and historical developments. Scholars who want to carry out research in the Vatican archives are severely screened and are given access only to selected files, none earlier than 1903, the year of Pope Leo XIII's death. A determination to allow access to files after 1903 is reserved by the pontiff, and there is no way to tell when such a determination may be expected.

Not all assessments by the Vatican's agents have been accurate. For example, the French Revolution had already started, King Louis XVI had yielded to the National Assembly, and further upheavals were looming, but the papal representative in Paris, in a secret dispatch, urged the Vatican not to waver in its support of the royal court: "Despite the [French] nation's desire to do great things in this assembly . . . the court will have the greatest influence." Two years later, the king was executed, the royal court swept away, and the papal envoy had been forced to leave France.

Compared with the embassies of the major powers, which

sometimes have hundreds of diplomats and support personnel, the staffs of the apostolic nunciatures and delegations are small. The mission chief, usually a titular archbishop, may have a secretary and perhaps one to three assistants of councillor rank, all priests. There may be a majordomo-driver, a few part-time consultants or interpreters from the local Roman Catholic laity, and a few nuns for housekeeping. (When Archbishop Angelo Felici was apostolic nuncio in The Hague during a tense period in the relations between a part of the Roman Catholic Church in the Netherlands and the Vatican, he taught himself Dutch to be able to translate documents and the local newspapers without any help.)

The apostolic delegation in Washington and the permanent observer mission of the Holy See in New York are said to cost less than $500,000 a year combined. Many small countries spend much more on any one of their embassies.

The Vatican foreign service operates on a shoestring in other respects, too. When Pope John Paul II visited the Philippines and Japan in 1981, he asked his secretary of state, Cardinal Casaroli, who was traveling with him, to make a quick side trip to Hong Kong to meet a Chinese bishop and sound him out regarding a possible accord between the Holy See and the People's Republic of China. Cardinal Casaroli made his own plane and hotel reservations and flew off to Hong Kong alone, without even a junior aide. (The mission to Hong Kong was unsuccessful.)

Confidential messages to and from the Vatican have been enciphered since the Middle Ages—and the methods haven't changed much since then. Today's code system used by the Roman Curia is, according to experts, unsophisticated and could be cracked by any competent cryptographer. Bishops and other prelates who happen to travel to Rome sometimes serve as couriers. Quite often the nuncio in one of the world capitals will use the diplomatic pouch of a friendly embassy, most often Italy's, to forward confidential mail to the Vatican. Much business today is transacted by telephone between the Vatican's Secretariat of State and its representatives abroad; all calls are made without scramblers and can easily be monitored. It needed Archbishop Giovanni Cheli, one of the most efficient and diligent papal diplomats, to alert the curia to the advantage of telex service. However, only his permanent observer mission in New York and a handful of the most important nunciatures and apostolic delegations were authorized to install telex equipment.

Diplomats in Rome, who regularly discuss bilateral and international affairs with the pope's top aides, agree that the Vatican appears to be very well informed on some areas—like Europe, the Middle East, and Latin America—and much less so on other parts of the world. The Vatican knows much about international organizations and conferences, little about what is going on in the Soviet Union and China. "They appreciate it whenever I can give them some goodies from our cables," a Western envoy told me. Trading information is as old as diplomacy.

Ambassadors from more than one hundred nations are formally accredited to the Holy See. However, many of them serve principally in diplomatic posts in Berne, Bonn, Madrid, Paris, or other European capitals and visit Rome only to present their letters of credence to the pope, and on a few other occasions. The Holy See does not officially deal with diplomats who are accredited to the Italian Republic, unless they are carrying out an occasional once-only assignment at the Vatican, like representing their government at the funeral of a pope or the inauguration of a new head of the church. The Vatican, furthermore, does not extend accreditation to ambassadors or other diplomats who are divorced, or whose spouses have gone through divorce; the religion of the ambassadors, on the other hand, is considered irrelevant.

The number of permanent missions to the Holy See exceeds fifty. Among them are a shadowy legation of Lithuania, whose annexation by the Soviet Union during World War II has never been recognized by the Vatican, and an embassy of the Sovereign Military Order of Malta, an international association that claims to be an autonomous entity, although it lacks a territory of its own. Permanent ambassadors to the Vatican live and work in embassy buildings around Rome, and visit the Vatican only for talks with papal officials or for ceremonies. However, during World War II, the Holy See offered living and working quarters inside the Vatican to diplomats whose countries were at war with Italy—among them the ambassadors of Britain and France, the personal representative of President Roosevelt (1939–43), and the ambassador of Nazi Germany after Italy had changed sides.

In the cosmopolitan fraternity of diplomats, a resident ambassadorship at the Holy See is regarded as a pleasant sinecure, often the last posting in a distinguished career. Senior members of the diplomatic corps at the Vatican sometimes write their memoirs, work on other books, or cultivate hobbies. They are often treated patronizingly by their busier colleagues who are accredited in Italy, and they repay such condescension with mordant remarks about the irrelevance of Italian politics as compared with the universal nature and interests of the papacy. The presence of the Vatican in the capital of Italy results in a situation where Rome boasts more embassies than Washington, Moscow, or London—a full set of missions accredited to the Quirinal, the former papal summer palace that is now the official residence of the president of Italy, and a second tier of missions to the Holy See.

Some envoys to the Vatican attend an occasional ceremony in St. Peter's, confer now and then with some official in the Apostolic Palace, and mainly enjoy the pleasures of living in Rome. Others are convinced they have been assigned to an international observation post of the first magnitude, and transmit voluminous reports to their home governments. Even diplomats from powers that maintain no formal ties with the Holy See often call at the Apostolic Palace. Foremost among them is the personal representative of the president of the United States to the pope who visits Rome several times a year and has a permanent office and a staff in Rome that report to the Department of State in Washington. For several years, Robert F. Wagner, Jr., former mayor of New York, served as United States representative at the Vatican. President Reagan named a California supporter, William Wilson, as Wagner's successor. The Israeli embassy in Italy also has its Vatican specialist who sees officials at the Secretariat of State from time to time, as do diplomats from Poland and a few other nations that are officially unrepresented at the Holy See.

The expansion of the papal foreign service since the end of World War II is due to decolonization, the emergence of new sovereign countries, and the heightened prestige of the Vatican. In 1945 the Holy See maintained full diplomatic relations with 41 nations and was represented by apostolic delegates in another 20. Now, Vatican diplomats are stationed in more than 100 capitals around the globe, and are accredited observers at 10 international bodies.

Officials familiar with the kind of information that pours into the Vatican daily from its diplomatic outposts and from church hierarchies on all continents say outsiders would be surprised by the frequency of reports concerning personnel and other administrative matters. The mother superior of a nuns' order protests against what she denounces as the high-handed ways of a local bishop. A seminary in the Philippines is under suspicion of having given asylum to rebels against the government, and a group of conservative Roman Catholics warns the pope against an alleged plot to destabilize the nation. An archbishop in France wants the transfer of his auxiliary bishop who, he is convinced, is scheming to take over his see. Jesuits in Mexico intend to close a high school and sell the building; does the Holy See agree? A priest in Slovakia smuggles a letter to the apostolic nunciature in Vienna asking it to tell the Vatican that a certain prelate is playing a "double game," working on the side as an informer for the Communist authorities. The son of a tribal chief in Central Africa who recently has been consecrated as a bishop is discriminating against seminarians and priests from other tribes; can't the pope do anything about it?

Most of such business ends up at the Secretariat of State. Somebody has to decide whether a matter ought to be brought to the attention of the pontiff or, if not, who should handle it. To make the system function, the Vatican's superagency requires a team of all-round men who can cope with an immense amount of paperwork. And they must be able to consider the latest move in the East-West disarmament talks (should the pope make another pronouncement on nuclear warfare?) then, half an hour later, deal with the complaint by the mother superior.

HARD WORK AT THE TOP

The governments of the world powers and the productivity experts of multinational corporations would be envious if they could see how the top unit of the papacy's executive structure handles a staggering volume of administrative tasks with a very small staff at relatively low cost. The cardinal secretary of state, his "substitute" or deputy, and their closest aides are in service or on call around the clock, day after day. Maybe they can take off a couple of weeks in summer, maybe not. There are no material incentives to speak of. Exercising power (an enjoyment that doesn't pall with age); the feeling of usefulness to a great and enduring institution; and, if they are believers, the satisfaction of serving their God to the best of their faculties, are the motivations for such hard work.

Secrecy is most rigorously enforced and maintained, and siestas are shortest in the Secretariat of State. Lights burn late in some of its offices in the Apostolic Palace, close to the pontiff's own private quarters. Many of the one hundred twenty or so officials of the papacy's chief executive arm work in rather spartan rooms, built after World War II on top of the southwest wing of the Renaissance structure that is the pope's main residence.

Despite the grueling hours, the monsignors of the all-important office, often comparatively young for their rank, and the even younger priests, are always well shaved—which is more than can be said of the personnel in other curia departments—and well groomed. Their round Roman hats, sometimes worn at a smart, though not rakish, tilt, look silken. Their cassocks are often of finer fabric than those of other ecclesiastics. (However, in the 1970s and early 1980s fewer and fewer priests in Rome wore their traditional garb, preferring dark business suits with or without the Roman collar, or even open-necked windbreakers and blue jeans, and berets instead of clerical hats. But then John Paul II sharply reprimanded the clergy of his diocese for their laxity in clothing, and the long black cassocks, Roman collars, and round hats reappeared in the city's streets, especially in neighborhoods close to the Vatican. The pope's vicar for Rome, Ugo Cardinal Poletti, who on John Paul II's behest had issued formal orders to the city's clergy to observe strictly the clerical dress code, was called "Cardinal Colletti" (Cardinal Collars) by priests and seminarians who were disgruntled at having again to wear their Roman collar.)

There is an air of authority and elitism about those working in the Secretariat of State that recalls the ways of officers in an army's general staff or, in Communist-ruled countries, of functionaries in the party's central committee. The priests, young monsignors, and titular archbishops of the top curia body handle business that in Washington would be split up between the White House staff, the Department of State, and various other United States government agencies. They do secretarial work for the pope, answer much of his voluminous mail, help him prepare many public addresses and other pronouncements and translate them, and carry out whatever special assignments he may give them. The Secretariat of State is also in charge of the papacy's relations with Italy and other nations all over the globe. Through a subsidiary body, known as the Council for the

109

Public Affairs of the Church, the papal secretariat directs the network of apostolic nuncios and other pontifical envoys abroad, and maintains contacts with the ambassadors of civil powers who are accredited to the Holy See.

In addition to all this, the Secretariat of State, since Pope Pius XII, has developed into a superagency that monitors and oversees what all the other curia departments do. The chief officers of the Sacred Congregations and other curia bodies don't always have easy access to the pope, but the cardinal secretary of state and his substitute see him daily, often several times a day. They can submit, or at least mention, to him not only the matters their own office is treating but also urgent business from other administrative units of church government. The Secretariat of State has thus become a filter between all branches of the Roman Curia and the pope—a supercuria.

A remarkable line of able and dedicated men passed through the offices of the Secretariat of State this century, while the core of the Vatican's bureaucratic machinery was becoming increasingly important and busy. Pope Pius XI, himself a strong personality, was served by two brilliant secretaries of state, Pietro Cardinal Gasparri—who negotiated the Lateran Treaties with Mussolini—until 1930, and Cardinal Pacelli afterward. When Pacelli became Pope Pius XII in 1939, he named a rather colorless prelate, Luigi Cardinal Maglione, as his secretary of state and continued doing much of what he had done during the years when he himself had occupied that post.

After Cardinal Maglione's death in 1944 Pius XII did not replace him, and for the pope's remaining fourteen years of life kept acting as his own secretary of state. During Cardinal Maglione's years in the Secretariat of State, Pius XII had relied mainly on a pair of aides who were heading the two main sections into which that bureaucratic body was then divided, one for "ordinary" and the other for "extraordinary" affairs. The competence of the two branches was ill-defined and overlapping. Msgr. Giovanni Battista Montini was mainly concerned with intramural and Italian matters, Msgr. Domenico Tardini with the Vatican foreign service. Pius XII would give special assignments to either prelate, and also use the tireless Montini as a private secretary. The Montini-Tardini team worked closely together for fifteen years. Montini was eventually to become pope, and Tardini died as secretary of state. When they were both simple monsignors in high positions in the Apostolic Palace, the contrasts between their personalities and their inevitable rivalry were sources of perpetual gossip in the curia. Pius XII must have been aware of it.

Montini, thin and humorless like his patron, was attracted by French culture, while Tardini was robust, energetic, loved hearty food and a good joke, and would occasionally lapse into Roman dialect. Montini, the son of a well-to-do newspaper publisher in the northern Italian city of Brescia, was a shade more liberal than his partner. His one interest outside his Vatican work was a church-affiliated organization of university graduates that was barely tolerated under the Fascist dictatorship. After World War II the group furnished several national leaders to the Christian Democratic party, which had emerged as the country's strongest political force. (A brother of the future pope, Ludovico Montini, was elected into the Italian senate on the Christian Democratic ticket.) Tardini, who came from Rome's *popolino*—the "little people"—had unhappy childhood memories, and tended toward political and theological conservatism. Though he used to work almost as long hours as did Montini, he also had an outside pursuit—Villa Nazareth, an institution for orphans and homeless youngsters on Mount Mario. Whenever he had an hour to spare he would visit "his" boys there.

Tardini, though often gruff, was more popular in the Vatican than Montini, especially with subalterns. One day, angered by the clumsiness of an apostolic nuncio, he rushed out of his office into the corridor and said loud enough that many of his aides could hear him: "People always say that the diplomacy of the Holy See is the first in the world. If ours is the first, I'd really like to see the second. . . ."

Archivists, who register and file away every scrap of paper from the desks of the top curia officials on which they manage to lay their hands, became addicted to the sardonic, or plainly rude, comments in Tardini's handwriting that they found scrawled on or clipped to many documents. "Imbecile!" might be a typical Tardinian comment on the report from an apostolic delegate, committed for the ages to the Vatican's Secret Archives. When President Roosevelt, in a personal message to Pope Pius XII after Pearl Harbor, declared that the United States forces would liberate Europe and Italy, Tardini noted: "Too condescending!"

Three years later, Tardini had occasion to receive a prelate,

Angelo Roncalli, whom Pope Pius XII had just named apostolic nuncio to liberated France. The future Pope John XXIII had been apostolic delegate to Bulgaria and later to Turkey and Greece, and was just stopping over in Rome on his way from Istanbul to Paris. Roncalli thanked Tardini for the assignment to Paris, and said he had been most surprised to be chosen for such an important post. "You may be sure all of us here were more surprised than you," Tardini had said dryly, unimpressed with Roncalli's diplomatic skills. Then Roncalli had an audience with Pius XII (who could hardly have imagined he was speaking to his successor). "Monsignor, we have only ten minutes for you," the pontiff said to the new nuncio. "We want to tell you one thing. For this new assignment you do not owe any gratitude to anyone except the pope. We have meditated, prayed, and decided."

When Roncalli was about to receive the red hat in a consistory in 1953 preliminary to his transfer to Venice as patriarch, Montini and Tardini were both due for promotion too. Pius XII called in the two men who for many years had jointly run the Secretariat of State and announced to them his intention of raising both to the cardinalate. According to an official disclosure made later, both Montini and Tardini pleaded with the pontiff not to confer such a high honor on them because they didn't feel worthy of it and preferred to serve the head of the church in their old capacity.

If the duo really said so, they only conformed with clerical etiquette. Usually a pope doesn't tell a churchman he wants to make him a cardinal. If he does, the correct conduct for the prelate thus honored is to display the right amount of humility without overdoing it. Then it is up to the pope to go ahead with his plans for preferment. Curialists think Tardini sincerely didn't want to become cardinal at the time, fearing that Pius XII might ask Montini to serve as cardinal secretary of state while he himself might be shunted into a less influential position. Montini, on the other hand, is believed to have very much coveted the red hat then, but was foiled by the convincing reluctance his colleague was showing. And the pope? Old Vatican prelates who knew Pius XII say that he wasn't above playing one of his aides against the other, and that in 1953 he really wanted to keep Montini and Tardini in their old jobs.

The consistory was held without either of the two men joining the sacred college, but Pius XII gave them both a new title, "prosecretary of state." The Vatican explained that the proper form of addressing either Montini or Tardini henceforth was "Your Excellency," the way one speaks to bishops. More than a year later, a new twist in the relationship between Pius XII and his diligent pair of aides baffled the curia. Suddenly, the pope sent Montini as archbishop to Milan, a see that had become vacant, and from then onward relied on Tardini alone as his principal lieutenant in the Secretariat of State.

When Montini arrived in his new archdiocese, he kissed the ground as if to signal he hadn't wanted anything more ardently than his new job. Yet churchmen who had witnessed Montini's departure from Rome said he left the Vatican with a heavy heart. The benevolent explanation for Pius XII's decision to deprive himself of such a devoted curial aide was that he'd wanted to give Montini an opportunity for gathering experience in the largest archdiocese in Italy. Such pastoral work, it was said, would eventually be an important asset for a candidate in the election of Pius XII's successor. However, Pius XII failed during his remaining four years to make Archbishop Montini a cardinal, thus barring him from participation in the conclave after his death and from any but a mere theoretical chance of becoming pontiff.

Pius XII's innermost motive for separating himself from Montini remains a mystery. The pope may have become tired of his long-time aide's martinet ways (Pius XII himself was a martinet), or he may have had misgivings about Montini's mild leanings toward left-of-center currents in the Italian Christian Democratic party and have preferred to work with the conservative Tardini. There was also gossip that for a long time Mother Pasqualina had wanted to get Montini out of the Vatican, and finally had had her way.

Montini and Tardini finally did get their red hats in 1958, when Pope John XXIII held his first consistory for the creation of new cardinals shortly after his election. He put the name of the archbishop of Milan on top of the list of his additions to the sacred college. Tardini became the pontiff's full-fledged cardinal secretary of state. This time neither of the two former colleagues declined the honor. "One can't say no to such a pope," Cardinal Tardini explained later. When he suddenly died, at 73 years of age, on June 30, 1961, during the preparations for Vatican II, Pope John thus announced the event to a crowd in St. Peter's Square: "This morning the angel of death entered the Apostolic

Palace and carried away the cardinal secretary of state . . . the closest and staunchest assistant to the pope in the government of our holy church."

John XXIII replaced Tardini with Amleto Giovanni Cardinal Cicognani, a former longtime apostolic delegate in Washington and a conservative whom he had made a cardinal in 1958 (to do so, he'd had to waive canon 232 of the Code of Canon Law, which prohibits the elevation to the cardinalate of someone related to a living cardinal—in this case Gaetano Cardinal Cicognani, member of the Roman Curia, friend of John XXIII, and brother of the former apostolic delegate in Washington). The eight years of Cardinal Cicognani's service as secretary of state coincided with Vatican II and the immediate "postconciliar" period during which various reforms that the great church assembly had adopted in principle were to be translated into specific ecclesiastical legislation. John XXIII seems to have considered Cicognani's conservatism a healthy check to the impatience of liberals in the church.

When Cardinal Montini, as Paul VI, succeeded John XXIII in 1963, he confirmed Cicognani in his post. After the end of Vatican II, the aged secretary of state often acted as a spokesman for the faction in the curia that sought to water down the liberal changes envisaged by Vatican II. Since Cardinal Cicognani had daily access to the pope, he could convey to Paul VI the conservative party's insistent recommendations for "prudence" in carrying out the decisions of Vatican II.

Cardinal Cicognani was 86 years old in May 1969 when Paul VI announced his replacement by a Frenchman, Jean Cardinal Villot. He was the first non-Italian secretary of state since the English-born Spaniard Rafael Cardinal Merry del Val served under Pope Saint Pius X. The tall, aloof-looking Villot was to be the head of the supercuria under three popes and to reach the height of his power in his unexpected role as a mentor to Pope John Paul I.

A native of the Auvergne in the heartland of France, Villot sometimes said that he had become "a Roman at heart." He nevertheless remained a typical Auvergnat, displaying peasant realism, energy, and distaste for rhetoric. He had become known as a conciliator when he was permanent secretary of the French bishops' conference, 1050–53. Pope John XXIII, who knew Villot well, had promoted him to the important see of Lyon, which he headed from 1965 to 1967. During Vatican II Villot served as one of several undersecretaries of the council, and impressed Pope Paul VI with his tact and discretion. Villot received the red hat in 1965, and two years later was called to Rome to head the Vatican's department for the clergy. In this post he showed understanding for priests who wanted to get married but to remain active in the church in some capacity, possibly in its education system. Conservatives in the curia overruled Cardinal Villot on this issue and blocked any compromise solution for such clergymen. (However, some liberal bishops in the Netherlands continued to help former priests who had acquired families.)

As prefect of the Sacred Congregation for the Clergy, and later as secretary of state, Cardinal Villot had a stock phrase when aides confronted him with prickly issues: "Let's not overdramatize," he would say in his almost accent-free Italian. He was cool-headed and was often proved right.

In 1974 he assessed the Italian people's mood much more accurately than did many influential Italians in the Vatican, and Paul VI himself. The church then was giving all-out support to a drive promoted by conservative Roman Catholic groups and politicians aimed at having the country's divorce legislation of 1970 repealed in a national referendum. Paul VI himself backed the campaign for having divorce banned again in Italy. Cardinal Villot counseled to keep the Vatican out of the issue. A friend of mine heard him say: "This is a battle we may win, but also lose." It was indeed lost, disastrously for the church and the hapless Christian Democratic strategists, when the electorate by a 3 to 2 majority upheld the 1970 divorce act. Had the Vatican heeded Cardinal Villot's advice not to let itself directly be drawn into the referendum campaign, it would have avoided having to acknowledge that three-fifths of the Italian voters had flouted the papal teachings and admonitions.

Although in effect the "prime minister" of the central church government, Cardinal Villot for years remained something of an outsider in the curia. He seemed more comfortable dealing with bishops and bishops' conferences in various countries—understandably, in view of his earlier career—than with nuncios and other Vatican officials.

He cherished his privacy in the sumptuous suite that is the secretary of state's requisite, on the floor below the pope's official apartment in the Apostolic Palace. He liked to see old friends from France, and on such occasions would show off his well-known connoisseurship regarding French and Italian wines. And Cardinal Villot didn't put up a fight when a younger man began taking more and more responsibilities away from him.

PAPAL CHIEF OF STAFF

The official who for years overshadowed Cardinal Villot was his "substitute," or deputy, Msgr. Giovanni Benelli. A round-faced, blunt Tuscan, he became one of the most forceful personages the Roman Curia has seen in this century. Monsignor Benelli seemed insatiable for work; he was an authoritarian and a stickler for detail. Vatican personnel called him "the carabiniere"— an unflattering reference to Italy's military policemen who aren't known for sophistication—or "the master sergeant." A papal diplomat who had worked under him for years, asked to characterize Benelli, also groped for a military simile: "He was like a general who gives orders to officers of a higher rank, as well as to colonels, captains, and noncommissioned officers, inspects barracks and uniforms, and tastes the food rations of the privates." However, the diplomat also recalled: "Whenever I sent a query to the Secretariat of State asking for instructions, I could be sure that next morning I'd have a reply and a decision from Benelli. He was the man of the pushbuttons—he would phone to Vienna and Washington, Buenos Aires and Manila, all in one morning." He was what the curia hadn't known before him, a modern chief of staff.

Benelli had served as a papal diplomat in Ireland, France, Brazil, Spain, and West Africa, but the most important period in his early career had been his years as secretary to Monsignor Montini when the future pope was himself an aide in the Secretariat of State.

As an assistant to one of the two chief executive officers of a demanding master, Pope Pius XII, the young ecclesiastic from a town near Pistoia in Tuscany had learned round-the-clock discipline, and early on become an expert in the bureaucratic meanders of the curia. When Montini himself, at last, was the head of the church, he called his former secretary back to Rome and made him the number two man in the supercuria.

As "Monsignor Substitute," Benelli, a titular archbishop at the relatively early age of 45 years, handled almost all of the really important church business. The reports, complaints, and requests from the world's Roman Catholic bishops sooner or later came to his desk, along with the memos, drafts, and documents that are the steady output of the church's administrative mills. He would personally act on some matters, and refer others to Pope Paul VI, often without informing the prelate who nominally was his direct superior, Cardinal Villot. The pontiff, in his customarily hesitant way, would tell the substitute what he wanted to be done, and Benelli would see to it—in dispatches to nuncios, circulars to the world hierarchy, and impatient telephone calls to bishops or curia departments—that it was done. Benelli seemed much more interested in efficiency than in ideology. In the tug-of-war between conservatives and liberals in the church that marked the years after Vatican II, he held the middle ground like the pope whom he served. The only roadblock in Benelli's daily informal contacts with the pontiff was Paul VI's personal secretary, Msgr. Pasquale Macchi, whose role will be described at length later.

The powerful papal chief of staff also had a finger in many Italian pies that appealed to church appetites. During a crisis in the Roman newspaper with the largest circulation, *Il Messaggero,* I discovered by chance that Benelli was actively backing a group that tried to gain control of it. *Il Messaggero* for years had angered Paul VI by its anticlericalism; Benelli clearly wanted to change the newspaper's editorial line to be more palatable to the pope.

In the Vatican, Benelli was feared as a taskmaster. He supervised the pontifical Swiss Guard and the gendarmerie (soon renamed Vigilance Force) with an apparent flair for military things, and insisted that Vatican personnel keep office hours. He aroused particular fury in many Roman families when he pruned the list of persons holding passes that entitled them to shopping in the Vatican commissary.

To be able to buy cigarettes; Scotch whisky; chocolates, coffee, spaghetti, and other food items; woolens; and some appliances at the Annona, the Vatican supermarket near the post office and the printing plant of *L'Osservatore Romano,* is a coveted privilege in Rome. Prices are substantially lower than in the stores outside the ramparts of Michelangelo that protect the papal enclave; no Italian import duties or sales taxes are levied on the merchandise. The well-stocked commissary is meant as a fringe benefit for the persons who live in Vatican City and for those who commute to Vatican jobs from other Roman neighborhoods, the cheap prices of the Annona making up to some extent for the comparatively low pay scales of the pontifical administration.

Before Benelli, thousands of Roman families with the most tenuous links to the papal state also enjoyed access to the shopping paradise—nieces of long-deceased cardinals, distant cousins of persons who had once held a job in the curia, friends of prelates, people who years earlier had rendered a favor to some nuns' order. Benelli, like an archangel with a flaming sword, barred such freeloaders from the Annona. It wasn't a posture conducive to popularity.

The outrage over Benelli's "ruthless" purge of Annona customers seeped back to the cardinals of the curia, who had their own good reasons for detesting Pope Paul VI's de facto chief of staff. One of these was Paolo Cardinal Bertoli, at the time head of the Sacred Congregation for the Causes of Saints, the Vatican department that prepares beatifications and canonizations. A former papal diplomat and apostolic nuncio in Paris (where he wasn't too happy to have young Benelli as an aide), Cardinal Bertoli brusquely resigned as head of the Sacred Congregation in 1973, when his former nunciature assistant started bullying him. Among other things, Benelli wanted an impressive array of new saints for the 1975 Holy Year because the canonization ceremonies would be an added attraction for pilgrims and tourists. The church jubilee, normally held every 25 years, always brings millions of visitors to Rome; it is a boon for local business, and in a variety of ways also bolsters the Vatican's finances. (The Vatican, nevertheless, denied that monetary considerations were responsible for John Paul II's proclaiming an "extraordinary" Holy Year in 1983 to celebrate the 1,950th anniversary of Redemption by Jesus.)

Pius XII had provided an extra highlight for the 1950 Holy Year by proclaiming the sainthood of a fourteen-year-old Italian girl, Maria Goretti, who had died in 1935 while resisting rape. To the delight of the media, both the mother of Saint Maria Goretti and her murderer were still alive when she was canonized. (The assailant later made his living as a gardener for a monastery, after serving 30 years of a life sentence.) Many churchmen at the time had grave reservations about the procedure by which the cause of the girl saint was pushed through in a few years, quite clearly to meet the 1950 deadline. There were also less than reverent comments in the world press.

Cardinal Bertoli didn't want to lend himself to a replay of the hasty preparations for the 1950 Holy Year and lay the church and himself open to public reproach. He insisted that the customarily slow and painstaking proceedings in the making of new saints be observed, and rather than yield to Benelli's impatient urgings to think of 1975, stepped down from his curia post to join the group of jobless cardinals in Rome. The Vatican often announces that some curial department chief has resigned, but such a move is almost always due to papal pressure. A cardinal's voluntary withdrawal from a curia post is exceptional, and it caused a Vatican sensation.

Ill will against Benelli built up in the curia and in Paul VI's own household during the next few years. Early in 1977, the pope told Benelli he intended to transfer him to Florence and make him a cardinal forthwith. Paul VI's private secretary, Msgr. Pasquale Macchi, was generally believed to have influenced the decision.

Not surprisingly, everybody in the Vatican at once pointed out that Paul VI was relegating Benelli to Florence in the same manner as he himself had been exiled to Milan by Pius XII 23 years earlier. But the circumstances weren't really the same. The difference was the red hat that Benelli received with the assignment as archbishop in the capital of his native region. He now had the same rank as his powerful critics and would play a decisive part in the election of a successor to the aging pontiff. In fact, Benelli was himself mentioned as a leading candidate for the papacy in both conclaves of 1978, and he was the architect who built the coalition of Italian and non-Italian cardinals who elected Pope John Paul I. Had that pontiff lived longer, he might have called Benelli back to Rome.

In 1981 I visited Benelli in his archiepiscopal palace in Florence, which looks out on the Cathedral of St. Maria del Fiore, its campanile and its baptistery. He told me: "I am happy here and I am busy. I have to do a lot of things myself because I have only one auxiliary bishop, and it is a large archdiocese. Last week I took sick people to Lourdes, on Sunday I led another group of pilgrims to a shrine in the neighborhood. It is a great pastoral experience." The former Vatican chief of staff didn't sound convincing. He was then 60 years old and in his fifth year as archbishop of Florence. A former aide commented to me: "Benelli misses the Vatican tremendously. He misses the work, the pressures, the power. He feels beached. Whatever he says about the great pastoral experience, he is doing exactly what Wojtyla did in Krakow—trying to get in on international issues like peace and disarmament, keeping in touch with important churchmen all over the world, never mind the phone bills—cultivating his own image."

Cardinal Benelli's large study in the archbishop's palace in Florence didn't look like a powerhouse, but he was working the telephone assiduously and making frequent trips to Rome in a car that still bore Vatican City license plates. He received detailed reports on what was going on in the Secretariat of State by his former secretary who had remained on its staff, Msgr. Giovanni Battista Re, and by other informants. Benelli seemed ready and eager to return.

He was still considered a potential candidate for the papal throne in case John Paul II's pontificate were to end unexpectedly early. However, in October 1982, the cardinal-archbishop of Florence suffered a heart attack, and died a few days later.

To step back a few years—Benelli's departure from the Vatican in 1977 brought an instant and automatic increase in the prestige of Cardinal Villot. Paul VI had his secretary of state also named camerlengo of the Holy Roman Church, and in this ancient office the Frenchman served twice as the chief administrator of the Holy See during the interregnums of 1978.

When the patriarch of Venice, Cardinal Luciani, was elected successor to Paul VI, he almost immediately confirmed Cardinal Villot and all other Vatican dignitaries in their posts. "With this rash action, probably meant as a kindness," a gray-haired monsignor told me then, "the Holy Father has tied his own hands and has completely surrendered to the curia."

A little later a picture was published that seemed to illustrate the remark. It showed Pope John Paul I walking in the Vatican gardens with his secretary of state and listening to him with apparent respect. It looked as if the tall French cardinal was instructing the new head of the church in what he had to do, and what was the most urgent business to be tackled.

Or maybe the cardinal secretary of state was explaining to the new pontiff, who was still naive in such things, why he couldn't address a letter to "Jerusalem, Israel." That was indeed what John Paul I had written on the envelope when he meant to send a personal note to the president of Israel as thanks for Yitzhak Navon's good wishes on his accession to the throne of Saint Peter. Horrified aides in the Secretariat of State caught the let-

120

ter before it was put in the mail. The address, in the papal hand-writing, would have been tantamount to a Vatican acknowledgment that Jerusalem was the capital of the Jewish state. Ever since the end of World War II the papacy had advocated a special international status for Jerusalem, and had never recognized Israel's claim, after the 1967 war, to exclusive and sovereign jurisdiction over the Holy City. The incident of the letter to the Israeli president must have brought home to John Paul I the awesome complexity of his new office. After the death of the "smiling pope," cardinals and other churchmen said openly that he had appeared overwhelmed by the Vatican bureaucracy and felt unprepared to cope with the pressures awaiting him. The resulting stress is a possible explanation for his unexpected death.

His successor, the Polish pope, avoided the trap of a blanket confirmation of all curia officials in their jobs, and took his time reshaping the church's government according to his wishes. Shortly after John Paul II's election, Cardinal Villot—who said he felt fatigued after the many demands on his energy in the "year of the three popes"—offered to resign from his post as secretary of state.

The French cardinal suggested to the pope he should name an Italian in his place, implying that the Italian element in the curia would welcome such a gesture, which would create a local counterweight to the first non-Italian pontiff in the modern era. John Paul II told Villot, and repeated in a formal letter for publication, that he must stay in office for some time because his long experience was still needed. Villot had remained the nominal head of the Vatican administration when he died in March 1979 at the age of 73.

By then, day-to-day work in the Secretariat of State had long been handled by Archbishop Casaroli who, though in an entirely different style, had built for himself a position similar to that once held by Benelli. Assuming that the Polish pontiff would indeed want an Italian as his new secretary of state, curialists and the Roman church establishment were excitedly speculating to whom the job might go. Would the forceful new pope give it to the pliable Casaroli or to someone with a stronger personality, perhaps even to Benelli? John Paul II's decision came soon: Casaroli.

When the Polish pope's choice was announced, many diplomats in Rome and governments throughout the world interpreted it as a sure sign that he wanted to continue the Vatican's Ostpolitik. Casaroli, it was recalled, had first become known internationally as Pope John XXIII's agent for negotiating with Communist regimes in Eastern Europe and was the Vatican's leading specialist in that field.

It soon became apparent, however, that the first Slav on the papal throne was reserving Eastern European affairs for himself, sometimes even bypassing his own secretary of state. The curia eventually realized that in appointing Casaroli as his chief aide, John Paul II had wanted to make sure that the Secretariat of State would not become a power center of its own under an ambitious leader like Benelli. A skillful negotiator and administrator with a prodigious capacity for paperwork, and a penchant for taking on more and more chores, Casaroli seemed certain to remain a loyal servant and not become a power broker. Two months after being promoted to the top spot in the Secretariat of State, Casaroli received the red hat. An office rival, Archbishop Giuseppe Caprio, also became a cardinal, and was promptly transferred to the Holy See's financial administration. In this post he inherited a splendid apartment in the Vatican, but could exercise little influence. (The reader has met Caprio as the prelate who told John Paul II the day after his election that the pontiff had forgotten to impart the apostolic blessing.)

The slender, bespectacled Casaroli with the very Latin features has been billed as "Vatican foreign minister" under four popes. He is a graduate of the priests' seminary of Piacenza, southeast of Milan, a foundation-supported elite institution that has furnished so much talent for high church posts since World War I that envious curia bureaucrats speak about a "Piacenza set." At the age of 26, Casaroli was already an archivist in the Secretariat of State, an excellent starting point in the Vatican because a diligent young priest in that post can familiarize himself with plenty of confidential business, current and past. Later, Casaroli worked in the Latin American section of the Secretariat of State. During off hours he worked doggedly to become proficient in many languages, and at the office he handled diverse assignments with remarkable versatility. While drafting documents and rewriting them again and again, he would listen to soft background music, mostly Bach and Mozart.

Pope John XXIII became impressed with Casaroli and sent him to international conferences as representative of the Holy See. When that pontiff embarked on his Ostpolitik, he entrusted the polyglot aide with sensitive missions. The smiling Casaroli became a familiar figure in the government offices of Belgrade, Budapest, Prague, and Warsaw, "the pope's Henry Kissinger." His unflappable manner often encouraged Communist officials to be quite blunt and tell him exactly what was in their instructions and on their minds. Casaroli never seemed to be shocked by anything, and would proceed from noncommittal reply to tension-easing joke to the frank acknowledgment that, yes, the other side too had a point and was entitled to defending its interests. Then, with a characteristic movement of his fine hands, as if he were forever washing them, Casaroli would smilingly suggest that they all find some common ground.

In tortuous negotiations over eight years, Casaroli personally and through an aide, Monsignor Cheli, worked out the arrangement whereby Cardinal Mindszenty left his refuge in the United States embassy in Budapest and went into exile in 1971, removing himself as an obstacle to better church-state relations in Hungary. By that time, Pope John XXIII had died, and Paul VI was continuing to use Casaroli as the Vatican's chief diplomatic agent. Casaroli became a titular archbishop in 1967.

In 1973 he was the first high Vatican dignitary ever to travel to Moscow in an official capacity. There he notified the Soviet government of the Holy See's adherence to the treaty to curb the spread of nuclear weapons, the so-called nonproliferation pact. The move by the Vatican, which has no armaments other than the halberds of the Swiss Guards and the handguns of its security personnel, and operates a small oil-powered generator but no nuclear reactor, was intended as a gesture of moral support for international efforts to control nuclear arsenals.

In 1975, Casaroli paid an official visit to Cuba, and got on famously with Fidel Castro. Later that year he sat, together with government chiefs and foreign ministers of 34 European nations, the United States, and Canada at the same table at the Conference on European Cooperation and Security in Helsinki. That the Vatican was recognized as a full-fledged partner in the parley was considered a triumph for the papal—and Casaroli's—diplomacy. It didn't matter that the pope's "foreign minister" was listed as the representative of the State of Vatican City rather than, as he would have preferred, of the Holy See. About the same time, the far-looking agent of papal Ostpolitik began studying yet another language—Chinese.

Archbishop Casaroli's dealings with Communist authorities

caused suspicions and resentment among conservative prelates. Archbishop Marcel Lefebvre, a Frenchman who kept criticizing the liberal reforms of Vatican II, let it be known publicly that he regarded the pope's "foreign minister" as a dupe of communism. (The French prelate, once archbishop of Dakar, Senegal, was suspended from his priestly duties by Pope Paul VI on the ground of disobedience, having insisted on ordaining priests despite Vatican prohibition.) In the curia itself, Casaroli's pragmatism was opposed by such diehards as Cardinal Felici, the Vatican's ranking canon law expert and an audiovisual gadgetry buff, and Silvio Oddi, a traditionalist member of the "Piacenza set."

Seemingly unperturbed by the conservative criticism, Casaroli kept himself informed on the latest advances in many fields and on contemporary problems. "He is interested in everything," an assistant told me. A friend who once accompanied Casaroli on a train trip from New York to Washington said that there was little small talk because Casaroli had appointments with United States government officials and was studying a thick volume on the neutron bomb.

In Rome, the cardinal secretary of state still found time to look after youngsters whom he considered his charges, much as Cardinal Tardini had done before him. Casaroli had served as a chaplain in a prison for juvenile offenders in the Trastevere section of Rome, and later supervised an institution for troubled and homeless youths in the Monteverde Vecchio district, the Villa Agnese. Named after an American donor, Agnes Lincoln, the "house of reeducation" became something of a home to the high Vatican dignitary. Whenever Archbishop Casaroli had a free evening, he would spend it there with his young friends. Then, one of the youngsters disappeared and was later found dead in one of the many tufa caves on the city's southwestern outskirts. The police said he had been slain in a crime with a homosexual background.

While the local press was still discussing the case, *Il Tempo* of Rome published a photo showing the young victim close to Archbishop Casaroli with other boys at the Villa Agnese. The caption was bland, but the innuendo was overt and none too subtle. Casaroli happened to be absent from Rome at the time, engaged in church-state talks in Madrid. The newspaper picture caused a subdued stir in the Vatican where *Il Tempo* is regularly read by many members of the papal bureaucracy. The strongly anti-

Communist daily is also a favorite conduit for leaks and plants from the conservative faction in the curia. (Some of the church-related news in the Italian press must be read as code signals in clerical feuds.)

Villa Agnese was closed, but Casaroli remained faithful to his pastoral vocation of caring for troubled youngsters. When he returned with Pope John Paul II from a long and tiring journey to various black African countries, the cardinal secretary of state, unlike the other members of the pontifical party, didn't retire for a rest but had his Fiat car pulled out of the Vatican garage and drove to the detention center for juveniles on Mount Mario of which he had taken charge after the Villa Agnese episode. "When I retire, I want to live in two rooms in a prison for youngsters," he used to say.

The curia conservatives kept launching torpedoes against Casaroli. *Il Tempo,* again an instrument in Vatican infighting, attacked the Holy See's diplomacy as clumsy and ill-advised when Peking brusquely rebuffed a move by Pope John Paul II, aimed at opening a dialogue with the People's Republic of China. The pontiff, returning from a visit to east Asia in February 1981, had sent Casaroli to Hong Kong. The cardinal secretary of state met there with Bishop Deng Yiming (for the Vatican, Dominic Tang), a 72-year-old Jesuit who had been permitted by the Communist authorities to exercise the ministry in Canton, and even to seek medical treatment in Hong Kong. In the spring of 1981, after Casaroli had returned to Rome, the Vatican announced Deng's appointment as archbishop of Canton. Both the Chinese government and the state-controlled Catholic Patriotic Association branded the Vatican announcement as an intolerable interference in the People's Republic's domestic affairs.

On May 13, 1981, Cardinal Casaroli was on his way to the United States for a long-planned visit when Pope John Paul II was shot and wounded in St. Peter's Square. The cardinal never left John F. Kennedy Airport in New York; he took the very next flight back to Rome. After a brief stop at the Vatican, he was at the pope's bedside. For the next several weeks, the cardinal secretary of state shuttled between his office in the Apostolic Palace and the Gemelli hospital daily. During John Paul II's long recovery, Cardinal Casaroli, working even longer hours than usual, managed to keep the curia machinery running. His performance was closely observed by his Vatican critics, who were watching for signs that Casaroli might be tempted to act in the manner of a "deputy pope." However, the secretary of state remained duly self-effacing.

He nevertheless succeeded in tightening his grip on the levers of command in the church's government. One all-important branch had until then eluded him, the management of Vatican finances, but now Casaroli managed to increase his influence in that sector as well.

An aide characterized John Paul II's deceptively suave cardinal secretary of state as a "gentle centralizer." However, Casaroli couldn't control everybody and everything. As always, and maybe more so than in recent history, the Vatican bureaucracy and its chief were stymied by a small, powerful coterie— the pope's entourage.

CHAPTER 5

PAPAL KITCHEN CABINET

TO HOLD THEIR own against the cardinals or against cama-
rillas at the pontifical court, and to avoid being smothered by the
Roman Curia, popes often brought into the Vatican personal
aides whom they felt they could trust. In past centuries relatives
of the reigning pontiff, ordinarily nephews, acted as his confidential advisers or agents. At times, some papal kin who had
become assistants and favorites were able to pile up much wealth
while the going was good and the pontificate lasted—whence the
derogatory flavor of the term "nepotism," which had its origin
in papal Rome (the Latin *nepos* means both "grandson" and
"nephew"). The system and, in a whispering campaign, also the
word were revived under Pius XII.

The tendency of many pontiffs to surround themselves with
persons enjoying their confidence, and in many matters to rely
on them rather than on the church bureaucracy is understandable, maybe even inevitable. Rulers of every era have had their
secret councillors and middlemen. As an elective, absolute monarchy, the Roman Catholic Church catapults a prelate, who until
the day before may have been archbishop of a quiet provincial
city, into the Apostolic Palace, where he is expected to grapple
with a multitiered administrative machinery possessing worldwide ramifications. Fearing that he may be maneuvered by the
high ecclesiastical officials who have long been ensconced in the

curia, the new pontiff may often turn to the associates he knew before his elevation when he wants to gather independent information, discuss strategies, get things done, check up on church bureaucracy, or simply relax. The pope may or may not give official Vatican rank to such intimates. As he gets older he is naturally inclined to favor just a few members of his entourage, maybe only one, over the rest.

Much talk in the Vatican, in every pontificate, centers on the perennial question: who has the pope's ear? To find a direct channel to the head of the church and cut through curial red tape is of paramount interest to anyone seeking a papal decision or favor. When a pontiff gets tired, senile, or sick, his entourage normally covers up for him to make it appear he is still in full command; at the final stage of many pontificates, some personage close to the failing head of the church has virtually functioned as acting pope. Once the pontiff is dead, his favorites are quickly booted out of the Vatican. (In past centuries, Roman mobs would run them out of the city, loot the palaces or houses they and their relatives possessed, and harass their hangers-on.)

Papal nepotism can be traced to the early Middle Ages. During the turbulent tenth century, when more than one pontiff was murdered, Pope John XV, a native Roman, caused a scandal by the blatant favoritism shown toward his relatives. In the following centuries popes from the Colonna, Orsini, and Caetani clans found nothing wrong with their brothers, cousins, and nephews getting rich and becoming influential. Nepotism continued thriving when the popes preferred to be guests, or honored prisoners, of the French kings in Avignon rather than reside in tumultuous Rome. The cardinals who met in conclave in Avignon after the death of Clement VI, in 1352, drew up a document expressly barring relatives of any future pope from high church positions during his pontificate. The prohibition was soon ignored. During the Great Schism, 1378–1417, each of the three rivaling popes put members of his own family into key jobs to strengthen his power base.

The Renaissance era saw what in church history is known as "grand nepotism." The first Borgia pope, Calixtus III (1455–1458) gave the red hat to several of his nephews. One of them himself became pontiff—Alexander VI, the gifted and thoroughly unscrupulous Spaniard whose reign has become an enduring embarrassment for the church. His son, Cesare Borgia, whom Machiavelli took as model for his Prince, was a sinister figure who dominated the Vatican and the pontiff, and tried to carve out a central Italian state for the Borgia dynasty he intended to found. When Alexander VI died in 1503, probably poisoned by the "Borgia powder" that was destined for a number of cardinals, Cesare was sick; eventually he had to abandon his Italian ambitions. A multitude of other Borgias who had been holding jobs in the curia or in the pontifical domains were ousted by Alexander VI's successors to make room for new favorites. Adrian VI, the earnest Dutchman whose brief pontificate, 1522–1523, was recalled earlier, provoked mirth among the cynical Romans because he didn't bring a bunch of relatives from Utrecht into the Vatican.

Even the stern pope of the Counter-Reformation, Paul IV (1555–1559) wasn't free of the temptation to favor his own family. He placed a nephew, Carlo Caraffa, at the head of the Holy See's temporal (political) administration. However, when the pontiff found out that his nephew was misusing his position, he stripped him of power.

Not all papal favorites were evil. At least one of them became a saint—Carlo Borromeo, whom his uncle, Pius IV (1559–1565), had made a cardinal and head of the papal secretariat. (John Paul II, who was Karol Wojtyla, has repeatedly avowed his veneration for Saint Carlo Borromeo, his patron saint.)

In the seventeenth century most popes had a "cardinal nephew" at their side in what was considered the normal way of running the Vatican. The role of these nephews explains the wealth they and their families were able to accumulate—the palaces, castles, and land holdings of the Aldobrandini, Barberini, Boncompagni, Borghese, Chigi, Ludovisi, and Pamphili clans. Made marquesses and princes, these relatives of popes and their nephews became the pillars of what to this day is known as Rome's "black," or pontifical, nobility—an aristocratic caste—much of whose riches are based on corruption.

The scion of a Neapolitan family, the Pignatellis, the austere and zealous Innocent XII (1691–1700), found nepotism indecent. In 1692 he issued a bull, "Romanum decet Pontificem," forbidding the head of the church to enrich his relatives. (Bulls and other papal documents are quoted by their first words in Latin; the initial words of Innocent XII's bull mean "It behooves the Roman pontiff . . .") Every pope since then has had to swear in secret conclave, right after his election, to observe Innocent's rule.

Nepotism in various forms has nevertheless survived. Pius VI (1775–1799), who died as Napoleon's prisoner in Valence, France, was particularly nonchalant about favoring members of his family, the Braschis of Cesena. Nepotism again became quasi-official in the Vatican under Pius XII, whose three nephews all played important roles during his pontificate. But the trio was overshadowed by a woman who was not a relative of the pontiff, Mother Pasqualina.

PUISSANT VIRGIN

A year and a half after the election of John Paul II the Vatican felt it necessary to deny formally that any member of a female religious order was playing a conspicuous role in his private establishment in the Apostolic Palace. "There is no nun who might be thought of as following in the footsteps of that Sister Pasqualina of Pius XII's time," declared the official press spokesman of the Holy See, the Reverend Romeo Panciroli. He was responding, with what seemed annoyance, to an Italian magazine article that had mentioned a Sister Teodolina, and asserted that she followed the Polish pope everywhere "like a shadow." There just was no nun of that name and of such ubiquity in the pontiff's private household, the spokesman affirmed.

His statement appeared to mirror high-level abhorrence of any suggestion that someone in the pontiff's entourage—let alone a woman!—might exercise hidden power. Mother Pasqualina (the spokesman had downgraded her to a mere "sister") had played such a part, especially during the last years of Pius XII's pontificate. When the Vatican denied that a "Pasqualina" situation existed in John Paul II's entourage, it sounded like disapproval of an irregularity in Pius XII's reign that was still vividly remembered. Father Panciroli, who had held almost daily briefings for Vatican news reporters under Paul VI, and continued doing so under John Paul I and John Paul II, was known for carefully sticking to his instructions from the Secretariat of State. He wouldn't say a word more or less than he had been told to say. His remarks on the papal household had evidently been inspired from high up.

From Pope John Paul II personally? Probably not. Popes don't criticize their predecessors in public, not even indirectly, and whenever they speak about a deceased pontiff they will invariably make a point of mentioning that his memory is "venerated." It is unlikely that John Paul II would have authorized an oblique censure of Pius XII or an unkind word about his housekeeper. At any rate, when I saw Mother Pasqualina, several months after the unusual Vatican denial, she told me that the Polish pope had some time earlier invited her to attend morning mass said by him in his private chapel, and he had afterward shown her around his private apartment to let her see what changes had been made since the time she lived there herself, directing Pius XII's household.

"The Holy Father was very kind to me," she said. It was a gracious gesture toward a once-powerful woman who, after her patron's death, had found she had few friends and many enemies in the Vatican. When Mother Pasqualina spoke to me about her latest—maybe her last—return to the Apostolic Palace, she was 87 years old. The small Bavarian nun in her black garb had become a little stouter than I had remembered her, and was slightly stooped. Her broad face with the high cheekbones was almost unlined, she had a warm smile and a firm handshake, her small, dark eyes were as vivacious as ever, and her mind was quick. Her hair was, as always, covered by her order's black and white coif. She looked twenty years younger than her age.

Mother Pasqualina received me in a home for elderly women, the House Pastor Angelicus on Mount Mario, two and a half miles from the Vatican. The rest home, named after Pius XII by the epithet that the apocryphal prophecy of Saint Malachy had assigned to him, is operated by Mother Pasqualina's Swiss-based order, the Teaching Sisters of the Holy Cross of Menzingen. Although younger nuns had administrative responsibilities, there was no doubt that the former papal housekeeper was in charge. "I built it," she remarked with a sweeping gesture taking in the modern complex and the sloping garden. The institution was inaugurated fourteen years after Pius XII's death.

During those years Mother Pasqualina had also worked on her reminiscences, which she had to write at her order's request. The order is the beneficiary of the earnings from these memoirs in all media. Mother Pasqualina also talked at great length about her experiences as a key witness in the proceedings for the proposed beatification of Pope Pius XII.

Beatification, the formal statement that a dead person is "blessed" in heaven, is a step on the lengthy road to sainthood in the Roman Catholic Church. In earliest times, the sanctity of a dead Christian was proclaimed by the consensus of the faithful or by a bishop. The first solemn canonization by a pope is recorded as having taken place A.D. 993, when John XV—who earlier in this chapter was mentioned in connection with his nepotism—inscribed Saint Ulric of Augsburg in the list, or "canon," of the church's saints. Since the twelfth century the proclamation of saints has been a monopoly of the popes.

A procedure developed in which the lives of candidates for sanctity were posthumously examined by clerical judges. This process is now entrusted to the Vatican's Sacred Congregation for the Causes of Saints. This department of the Roman Curia acts only following petitions from groups of the faithful, and authorization by the pontiff. A "promoter of the cause" has to make an official nomination. In the painstaking process, an official of the congregation, popularly known as the "devil's advocate," has to search the candidate's life and writings for any element that might speak against the recognition of sainthood.

Some saints took centuries to be acknowledged officially. Saint Joan of Arc died on the stake in 1431, but was beatified only in 1909, and canonized in 1920. Several medieval popes and many other persons—mostly priests, friars, and nuns—have been declared "blessed," but haven't attained sainthood so far. Repeated efforts by groups of admirers to have Christopher Columbus proclaimed blessed, and eventually sanctified, have led nowhere. The discoverer of America shares such posthumous frustrations with many others.

The canonical process for Pius XII was opened simultaneously with that for the beatification of John XXIII. Paul VI, who throughout his pontificate felt he was overshadowed by the lasting popularity of his immediate predecessor, had wanted John XXIII's case of presumed sanctity to be coupled with that of Pius XII, with whom he himself had been so closely associated. It seems that support for the cause of John XXIII was much broader and more spontaneous than that for Pius XII.

The head of the Roman Catholic Church is addressed as "Holy Father," but holiness in the doctrinal sense of glory in heaven doesn't go automatically with the high office; far from it. The last pope to be canonized was Saint Pius X (1903–1914), the benign-looking mainland Venetian who knew how to talk to the "little people," and permitted the Vatican inquisitors to hound priestly intellectuals as "modernist" heretics because they had sought to reconcile faith and science.

Before Saint Pius X, one has to go back to the seventeenth century to find a head of the church who achieved even the pre- liminary step toward sainthood, the Blessed Innocent XI (1676– 1689). From the sixteenth century, Pope Saint Pius V (1566–1572), a Dominican who became a champion of the strug- gle against Protestantism, is represented in the church's catalog of saints. (This list, repeatedly purged of spurious saints, in- cludes two thousand or three thousand names; nobody knows ex- actly how many.)

The Renaissance wasn't productive of papal holiness, but seven blessed and three sainted pontiffs can be found in the elev- enth through the fourteenth centuries. Holy popes abounded in the first millennium of church history, especially in primitive Christianity, but the list shows that sanctity was rather scarce among the pontiffs of the second millennium. If, in addition to Saint Pius X, two or even more of the recent popes were to be raised to the glory of the altars, as the ecclesiastical phrase goes, the twentieth century would appear to have brought a bumper crop of holiness in the Vatican.

In the procedures to establish Pope Pius XII's "heroic virtues," a prerequisite for beatification and canonization, his housekeeper was a key source. (Another condition for the proclamation of saint- hood is verification of a number of posthumous miracles attrib- uted to the heavenly intercession of the candidate.) Mother Pasqualina told me she had thus far been questioned by officials of the congregation of saints in 33 sessions lasting about two hours each. "I had to report everything I knew about the Holy Father, Pius XII," she said. Wistfully, she added: "Forty-one years I was with him—nuncio in Munich, nuncio in Berlin, card- inal secretary of state, pope. Forty-one years . . ."

A farmer's daughter from the town of Eberfeld in Bavaria, she was known as Josefine Lehnert before she took religious vows and became Sister Pascalina, Italianized as Pasqualina.

She was not yet 23 years old when she first met Monsignor Pacelli, then 41, at her order's mother house in Rorschach on the Swiss side of Lake Constance. The frail, earnest Roman prelate, recuperating from serious illness, was spending a period of rest there. Not much later he obtained the transfer of the pert little nun to the apostolic nunciature in Munich, where she was to be his housekeeper.

That the new papal envoy to the Kingdom of Bavaria was permitted to have a nun eighteen years his junior to take care of his household was an extraordinary departure from church rules. The Code of Canon Law, promulgated by Pope Benedict XV in the year he sent Pacelli as nuncio to Munich, enjoined all clerics in its canon 133 (which rephrased earlier norms) to avoid "cohabiting" with women who might give rise to the suspicion of "something evil." The same provision in the church's lawbook advised priests that their mother, a sister, an aunt, or some virtuous elderly woman could conveniently look after their household. Until his move to Munich in 1917, Pacelli had indeed lived with his mother, as many Italian priests and other unmarried men do.

It may be due to the austere personality of the nuncio in Munich that apparently nobody had anything to say about his housekeeper's being far from the "canonical age," a clerical euphemism for the menopause. Not yet 30 years old, Sister Pasqualina followed Pacelli to Berlin when he took up residence there as the apostolic nuncio to the German Reich. She then followed him to Rome when Pope Pius XI made him a cardinal and appointed him secretary of state.

After Pius XI's death in 1939 Sister Pasqualina was—again, quite exceptionally—allowed to enter the secluded area where a successor was to be elected, in order to serve Cardinal Pacelli as a conclavist, or assistant. The next day she moved with him, now the new pope, into the pontifical apartment. Pius XII, who from his long years in Germany had retained a partiality for all things German, spoke to his housekeeper in her native language until his death, although her Italian had become fluent. In the pontiff's private quarters she had the help of two other members of her order—the last of them were Sister Ewaldis and Sister Maria Conrada—and, being the head of a small nuns' community, began to be addressed as Mother Pasqualina. Technically she was never a mother superior.

There was little gossip about her personal relationship with Pius XII, although Pasqualina had remained remarkably good looking. Romans would say with a wink that she was "like the wife" of the pope, but nobody really seemed to believe that the ascetic, often sickly, pontiff was interested in, or even capable of carnality.

Totally trusting his housekeeper's loyalty, discretion, and intelligence, Pius XII increasingly used her for confidential work.

He dictated memoranda to her, and asked her to make telephone calls and visits on his behalf. During the 1950s I often heard accounts of persons in need who had received an unexpected visit by Mother Pasqualina with a money gift from the pope. I was told she was making such errands of mercy around Rome in a small Vatican car, and would urge the driver to hurry: *"Più presto, più presto!"* When I last saw Mother Pasqualina I asked her about this. She said: "The Holy Father [Pius XII] helped everybody, and nothing was too much for him. One could always take what was necessary from his private funds, and his greatest joy was being able to ease hidden want." She wouldn't talk about her own role in Pius XII's private charities.

With all her devotion to the pontiff, Mother Pasqualina managed to rule over a little realm of her own in the papal suite. During the last grim Roman winters of World War II, she told me, Pius XII insisted on doing without any heating in his study and bedroom, and consequently his hands were covered with chilblains. "We sisters decided we did want some warmth, at least during the chilliest days, and we smuggled an iron stove into our quarters," Mother Pasqualina reminisced with a nun's roguishness. "But try to heat those high-ceilinged rooms with a small stove, especially when you have very little coal!"

The fact that Pius XII throughout his pontificate used some German Jesuits as personal aides was at the time attributed to Mother Pasqualina's influence, although it may have been due to his general pro-German sympathies. In Rome she always showed deep respect for the Society of Jesus, then an important force in the Vatican.

Pasqualina was a commanding, though hardly visible, presence in the Apostolic Palace. High prelates and obscure priests, diplomats and Pius XII's own relatives sought to win the little nun's support when they wanted some favor from the pope. Pasqualina herself recalled that one day the pope's elderly sister had asked her to use her influence to ensure that Pius XII would receive the members of his family more often. The pontiff replied he had no time for such commitments. (He saw his three nephews often on church business, but only received the other members of his family, children included, jointly, in his private apartment once a year, on the afternoon of Christmas Day.)

Mother Pasqualina was supposed to be able to obtain from the pontiff the nomination of bishops and even of cardinals; small wonder that ambitious ecclesiastics wooed her. She was swamped with letters and petitions begging for money, the church annulment of some broken marriage, or a Vatican job. Many members of the church hierarchy in various countries (especially in Germany) who had grievances against the bureaucrats in the curia turned to Mother Pasqualina as an ultimate resort, hoping she would take up their complaints with the pontiff.

By the early 1950s she was a firmly established, though unofficial, Vatican institution, an independent and direct channel to the pope. In addition to her household chores she handled matters related to the government of the church and other sensitive business. She could have used a secretary of her own, but remained a one-woman operation. Many people believed she had had a hand in removing Monsignor Montini, the future Pope Paul VI, from the Vatican. While he was closely associated with Pius XII, there had been subterranean rivalry between Montini and Pasqualina.

The name Pasqualina has remained impressed in the minds of the Romans as a byword for an éminence grise. When Italian Communists, more than twenty years later, were grumbling about the alleged undue influence on their party's poker-faced secretary-general, Enrico Berlinguer, by one of his aides, Antonio Tatò, they jokingly called Tatò "Berlinguer's Brother Pasqualino." (The sobriquet also betrayed a sense of parallel lives in the Vatican and the Communist apparatus: the atmosphere at Communist party headquarters on the Via delle Botteghe Oscure in Rome's center is curial; Communist functionaries and central committee members often move and talk like prelates; one of the party's top leaders, Giancarlo Pajetta, remarked publicly that of all the institutions in the non-Communist world he had the highest admiration for the Jesuit Order.)

One day Mother Pasqualina slipped and broke a leg. She was taken to Salvator Mundi International Hospital on the Janiculum Hill, a fashionable clinic operated by the Sisters of the Divine Savior. While she was under treatment there, the security measures were as tight as if the pope himself or royalty were being protected. Every day flowers arrived for the exceptional patient; she sent them all to the house chapel.

During the 1950 Holy Year when the pontiff cited his own infallibility in defining the dogma of the Virgin Mary's bodily assumption to heaven, the Romans were convinced that Pasqualina, a devotee of the Madonna, was really responsible for the new tenet of faith. Cynical clerics suggested that one of the litany invocations to Our Lady, "Virgo Potens!" (Powerful Virgin) might refer to Mother Pasqualina. During the outdoor rite in St. Peter's Square for the proclamation of the new dogma, the German nun, her face framed in her order's severe coif, was seated in a special place near the pontifical altar.

Eminently practical-minded though Pasqualina seemed, she appears to have had a strong belief in the supernatural. She was understood to have contributed to Pius XII's mystical moods as he was getting older and his fragile health was declining. Twenty-five years later she spoke in a matter-of-fact way about how Pius XII had told her that Jesus had appeared to him "at the foot end of his bed." (At the time, irreverent Romans joked that Pius XII had ordered two espressos instead of the usual one—one for himself and one for the Lord.)

Ever protective of the pontiff, during the last years of Pius XII's life Pasqualina sought to regulate his day even more tightly and keep callers away when she suspected they might upset or fatigue him. Leading curia figures—even Cardinal Tisserant, the dean of the sacred college—found it hard to obtain a private audience with Pius XII, although the pope kept receiving diverse groups of people and giving lengthy addresses to them. Mother Pasqualina knew that the aging pontiff felt invigorated by such group audiences with their emotional atmosphere. During the last days of his life he still admitted a great number of visitors to Castel Gandolfo and, although weakened by bouts with hiccuping, delivered speeches to such groups as Italian news vendors, plastic surgeons from various countries, and American pilgrims led by Cardinal Spellman.

Mother Pasqualina was known to have been distrustful of Pius XII's personal physician, Dr. Galeazzi Lisi, and 23 years after the pope's death still didn't want to talk about the disgraced and long dead archiater. What she had to say about him is in the files of the church inquiry into Pius XII's presumed sainthood.

The order to the German nun to leave the pontifical palace in Castel Gandolfo and to stay away from the papal premises in the Vatican came hours after Pius XII's death. It was conveyed to Mother Pasqualina by a low-ranking official on behalf of Cardinal Tisserant, who as dean of the sacred college was, in the absence of a cardinal camerlengo, the acting head of the church government during the interregnum. Before the ouster there had been a clash between Pasqualina and Tisserant. As she told it much later, the cardinal had learned that she had burned documents. Pasqualina recalled she had told Tisserant: "Yes, I have burned two bags of documents, but I had received the Holy Father's order to do so in case he hadn't time to burn them. All my life I have obeyed; Your Eminence, would you have done otherwise? A pope's orders must be carried out." Pasqualina said she didn't know the nature of the documents she had destroyed, but believed they included drafts of addresses Pius XII had planned to give, and notes regarding private audiences.

Following Cardinal Tisserant's order, Pasqualina departed at once from Castel Gandolfo. (She would later say that the dean of the cardinals had told her she might stay as long as she needed to get her and the other nuns' affairs in order.) Pasqualina was then 64 years old. None of the Vatican dignitaries who had fawned on her for so long saw her off.

It was Cardinal Spellman who found her a refuge in Rome. He made it possible for the German nun to join the housekeeping staff of the Pontifical North American College, the institution for United States seminarians in Rome, whose vast new building on the Janiculum Hill had been inaugurated by Pius XII. American churchmen who have studied in Rome remember the kind little nun who used to mark their saint's day by placing flowers in their room. From the North American College, Mother Pasqualina could walk to St. Peter's to pray at the tomb of "her" pontiff. During the following years the indomitable nun canvassed prospective donors and battled Italian red tape to get the area on Mount Mario, the construction permits, the waivers from zoning regulations, and the funds for building House Pastor Angelicus, her monument to Pius XII.

In Pius XII's lifetime his three nephews—Carlo, Marcantonio, and Giulio Pacelli—and Enrico Galeazzi, the architect and half brother of the pope's personal physician, formed a tight little group that wielded great power in the Vatican, sometimes counterbalancing Mother Pasqualina's influence. All four men held lay posts in the pontifical administration; Giulio Pacelli could also claim diplomatic privileges because the government of Costa Rica had been nudged into naming him its envoy to his own uncle, the pontiff.

In modern times no head of the church was so indulgent in favoring members of his own family as Pius XII. He was still a cardinal when King Victor Emmanuel III of Italy, at Mussolini's behest, conferred on the future pope's brother, Francesco Pacelli, the hereditary title of a prince of the realm in the early 1930s. Until then the Pacelli family, connected with the Vatican over three generations, had belonged to the petty "black" (papal) nobility, a lowly class of aristocrats far apart from such proud Roman princely houses as the Colonnas and the Orsinis. Cardinal Pacelli had no objection to his brother's accepting the aristocratic title from the Savoy dynasty; only 60 years earlier the House of Savoy—the Italian royal family—were considered enemies of the church when their soldiers conquered Rome and ended the temporal rule of the papacy.

Francesco Pacelli, a church lawyer and legal adviser to the Holy See, who had been instrumental in the negotiations that led to the Lateran Treaty of 1929, died in 1934. His title passed to each of his three sons. The three Princes Pacelli were all lawyers qualified to plead cases—mostly marriage annulments—before ecclesiastical courts, and all three did remarkably well in their professional activities. They also found time to serve on the boards of directors of many financial and business corporations that were controlled by the Vatican or by other church bodies. Thus, the family of the "angelic shepherd" was deeply and most profitably enmeshed in money matters.

By contrast, another segment of Pius XII's inner circle, the German Jesuits, had a reputation for asceticism. Foremost among them was the pope's father confessor, Augustin Bea, the Bible scholar who was later to become one of the advocates of ecumenism during Vatican II. Popes, like all other Roman Catholics, are supposed to confess their sins to a priest periodically. Since the oldest times, many pontiffs have appointed their own father confessors, often choosing him from one of the religious orders, like the Jesuits, Franciscans, or Dominicans. The father confessor usually became a member of the pope's ecclesiastical household, or "pontifical family," without attaining any special rank. Many of these simple priests or monks who would hear the pope's confessions acted also as his "spiritual adviser," meaning that the head of the church had somebody with whom he might discuss crises of conscience and other problems weighing on his mind. Profound theological learning was always regarded as a requisite for the pope's confessor.

One might imagine that the priest who was supposed to know the pope's sins and all the secrets of his mind always held a formidable position in the Vatican. Historically, however, hardly any papal confessor ever did. Either they were just saintly men, or the courtiers and prelates at the Holy See assumed that the pope didn't tell his confessor everything, and therefore weren't impressed by his position.

As for Father Bea, whenever he was summoned by Pius XII, the Jesuit hurried on foot from the Pontifical Bible Institute in the heart of Rome, where he lived, to the Vatican, managing to cover the 1.25-mile distance in less than twenty minutes. The Vatican never sent one of its many cars for him. Father Bea and other German priests of the Society of Jesus also conducted research for Pius XII in libraries and archives, digging up learned quotations and other material that went into the pontiff's public pronouncements.

Robert Leiber, also a German Jesuit, handled sensitive secretarial work for the pontiff. Over the years, Father Leiber came to know the head of the church better than most Vatican officials did. After Pius XII's death, Father Leiber wrote in an article about the pontiff: "One of his classmates said that as a boy he had been difficult to approach. He stayed that way. He could be exceedingly charming in his personal relations; informal kindness and fatherliness characterized his audiences. Yet he remained solitary. It was hard to penetrate the depths of his soul."

GOOD POPE JOHN'S "SHADOW"

Pius XII's successor, John XXIII, was at ease with people, welcomed many visitors to his private quarters, and liked to have guests at table. Friendly, even jolly, though he used to be, he knew from his first moment as pontiff how to keep an air of great dignity. There were moments when the inborn shrewdness of the peasant's son showed. During his public appearances people would often grab his hands, kiss his ring, and then start asking for some favor. John XXIII would suddenly have the distrustful look of a farmer waylaid by an aggressive salesman; he quickly would pass the petitioner on to his secretary.

Msgr. Loris Capovilla, the bespectacled, intense secretary, used to smile much less than his patron did. Capovilla was fiercely loyal and could be quite brusque to people when he thought the aged pontiff was getting tired and should be left alone. The secretary was also inclined to overrate his own importance, as key aides to important personages often will, and John XXIII seemed amused by it. "Look at Capovilla," the old pope once whispered during a Vatican ceremony to a curial friend, Msgr. Carlo Grano (who later became a cardinal). "He is convinced he is running the church."

Yet John XXIII was genuinely fond of his secretary. A native of a small mainland town near Padua, Capovilla had lost his father early and had known poverty before entering a Venice seminary. After his ordination to the priesthood, he had served as a curate and taught the elements of religion in high schools. He had been drawn into a group of young clerics who shared what they called progressive views and had become editor of *La Voce di San Marco* (The Voice of St. Mark's), the local church weekly. At that time, Cardinal Roncalli, the new patriarch of Venice and the future pope, had just come from Paris and was finding the intellectual climate of Venetian Catholicism that of a backwater. He was favorably impressed by Capovilla's range of interests and concern with social problems, and made the well-read priest his secretary. Something like a father-and-son relationship soon developed. The secretary accompanied his patriarch to Rome for the 1958 conclave, and after Cardinal Roncalli's elevation to the papacy he offered, with due humility, to return to Venice. Pope John XXIII would have nothing of this.

The thin, earnest secretary became chubby Pope John's "shadow," as he was soon called in the Vatican with the tone of envious backbiting that is customarily reserved for a pontiff's intimates. Capovilla did not get along well with Cardinal Tardini, the crusty, conservative Roman who was John XXIII's secretary of state, and made little effort to ingratiate himself with other curia officials. He didn't even seem eager to accept the title of monsignor that is routinely given to a pope's secretary, and never gained much influence in church government. But Capovilla was around the old pope from early-morning mass to late at night. The two men had long talks about faith and grace, about the situation of the church and the world, and about the events reported in the daily press, which the former editor of *The Voice of St. Mark's* excerpted for the pontiff.

Capovilla is credited with having offered substantial suggestions and serving as an adviser when Pope John was preparing his landmark encyclicals. On occasion the seemingly undiplomatic secretary also acted as a discreet go-between from the pontiff to Italian politicians and other personages. When Khrushchev's son-in-law called on Pope John, Italian newspapers speculated that Capovilla had arranged the meeting, although there is little doubt that the pragmatic diplomacy of Monsignor Casaroli was mainly responsible for it.

Apart from Capovilla, there was no inner circle in the Apostolic Palace. In the pontifical apartment, nuns of the Poor Sisters of Bergamo, from the pope's home province in northern Italy, had replaced Mother Pasqualina and her German-speaking assistants. The pontiff would discuss with his housekeepers in their common dialect what he wanted for lunch or dinner. He enjoyed food, and a glass of wine or two with it, and wanted his guests to enjoy their meals with him too. In the papal suite and in the state rooms below it, brighter tapestries with John XXIII's coat of arms were substituted for Pius XII's somber damasks. (According to old usage, each cardinal, as prince of the church, has his own coat of arms; if he becomes pope it is often redesigned by Vatican heraldry experts. The Vatican also has its own tapestry workshop, staffed by nuns.) Leather armchairs were moved into the papal suite for the many visitors the new pontiff wanted to see; but he didn't make any other changes in the Apostolic Palace.

As Vatican II was being prepared and opened, Cardinal Bea, the Jesuit ecumenist who had already worked for Pius XII, again became a frequent visitor in the pontifical suite.

He briefed Pope John on the mood among the Eastern Orthodox and Protestant churchmen who were attending the council as observers; Bea and other liberals discussed with the pontiff how best to overcome conservative resistance to the church reforms that Vatican II was considering.

During John XXIII's pontificate, papal relatives were rarely seen in the Vatican. At his coronation three surviving brothers and a sister—the pope had been one of thirteen children of a rural couple—were present, but returned at once to their farm work near Bergamo. Pope John did not encourage them or other members of the large Roncalli family to visit with him again, nor did they apparently feel the urge to do so or to ask the pope for any favors; they seemed overwhelmed by Vatican grandeur.

Only when the end came did the three brothers and the sister again journey to Rome to be at the dying pontiff's bedside.

Capovilla had known for two years that John XXIII had inoperable cancer, and was the person closest to the pope during the harrowing months of the terminal phase. The edifying death of John XXIII, who had endured great suffering with courage and prayer, for once silenced the habitual scoffers; there was a sense of grief in Rome such as I have never before or afterward witnessed in that city.

Capovilla cleared out of the Vatican after the funeral, lived quietly in the homes of clerical friends, began to edit John XXIII's posthumous papers, and prepared to write the pope's biography. For the Vatican, the status of a just-deceased pontiff's secretary is always, to use a favorite curial phrase, a delicate problem.

As a new head of the church takes over and brings in his own entourage, nobody wants an insider of the ancien regime around. On the other hand, the closest aide to the new pope's immediate predecessor knows many secrets concerning important persons and matters, and—since not everybody has the discipline of a Mother Pasqualina—might be tempted to make improper use of them, like leaking them to anticlerical journalists or politicians, out of resentment if he is slighted or humiliated. A post rather distant from the Vatican, but dignified enough to propitiate the ex-secretary must be found.

As often happens in such dilemmas, it took the Vatican some time to decide what to do with Monsignor Capovilla. At last, in 1967, he was offered and accepted an appointment as archbishop of Chieti, near the Adriatic coast. Though received with great honors by the local clergy and population, Capovilla did not turn out to be a success in the pleasant city in the foothills of the Abruzzi mountains. Conservatives in the region's church establishment and in the Christian Democratic party machine soon suspected the new archbishop of left-wing sympathies. Confidential protests and complaints started reaching the Vatican, and Pope Paul VI became nervous about Capovilla when a group of priests in the Abruzzi region circulated a manifesto criticizing the Vatican's adamant insistence on the rule of clerical celibacy. It doesn't seem that Capovilla had anything to do with the document, but it was the final straw.

A few months later, after secret and rather tense consultations between the former papal secretary and the curia, Capovilla was transferred (the technical term is "translated") to Loreto. The place is an ancient shrine on a hill near the seaport

Ancona that affords a fine view of the Adriatic Sea and the Abruzzi ranges. Ecclesiastically, Loreto is a prelacy directly under the jurisdiction of the Holy See, meaning that the small church district with 11,000 population, 40 priests, 60 monks and friars, and 180 nuns belongs to no diocese and gets directives straight from the Vatican. For Capovilla, who kept the title of archbishop, it was a sinecure smacking of exile.

As a holy place dedicated to the cult of the Virgin Mary, Loreto, since the end of the nineteenth century, has been outclassed by Lourdes in France, and since World War I by Fatima in Portugal, both of which now attract more pilgrims and receive more publicity than does the old Italian sanctuary. Today Loreto is something of an embarrassment to many Roman Catholics because its fame rests on a medieval legend that even simpleminded pilgrims find hard to believe. At the center of the pious tale is a small structure in Italian Gothic style, in part rebuilt by Renaissance architects—the Holy House. It is supposed to have been the Virgin's home in Nazareth, which, when the infidels overran the Holy Land toward the end of the age of Crusades, was carried by flights of angels from Galilee by way of Dalmatia to the place where it now stands. This feat of heavenly air transport prompted Pope Benedict XV to grant a petition by Italian aviators to proclaim Our Lady of Loreto as their patroness.

The Holy House of Loreto adjoins an exuberant fifteenth-century church with a dome by Sangallo, a campanile by Vanvitelli, and mosaics by Guido Reni. Nearby is an Apostolic Palace, a reminder that Loreto once belonged to the State of the Church and was occasionally visited by popes; the setting must have brought back memories of Vatican splendor to Archbishop Capovilla. In September 1979 the former secretary of John XXIII had the satisfaction of welcoming another pontiff, John Paul II, to Loreto. The Polish pope, who had included the letter *M* for Mary in his coat of arms, made a point of visiting all major Marian shrines in Italy and, with a nod toward popular religion and an implied compliment to Capovilla, did not bypass the Holy House.

Apart from that rare papal visitation, Capovilla's life in Loreto has been quiet, with most of his energies devoted to keeping Pope John XXIII's memory alive through books, articles, lectures, and interviews, and to continue to press for that pontiff's beatification and canonization. After Mother Pasqualina,

Archbishop Capovilla: the surviving intimates of dead popes may find a new mission in life and a role in the church by asserting the sainthood of their former patrons.

MILAN MAFIA

Pope Paul VI, the apprehensive-looking successor to John XXIII, brought with him a cluster of aides, associates, and hangers-on, including laymen without any discernible church function, who were soon known in the Vatican as his "Milan mafia." Not everybody in this coterie hailed from the dynamic, well-to-do metropolis where the new pontiff had been archbishop for more than eight years, or from the surrounding region, Lombardy. A peripheral but ominous figure in Paul VI's Milan set, Michele Sindona, was a transplanted Sicilian who was eventually found by Italian investigators to have ties to the real Mafia. He was to implicate the Vatican in his disastrous financial adventures, clouding the Holy See's image around the world. An American prelate of the curia, Bishop Paul C. Marcinkus, soon joined Paul VI's inner circle.

At the center of the Milan mafia was a priest from Lombardy who for years had been close to the future pope and had become his secretary, Pasquale Macchi. Paul VI called him "Don Pasquale," even after he had named him a monsignor in 1964. There was little about Macchi, though, to inspire the mirth engendered by the hero of Donizetti's comic opera; in the Vatican the customary expression of Paul VI's secretary was a scowl. Curialists quickly referred to him as "Montini's Mother Pasqualina."

Macchi had been introduced to the future pope when the newly named archbishop of Milan, Montini, was looking for an assistant who knew the ropes in the city and its densely populated hinterland. A native of Varese, an industrial center 35 miles northwest of Milan, Macchi was then 30 years old, a seminary professor and a part-time prison chaplain.

The young priest appealed to the archbishop because he was an intellectual strongly influenced by French thinkers, as the future pope himself had been. Macchi had earned his university degree with a doctoral thesis on the problem of evil in the writings of Georges Bernanos, an author whom Montini held in high esteem. In the years to come, Macchi was always looking for new and old books to buy for his patron. Macchi also had a passion for modern art, and he got his archbishop hooked on it. In Milan the two started collecting works by contemporary painters and sculptors, a hobby that brought Montini in direct contact with a milieu new to him—artists, writers, and actors.

While such contacts broadened the future pope's intellectual and human horizon, they didn't make him a liberal. Indeed, having become acquainted in Milan with the ways of industrial society, Montini appears to have become even more indecisive and agonized than before when confronted with ethical issues. In Milan, Montini also met with the city's leading industrialists, bankers, and financiers, many of whom made contributions to the projects and charities of his archdiocese. Dealing with the business community strengthened the archbishop's taste for doing things the modern way, like a corporation executive, and as pope he would try to introduce modernity into the Vatican.

Soon after Montini became Paul VI in 1963, some of the architects and designers whom Macchi and he had cultivated in Milan were called to Rome to redecorate the Apostolic Palace. The pontiff retired to Castel Gandolfo while his own quarters and other parts of the building underwent the facelifting that has been described earlier.

Macchi set himself up in the Vatican as a vicarious patron of modern art. What the Renaissance popes had done for Raphael and Michelangelo, so Paul VI's secretary seemed to think, should be done on behalf of his pontiff for twentieth century talent. Macchi and his agents scouted in the art markets in Europe and in the United States for works to buy, and lined up private donors to finance the acquisitions. They enlisted the help of an American art dealer, Lawrence Fleischman, director of Kennedy Galleries in New York, and founded a nonprofit organization, Friends of American Art in Religion, as a purchasing arm. Terence Cardinal Cooke, archbishop of New York, agreed to function as president of the group; Fleischman served as vice-president. The Friends of American Art in Religion held two seminars in Rome to discuss acquisition strategy. The organization was later to help lay the groundwork for the "blockbuster" exhibition of works of art from the Vatican collections, held at the Metropolitan Museum in New York, as well as in Chicago and San Francisco in 1983.

In 1973 Macchi and his associates were ready to organize an exhibition of modern religious art in the Vatican, meant to mark the tenth anniversary of Paul VI's elevation, and to show off some of the treasures they had quietly assembled over the years. Space on three levels of the Apostolic Palace and in adjoining buildings had been adapted to house Macchi's modern art collection. Twentieth-century paintings and graphic works also were hung in the Borgia Apartment, once the living quarters of Pope Alexander VI and his tempestuous family. Macchi's decorators covered some of the old walls with burlap to create what looked like a modern museum environment, in odd contrast to the Pinturicchio frescoes on the vaulted ceilings.

The show in more than fifty rooms included paintings by Ben Shahn, Chagall, and Kokoschka; ceramics by Picasso; graphics by Klee and Kandinski; and six hundred other works, almost all of them figurative. Abstractionism was represented only timidly. Paul VI, in an address inaugurating the exhibition, said that modern art had marvelously proved it was capable of expressing Christian values. Italian art critics were less kind; they wrote that the new papal collection had been put together haphazardly and that all too many items in it were second-rate and none really outstanding. Macchi's 1973 project has, as Collection of Modern Religious Art, become a permanent addition to the Vatican museums, but many visitors skip it.

Long before Macchi's modern art collection was opened to the public in 1973, almost everyone in the Vatican was aware of extensive work going on in parts of the Apostolic Palace, but even high prelates of the curia ignored how many pictures, sculptures, and other objects had been brought together, and who had paid for them. Almost no details leaked out before the surprise announcement that the show was about to be inaugurated. The secretiveness prompted a wave of rumors about alleged shenanigans in purchasing all that modern art. Paul VI in his opening speech indirectly replied to such speculation by stressing that the exhibits had been assembled thanks to the generosity of donors, and that no funds had been diverted from the church's charities.

By that time Macchi, who at the age of 50 had become stooped and gray, was already one of the most formidable figures in Paul VI's Vatican, rivaling in influence Archbishop Benelli, then the de facto chief of staff. The secretary's reputation as an unfailing servant to the aging pontiff had been enhanced, in his patron's eyes as well, when he saved Paul VI from an assailant's knife in Manila in 1970. Various persons in the pope's traveling party have been credited with foiling the attempt on his life; I was present at the scene and have no doubt the merit was Macchi's. The news reporters traveling in the papal jet were just disembarking on arrival in the capital of the Philippines when we saw the Bolivian painter (an artist, too!) rush toward the pontiff, who was being solemnly welcomed by local churchmen and officials. Macchi, at the pope's side, hurled himself at the attacker in what looked like a reflex act, pushing aside the Bolivian's knife so that it barely grazed Paul VI.

During the last few years of Paul VI's pontificate, his secretary assumed an increasingly protective—some curialists said proprietary—attitude toward the pontiff. Macchi seemed to have become indispensable to Paul VI, who had turned moody and suffered from spells of depression and sleeplessness along with bouts of arthritic misery. Macchi nagged the head of the church into eating more, drinking an additional glass of wine, forcing himself to smile when he appeared in public, and to go to sleep instead of writing by hand long letters to friends and reading deep into the night. The secretary also intervened in church politics by arranging confidential papal audiences for bishops and other ecclesiastics, circumventing the curia. This, rather than substantive issues, inevitably increased tensions between Macchi and Benelli. A chief of staff detests nothing more fiercely than his commander doing things of which he is unaware and seeing people he hasn't vetted and introduced. When Paul VI sent his chief of staff as archbishop to Florence, the papal secretary seemed the winner in a long-smoldering conflict, although he himself was not equipped intellectually or by experience to take up the function of a chief of staff.

By 1977 church government was almost at a standstill because the pope's inveterate reluctance to make decisions had worsened with his illness and the absence of a dynamic aide like Benelli, who would take it on himself to keep things running. Macchi was then the dominant Vatican figure. He managed to stay in touch with his artist friends and to discuss new acquisitions for the pope's—and his—modern collection, as well as maintaining liaison with the curial apparatus and, on advice from the Vatican doctors, telling Paul VI when to cut his schedule of audiences and desk work.

Although it had been known for a long time that Paul VI was ailing and often in pain, his death at Castel Gandolfo in August 1978 came unexpectedly and with startling swiftness. Macchi acted competently until the cardinals took over. When the dead pontiff's will was opened three days later, nobody was surprised to learn that he had named "dear Don Pasquale Macchi" his executor.

The document ordered the secretary to destroy all personal notes, manuscripts, and other papers left by Paul VI as well as any letters "of a personal and spiritual nature not destined for the information of other persons." The will also authorized Macchi to keep a few souvenirs from the pope's belongings and to distribute some other mementos among "dear persons" who were not identified. Macchi, the collector, must have accumulated much property of his own during his fifteen years in the Vatican. Two high curia officials told me later, independently, that when Paul VI's former secretary left the Apostolic Palace, he took "several truckloads" of personal belongings, including works of art, with him. Macchi's trucks are remembered by people in the Vatican as tenaciously as are the suitcase and the birdcage that Mother Pasqualina took with her from Castel Gandolfo in similar circumstances almost twenty years earlier.

Macchi went to live with friends in Milan and his native Varese. The former secretary of Paul VI eventually obtained an appointment as pastor of the old pilgrimage church of Sacro Monte on a 2,885-foot hill near Varese. The pro forma job, conveniently distant from the Vatican, left Monsignor Macchi plenty of time for editing the speeches and writings of his former patron and establishing a "Paul VI Institute" in Brescia dedicated to sifting and collecting that pontiff's spiritual legacy. So far there has been no hint of any effort to have Paul VI beatified and canonized.

Another influential member of Paul VI's Milan mafia, Sergio Cardinal Pignedoli, was to be the runner-up in the conclave of 1978 that led to the election of John Paul I. A widely traveled curialist with an outgoing personality and a ready smile, Pignedoli once claimed to me that he had "ten thousand friends" all over the world.

A good part of his day was taken up writing letters to young people everywhere. However, the cardinal's most important friendship was that with Paul VI; it went back to World War II when Pignedoli was a dashing chaplain in the Italian navy, and the future pope, twelve years his senior, a hard-working Vatican official. The older man became Pignedoli's mentor, and found curia posts and diplomatic assignments for his protégé.

When Pius XII relegated the aide who had served him so long to Milan, Archbishop Montini called his old friend and made him an auxiliary bishop. The two worked closely together for five years, but then something must have happened between them; Pignedoli asked for reassignment outside Italy. He became a papal envoy to Nigeria and later to Canada, and was given more opportunities to travel and make new friends.

When the archbishop of Milan became pope he recalled Pignedoli to Rome, put him in a high post in the Vatican's missionary department, and in 1973 gave him the red hat. As a cardinal, Pignedoli was in charge of one of the new bodies set up after Vatican II, the Secretariat for Non-Christians. His "let's-be-friends" line seemed successful in his new field—until 1976, when he fell into a political trap. At a symposium of Christians and Moslems in Tripoli, Libya, Pignedoli allowed himself to be maneuvered into endorsing a document that condemned Zionism, asserted the Arab character of Jerusalem, and demanded Israel's withdrawal from all territories it had occupied in 1967.

The statement was a glaringly pro-Arab departure from the Vatican's traditionally circumspect posture regarding the Holy Land. After tense telephone calls between Tripoli and the Secretariat of State, Pignedoli had to "clarify" that he really could not speak for the Holy See. The embarrassment raised serious questions about the diplomatic skills of the hail-fellow-well-met prince of the church, and may ultimately have diminished his chances for becoming Paul VI's successor.

The Tripoli incident apparently did not weaken the relationship between Paul VI and Pignedoli. Vatican gossip was that Pignedoli had secret power because he possessed material damaging to Paul VI from their time together in Milan. It was the kind of unsubstantiated rumor that abounds in Rome and in the curia, particularly in the later stages of a lengthy pontificate. Pignedoli was reported to have received between 12 and 20 votes in the final ballots of the papal election in August 1978 following Paul VI's death. In the conclave held in October of that year, after John Paul I's brief pontificate, Pignedoli was no longer considered a candidate, and seems to have climbed onto the Wojtyla bandwagon early. Kept on by the Polish pope as head of the Vatican Secretariat for Non-Christians, Pignedoli suddenly died in June 1980, at just 70 years of age, young for a cardinal.

Paul VI's household included four nuns for the kitchen chores, led by one Sister Giacomina, and a young priest from

Northern Ireland, Father Magee, who had begun sharing secretarial duties with Macchi after first having been borrowed from the Secretariat of State for translation tasks. A discreet curialist, well liked by Paul VI, Magee never left any doubt that he regarded himself as subordinate to Macchi.

The Irishman was to serve John Paul I in the same capacity and, as reported earlier, would be one of the first persons, if not the first, to learn of that pontiff's lonely death.

Two minor Vatican officials were considered members of the Milan mafia because they were Macchi's friends. They were Father Virgilio Levi, deputy editor of *L'Osservatore Romano,* the pontifical newspaper, and the Reverend Romeo Panciroli, who acted as the principal spokesman of the Holy See for the information media. Both men were to continue in their functions under John Paul I and John Paul II.

In his private quarters Paul VI occasionally saw members of the Milan intelligentsia and art world whom he had met when he was archbishop of that city, and other friends, such as Paolo Carlini, a well-known actor. The mix of Paul VI's inner circle, its alleged secretiveness, and its reputed aestheticism were soon subjects of malevolent whispers in Rome. In 1976 the scandalous rumors found their way into print as Roger Peyrefitte, the French author, asserted in an article in *Tempo* magazine that Paul VI was gay and "has for a boyfriend a movie actor whose name I am not going to mention but which I remember very well." Peyrefitte, an avowed homosexual, had caused Vatican indignation earlier, notably by his 1955 book, *The Keys of St. Peter,* and a 1958 newspaper article criticizing Pius XII. Italian authorities seized *Tempo* magazine on the ground that Peyrefitte had slandered the supreme pontiff. The pope himself, always sensitive to what French intellectuals were saying and writing about him, protested publicly. In his customary Sunday address before giving his noonday blessing on April 4, 1976, Paul VI in effect denied that he was a homosexual. The pontiff noted that his cardinal vicar for Rome and the Italian bishops' conference had urged the faithful "to pray for our humble person," and complained that he had been made the target of scorn and "horrible and slanderous insinuations by a certain press that lacks due regard for honesty and truth." Everybody understood that Paul VI was referring to Peyrefitte. No pope in modern times had ever before found it necessary to allude in public to his own alleged sex life, and many churchmen at the time deplored his statement as a papal overreaction.

THE POLISH NETWORK

The first pope in nearly five centuries who wasn't an Italian surprised Rome in more ways than one in his choice of the people closest to him. For one thing, the Polish pontiff surrounded himself with many more churchmen from his own country, and gave them greater influence in the Vatican than discretion might have counseled a newcomer to the age-old Italianate establishment. At the same time, far from appearing overawed by the complexities of the curia, John Paul II acted with self-assurance from the beginning, obviously determined to make the ponderous Vatican machinery work for him rather than the other way around. A Frenchman who remained an outsider in the curia although he headed its education department, Gabriel-Marie Cardinal Garrone, observed that the Polish pope was much more independent of the traditions and customs of the church's central government than Paul VI had been. "Pope Wojtyla is a man with great psychic equilibrium," Cardinal Garrone remarked, "which, I think, is in turn based on a great physical equilibrium."

After a while, Roman Vatican watchers were astonished to note that they were still unable to spot a papal favorite among the many Poles in John Paul II's entourage—somebody like Mother Pasqualina or Monsignor Macchi, whom one might approach for favors, and who would in turn become the center of a palace clique.

Eventually it was realized that the Pole on the throne of Saint Peter, with all his warmth in personal contacts, was a very private person, and had become even more so as bishop of Rome. Instead of relying on one intimate or on a few of them, John Paul II built a Polish network in and around the Vatican. It was comprised of dozens of ecclesiastics whose names Italians found hard to pronounce and spell, some of them shuttling between Poland and Rome, others permanently assigned to curial bodies, and yet others with undefined duties but with access to the head of the church. The loose, but efficient, grouping of Poles formed a new unofficial tier in the Vatican structure, monitoring what the administrative units were doing and reporting directly to the pope. Some of the curial Poles were given key jobs, others ostensibly subaltern positions, although everybody knew that they could reach the pope easily.

The social and political developments in John Paul II's homeland, especially after his memorable visit there in 1979, helped strengthen the Polish network at the Holy See. Remaining deeply enmeshed in the affairs of his native country, the pope closely followed the rise and suppression of the independent Solidarity labor movement and the subsequent events at home, asking for up-to-the-minute reports, giving detailed instructions to the Polish church hierarchy, and discussing strategy with Polish bishops and leaders of the Roman Catholic laity. A Western diplomat accredited to the Holy See remarked to me: "Pope John Paul is his own Polish desk officer." To stay abreast of the situation at home, the pontiff needed a staff of aides who could call telephone numbers in Poland, speak to Polish visitors in their language, read Polish newspapers and documents, and do other liaison work. A large Polish section was set up in the Secretariat of State.

From Krakow, the Polish pope had brought with him the nuns of the Servants of the Sacred Heart of Jesus, who took care of his household in the Apostolic Palace in much the same way as they had done in the archiepiscopal residence back home, and his private secretary, the Reverend Stanislaw Dziwisz. The five nuns from Krakow, occupying the rooms that once had been Mother Pasqualina's domain, picked up enough Italian to communicate with Vatican personnel, and learned to prepare pasta as well as John Paul II's favorite fare—borscht, kielbasa and other sausages, roast pork, cabbage, and rich Polish pastry. When nobody else was around, the pontiff might ask one of his household nuns to make a quick phone call to some Vatican official: "The Holy Father wants to see you as soon as possible."

Father Stanislaw, "Stash" to the Poles and the Americans in the Vatican, was given the rank of papal chaplain which is purely honorific, and the title of monsignor, but the curialists soon found that John Paul II's chief secretary, although near his patron around the clock, had little real influence. The baby-faced priest, the son of a railroad worker, lacked the linguistic skills and self-confidence of his principal, and appeared to be intimidated by the high prelates he saw from morning to night. "I wish I were home again," he was heard saying in his first months in the Apostolic Palace. "I am so lonesome in this place." Vatican officials also found Dziwisz to be much more in awe of his own chief than Mother Pasqualina, Capovilla, or Macchi had been of theirs.

"A papal secretary doesn't have to disinfect the boss's hands with alcohol after every audience the way Pasqualina did," an old archbishop observed to me. "But Dziwisz doesn't know the elementary things that a good secretary ought to do besides handing the pope the right text when he is about to read a speech. The secretary should always have a supply of clean scull-caps and collars ready, see to it that the boss never looks untidy, whatever the crush of people during a trip."

The quiet, taciturn Irishman, Monsignor Magee, whom John Paul II had taken over from his two predecessors and promoted to papal chaplain, like Dziwisz, served him as an alternate secretary for three years. Once the pope even sent Magee, a native of County Down, to Belfast on a special mission—to seek to end the hunger strike by Roman Catholic prisoners and to improve the conditions under which they were being held. In 1982 John Paul II appointed Magee as master of pontifical ceremonies, a post entailing attendance at papal rites and formal audiences, that was to keep the Irishman in daily contact with the head of the church. In his own household, the Polish pope replaced Magee with a black African, Monsignor Emery Kabongo, a Zairian whom he had first met during his 1980 visit to Brazil. Kabongo, then 36 years old, was serving as a secretary at the apostolic nunciature in Brasilia; he'd impressed the pontiff by the easy manner in which he dealt with the local authorities and the people. In 1981 Kabongo was called into the Vatican secretary of state, and a few months later took up his duties in the pope's personal quarters. Blacks in Vatican posts were no novelty, but Kabongo was the first black African in the immediate entourage of a modern pope. Curialists seemed rather pleased. "At least he's not another Pole on the third floor [the papal suite in the Apostolic Palace]," was a frequent comment.

John Paul II's two secretaries usually shared breakfast with their chief and were often at his table for other meals. The Polish pope seldom ate alone. Frequently he had half a dozen or more guests at lunch or dinner—visiting prelates from Poland or other countries, Italian bishops or cardinals, Roman pastors whose parishes he intended soon to visit, or Vatican administration officials whom he would quiz about their departments and problems.

Almost from the moment when Cardinal Felici as the senior cardinal deacon announced the election of Krakow's archbishop as the next pope, the few Poles who were then holding posts in the Vatican found themselves courted by people who up until then had ignored them. Suddenly it was important in the curia to have a Polish connection. After John Paul II, on the day following his elevation, made his surprise visit to his ailing friend, Bishop Deskur, at the Gemelli hospital, the prelate was showered with get-well messages and flowers. When he was moved to a clinic in Zurich for further treatment, members of his Vatican staff turned up there at short intervals to tell him that he was indeed looking much better already and that they were eagerly awaiting his return to Rome. (John Paul II personally telephoned Zurich many times to inquire how Deskur was coming along; the first time, the Swiss switchboard operator asked who was calling and snickered incredulously when the voice said, in faintly accented German, "This is the pope.") At least one Italian official of the curia's Commission for Social Communications, whose chief Deskur remained despite his illness, started learning Polish.

Another Polish prelate, Msgr. Juliusz Paetz, whose job for years had been to greet distinguished visitors to Paul VI, was now flooded with telephone calls and mail from people who claimed they were old friends, and from others who turned to him just because he was serving in the antechambers of the pontifical suite and was Polish.

One of the highest Polish dignitaries in Rome, Bishop Wladyslaw Rubin, as secretary-general to the Bishops' Synod had been in close touch with Cardinal Wojtyla for years. John Paul II made Rubin a cardinal in his first consistory and placed him at the top of the curia's department for the Eastern churches. A Slovak member of the Vatican bureaucracy, Archbishop Josef Tomko, became the new secretary-general of the Bishops' Synod. Slovaks are the neighbors of the Poles south of the Beskids and the Tatra Mountains, only a few miles from Krakow. That John Paul II had again called on a churchman from his part of the world to fill the sensitive synod post was regarded as a sign of ethnic favoritism in a kind of papal affirmative-action program for the Slavs who, as the Polish pontiff himself had repeatedly remarked, had too-long been neglected by the Roman Catholic Church. At the 1980 session of the synod, which was devoted to the problems of the Christian family, some Polish bishops were allowed to speak for twenty minutes at a time, whereas other participants were cut off by the chairman after ten minutes. "There is now a special space for Poles in the Vatican," an Italian archbishop said resentfully.

Ethnic solidarity was believed to have, at least in part, prompted John Paul II to strengthen Bishop Marcinkus's position. A Chicagoan of Lithuanian origin, Marcinkus had come from a people who historically have often shared their destiny with their neighbors, the Poles. Yet even Marcinkus at times seemed weary of John Paul II's nationalism. During the papal visit to West Africa in 1982, when the bishop was again acting as tour manager, he was asked whether the pontiff would meet with still another group of Poles who happened to live in that corner of the earth. (John Paul II's journeys brought out that there are Poles everywhere.) "If I hear the word 'Poles' again I'll scream," Marcinkus said.

A bias in favor of persons who were brought up in his own language seemed the main reason why John Paul II, to general astonishment, named the descendant of a Polish Jewish family, Jean-Marie Lustiger, the 139th archbishop of Paris in 1981. Lustiger, born in Paris, had become a convert to Roman Catholicism when he was 14 years old, and a priest at the age of 27. In charge of a parish in the well-off Saint Cloud district of French capital, he caught the attention of the future pope with a book, *The Sermons of a Parisian Pastor.* Cardinal Wojtyla wanted to meet the author, and the two men, conversing in Polish, hit it off famously. At the end of 1979 John Paul made Lustiger bishop of Orléans, and a little more than a year later he appointed his protégé as successor to François Cardinal Marty, then 77 years old, in Paris. In doing so, the pope bypassed Roger Cardinal Etchegaray, the respected archbishop of Marseilles, who was considered the favorite for the historic see of Paris. The appointment also ignored recommendations from the French bishops' conference and Archbishop Felici, the curial-conservative nuncio to France. Lustiger's promotion baffled President Valéry Giscard d'Estaing of France and the Roman Curia, where the new archbishop of Paris was almost unknown.

When another important see, Detroit, fell vacant in 1980 because of Cardinal Dearden's retirement, John Paul II nominated a Polish-descended prelate, Edmund C. Szoka, up to then bishop of Gaylord, Michigan, as his successor. Since Detroit has a large Polish-American population, the appointment was not as surprising as Lustiger's, but it was yet again an indication of papal priorities.

John Paul II's ethnic awareness also extended to deceased Poles, as was proved by a papal order to streamline procedures to make possible a 1982 canonization of the Blessed Maximilian Kolbe. A Polish Franciscan priest who was murdered in the Nazi extermination camp of Auschwitz (close to John Paul II's birthplace, Wadowice) during World War II, Father Kolbe had been beatified by Paul VI in 1977. To remove the formal ties standing in the way of an early proclamation of sainthood, John Paul II suspended canon 2138 of the church's law code, which provided that two additional miracles must be certified before a blessed person—who must already have officially recognized miracles to his or her credit—may be canonized. The papal waiver of canon law was exceptional, and felt to be high-handed. Curialists likened the favorable treatment posthumously accorded to the Franciscan martyr of Auschwitz to Pope Pius XII's decision to hurry the canonization of the adolescent rape martyr, Saint Maria Goretti, in 1950. It may be recalled that Cardinal Bertoli once resigned because he would not be rushed in causes of sanctity.

By the time John Paul II prepared the sainting of Father Kolbe as another Polish triumph in St. Peter's, the Polish element was already well entrenched in the Vatican. The Secretariat of State had its own Polish liaison staff, and Polish ecclesiastics had the run of all curial offices. The pope's successor as archbishop of Krakow and one of his closest friends, Franciszek Cardinal Macharski, often journeyed to Rome. He was regularly put up in a guest room of the papal apartment in the Apostolic Palace, and was entitled to give direct orders to John Paul II's secretaries. The Polish primate, Josef Cardinal Glemp, and other prominent and obscure visitors from the pope's homeland provided a floating Polish presence in the Vatican at most times.

In almost every public audience there was a distinct, vocal group of Poles who waved their red and white banners, chanted their hymns, and were greeted by the pontiff in their language, often with carefully worded remarks that were meant as messages for the people and the authorities back home. When John Paul II wanted a new guest house for Polish pilgrims to Rome, a site on the Via Cassia in the city's northern suburbs and the necessary money were quickly found. The institution, named after the Polish pontiff and staffed by Polish nuns, could put up nearly one hundred visitors in rooms with one, two, or three beds. It was often filled to capacity. In the convents and mother houses of religious orders around Rome, friars and nuns from

Poland moved into cells that for years had remained vacant as membership in the communities shrank; now personnel of their Polish affiliates were transferred to Rome.

In Rome's streets the Polish priests could be spotted easily, not only by their broad Slavic faces and their blond hair, but also by cassocks that seemed longer than those worn by Italian clerics, and by stiff birettas. In the pope's own diocese no other priest wore a biretta outside church. In Communist Poland, instead, the clergy made themselves conspicuous by wearing traditional garb at all times, as if to defy the Marxist regime and demonstrate their church's power. The presence of the many Polish priests helped John Paul II to enforce the ecclesiastical dress code in the Italian capital. The invasion of Polish clergy nevertheless made many Romans, clergy and laity, faintly uneasy.

An Italian churchman with vast international experience who held a key post in the curia remarked to me: "I just can't stomach [*"non mi va giù"*] this Polish chauvinism. Maybe it was a big mistake to elect a foreign pope at this time. For centuries Italian clerics have put the Holy See first and our nation afterward. This pope with all his enormous charisma, his pastoral skills, seems to be putting Poland first, the Holy See and the universal church afterward."

Another Italian, a bishop, said to me: "Interrupt me if you have already heard this one. It seems Jesus Christ visited His vicar on earth in the Vatican and asked Pope Wojtyla whether he intended to allow priests to take wives. 'Not as long as I live,' the Holy Father replied. And what about speculation that women may be ordained to the priesthood, and that the Vatican would permit the contraceptive pill? 'Not as long as I live,' John Paul II replied to either question. Jesus turned to leave. 'Lord,' John Paul said quickly, 'may I ask a question too?' Christ nodded, and the Holy Father inquired, 'Will there be another Polish pope after me?' 'Not as long as I live,' said the Lord."

John Paul II's unofficial, but highly efficient, Polish establishment in the Vatican continues to baffle curialists because they still can't identify any clear favorite. The pontiff from Krakow relies on the members of the ethnic coterie around him according to their capacities and the posts they happen to be filling at the moment, giving assignments now to one of them, now to another. The Polish network never gathers jointly with the pope in a formal meeting, but they report to him and also keep in constant touch with one another, exchanging information.

By diluting the influence that the papal entourage can exert on the curia and on himself, John Paul II remains his own man to a much higher degree than, for instance, Pius XII and Paul VI had been, especially in their declining years. Future church historians will probably agree with contemporaries of those two popes that Mother Pasqualina and Monsignor Macchi wielded substantial power in the Apostolic Palace. By bringing some individuals to their patron's attention and barring others, by suggestions and warnings, by conveying and withholding information, papal favorites have often influenced decisions on ecclesiastical personnel and policy with far-reaching consequences. The last stages of Pius XII's and Paul VI's pontificates are the most recent examples.

The nephew or secretary of some cardinal, a priest who a few years earlier taught theology in a provincial seminary, or—quite exceptionally—a nun may become a power behind the papal throne by events in which they had only a marginal part. But they must know that their sudden authority can be undermined by a cabal in the Apostolic Palace, and that at any rate it will end the very moment their patron dies.

The career of a Cardinal Confalonieri is quite unusual—he served as secretary to Pope Pius XI and after the death of that pontiff in 1939 lapsed into obscurity as a bishop in the Abruzzi region, reemerged later as a member of the sacred college, and eventually became its dean. The rule in the Vatican is that members of a deceased pope's entourage sink into oblivion for the rest of their lives. Yet such are the delights of exercising power while it lasts, that those who have a chance of enjoying it almost never back out voluntarily and are envied by all.

CHAPTER 6

MAMMON AT THE HOLY SEE

OUTRAGE OVER THE hard-nosed way the papacy was rounding up money all over Europe was one of the factors that led to the Protestant Reformation of the sixteenth century. Enormous sums were needed by the popes in those times to finance the construction of the new St. Peter's Basilica and other projects. Papal fund raisers were virtually selling indulgences—through which penitent sinners were said to be freed of divine punishment in their lifetime and in purgatory—to collect cash for the Vatican treasury.

The Church of Rome was haunted by financial machinations long before and long after the Renaissance. Charges of simony (the buying and selling of ecclesiastical benefices) and avarice were leveled at popes and their aides in the Middle Ages; in our time institutions and officials of the Holy See have been implicated in some of the many corruption and mismanagement scandals of post–World War II Italy.

The Roman Catholic Church, like other religious bodies, needs funds for its central government and its worldwide activities. However, no convincing reason has ever been adduced by the Holy See why its financial affairs should be transacted in impenetrable obscurity. One reason was certainly the papacy's age-old reluctance to admit it had anything to do with Mammon.

Up to the late 1970s no Vatican secret was more jealously

guarded than the secret of papal money. Only after the exposure
of highly questionable international manipulations in which capital and financial managers of the Holy See played parts was
public opinion aroused enough to prompt the cardinals to request clarity. From the start of John Paul II's pontificate a few
figures and facts regarding the Vatican budget have trickled out
—astonishingly, for the first time in history. A large part of the
Holy See's money affairs is nevertheless still left to guesswork.
Disregarding sensational allegations by avowed anticlericals and
by uninhibited media in various countries, this chapter attempts
to give a prudent assessment of papal finances, which are being
thoroughly revamped at the time of writing.

In the late 1970s and early 1980s the Holy See stated repeatedly that it was running up large budget deficits. Whenever the
pope's treasurers complain that they are short of cash they meet
with widespread incredulity inside and outside the Vatican.
What about the Holy See's fabulous riches? Even the most devout faithful, on being again dunned to give money "for the
Holy Father" may think, why doesn't he sell off some of his
possessions?

Apologists for the papacy usually retort: "How much is Michelangelo's *Pietà* worth? What is the international art market's
quotation for the Sistine Chapel?" True, St. Peter's Basilica
and the Vatican collections with their treasures are both price-
less and unsalable. However, the Holy See also owns plenty of
marketable and income-producing assets, although it does not
like to be reminded of them, and they may be incompetently
managed.

Anyone who tries to untangle the papal money affairs is
struck by the remarkable confusion, frequent bungling by officials, absence of independent auditing, and possibilities for
abuses in addition to the general reticence.

THE POPE'S SPENDING
MONEY

Foreign diplomats and Italian bankers were present in a Roman
club when one of John Paul II's top money managers, Cardinal
Caprio, gave a lecture on a subject that curialists don't like to
discuss with outsiders, "The Vatican's Finances." Reports that

the Holy See was fabulously rich, controlling enormous wealth—some said $10 billion, others $20 billion—in real estate, securities, and other assets had been published in the international press for many years. They had drawn indignant, even irate, denials whenever there had been a curial reaction at all. The trouble was that the pontifical spokesmen never came up with figures about the Vatican's resources, income, and expenditures. On the other hand, John Paul II himself had recently told the cardinals that the central government of the church was operating in the red, and that if nothing were done about the mounting budget deficits the Vatican would find itself short of cash in a few years. Cardinal Caprio's lecture was therefore awaited with more than polite interest, but listeners who expected to learn the hard figures at last remained disappointed.

The cardinal spoke much about the past and very little about the present. Going back to early Christianity, Caprio suggested that the first manager of church property had been Saint Lawrence, the deacon of Pope Sixtus II, who suffered martyrdom in the third century A.D. According to tradition, the saintly deacon, rather than obey an order to reveal and give up church wealth during the persecution of Christians in the reign of Emperor Valerian, resigned himself to being roasted to death on a gridiron. Before his ordeal he had gathered poor and sick Christians, and told the emperor's myrmidons: "These are the church's treasures." The Basilica of St. Lawrence Outside the Walls, which marks the martyr's presumed burial place and is one of Rome's major shrines, was gravely damaged by the first Allied air raid on the Italian capital in July 1943. Few other Roman churches suffered any harm during World War II; Saint Lawrence was luckless also seventeen centuries after his heroic death.

Cardinal Caprio could regard himself as a latter-day successor to Saint Lawrence. He had recently received the red hat, had been made president of the Administration of the Patrimony of the Holy See, and would soon be shifted to another financial department, the Prefecture for the Economic Affairs of the Holy See. The two bodies belong to a maze of overlapping, interlocking, and independent units that administer Vatican assets.

Caprio had served as pontifical envoy in east Asia and had picked up something of the Chinese way of expressing thought by indirection and symbols. He may have meant to say in the club lecture that, like Saint Lawrence, a financial manager of the Church of Rome should let himself be roasted rather than give away what he knows. That he did discuss Vatican finances publicly at all was due to a campaign in the Italian press demanding full disclosure. The Holy See, possibly John Paul II himself, decided then that some sort of explanation was in order. However, Caprio only hinted at the various bureaucratic bodies that manage Vatican money and assets, and he didn't supply figures. The cardinal also failed to mention that the pope personally needs cash, and usually disposes of considerable sums.

Pontiffs, like royalty, never carry money on them, whether they are in residence or journeying to faraway places. The head of the church nevertheless finds out soon after his election that he ought to have some cash stashed away for personal gifts or for emergencies, and that it is easy to build up such a reserve with or without the help of aides.

Quite a number of the people whom the pope receives in private audience, and even some participants in his general audiences, especially those in the coveted front row close to the pontifical throne, press envelopes with cash or checks in diverse currencies on him. "For your charities, your Holiness," the donors may murmur. The pope takes everything that is given to him, money or messages, and hands it to an aide at his side, often his private secretary. The assistant may later turn over the money to one of the Vatican's financial officers or directly to the pontiff. The voluminous mail that the head of the church receives, hundreds of letters on some days, also includes money —a generous check from some individual or corporate benefactor, or quite often the widow's mite, a $5 bill or 100 pesetas or a few pesos in an envelope with the handwritten address "Holy Father, Vatican."

The top officials of the Vatican bank, modestly called the Institute for the Works of Religion, and other financial agencies of the Holy See, for many years used to present a hefty check to the pontiff for his personal projects and charitable donations. It may have been a way of thanking the pope for not asking too many questions.

Mother Pasqualina told me that on July 19, 1943, after hundreds of American and British aircraft, wave after wave, had attacked the outskirts of Rome, Pius XII had asked for all the cash that was being kept in his household. She gave him the money that was stored in a box in a small room next to his study. Then he ordered to be driven to the city's eastern district where the bombs had fallen. The Basilica of St. Lawrence Outside the Walls had been hit, and hundreds of civilians had been killed. Many thousands of frightened residents had taken refuge at the Lateran where they thought, correctly, to be safe because the ancient complex was considered extraterritorial, an outlying dependency of the State of Vatican City. Romans who had been in Lateran Square when the pope arrived there from St. Lawrence's, accompanied by only two aides, told me later that Pius XII, so overcome by emotion that he could hardly speak, pulled a wad of 1,000-lire bills out of his white cassock and shoved them into the hands that were stretched out toward him. Before World War II an Italian family could live on 1,000 lire for a month; by 1943 the amount was still a lot of money even though there wasn't much one could buy with it. Mother Pasqualina remembered that he'd come back from St. Lawrence's and the Lateran with bloodstains on his dirtied white vestments.

John XXIII found plenty of cash in the papal apartment when the seals that had been put on its doors after his predecessor's death were broken. The new pontiff was not much interested in earthly possessions and had never accumulated much property. (Before his death he would give his fountain pen to his doctor, explaining that he owned no other valuables that would make a good souvenir.) On one of his first days as pope he asked Cardinal Siri whether it wouldn't be best to deposit the funds he had found in the pontifical apartment with the Vatican bank. The cardinal from Genoa, who had a reputation for financial acumen and himself nurtured pontifical ambitions, held up his hands like a handcuffed prisoner, and said: "Holy Father, if you do that, you'll end up like Saint Peter, in shackles." St. Peter in Shackles (San Pietro in Vincoli) is a Roman church, but the meaning was that a pontiff without ready cash is a captive of the curia's money men. John XXIII kept the cash.

Devoid as he was of acquisitive instincts, he did not mind spending the Holy See's funds. During Vatican II officials of the curia muttered about the cost of the vast church assembly. No exact figures have ever been published, but the council was estimated to have caused extraordinary Vatican expenditures of between $7 million and $10 million. Money well spent, John XXIII must have thought.

Paul VI with his Milan mafia and their patronage of modern artists engaged in financial dealings completely outside normal Vatican channels, on a level different from the usual "good works" of the popes. The role played by the Sicilian-born financial adventurer, Sindona, during Paul VI's pontificate will be discussed in detail later. The Sindona affair was a topic in many conversations between cardinals when the sacred college gathered in Rome twice in 1978 after the deaths of Paul VI and John Paul I.

The brevity of John Paul I's reign did not allow any guess as to how he would have handled money matters, his own or the Holy See's. True, as patriarch of Venice he had sold off church treasures to raise funds for social projects, but as a pope he seemed so thoroughly dominated by the curia that he could hardly have been expected to see through its confusing financial mechanisms. When he suddenly died, there was almost no money in the papal suite.

John Paul II appears to have availed himself early of the papal prerogative of creating a personal fund for which he was accountable to no one. Almost from the start of his pontificate the Polish pope could be observed during audiences giving cash —usually in United States currency—to countrymen and other people. He also reputedly made personal money contributions in less visible ways to needy persons or deserving institutions and projects.

His pontificate has also been marked by upheavals and changes in the Vatican's finances, due in large part to developments that had started under earlier pontiffs.

THE CARDINALS ASK QUESTIONS

Until the beginning of John Paul II's pontificate, even the vast majority of the sacred college, including most of the cardinals serving in the curia, were kept in the dark about the Vatican budget and finances. The popes themselves did not know all the details. As long as there were enough funds to keep the Vatican machinery running, pontiffs in recent times usually did not want to be informed day by day of what their treasurers were doing, and probably would not have grasped the technicalities of money management anyway. Even the supreme pontiff may get lost in the Holy See's financial labyrinth.

Before the archbishop of Krakow, Wojtyla, received the required majority in the conclave of October 1978, quite a number of cardinal electors asked him to promise that, as pontiff, he would insist on clarity regarding the Vatican's assets and budget. A year after his elevation John Paul II indeed summoned all cardinals, including those barred from a papal election because of advanced age, to a meeting in Rome to discuss the Holy See's economic situation and other issues. During the week-long gathering behind closed doors money problems dominated the debates. Even the public at large was, for the first time in many years, given a specific figure: it was told that the central government of the church was piling up increasing deficits, and that the difference between ordinary revenues and expenditures for the year 1979 was expected to amount to about $20 million at the lira-dollar rate then prevailing. (The Italian lira is also the currency unit of the State of Vatican City, and budget figures are in lire.) No other financial data were published, but an official statement said, rather tortuously, that the cardinals had discussed "the possibility of giving, in due course, favorable consideration to the proposal to supply public information" about Vatican finances. Only the pontiff could make a decision on such a policy of public disclosure. Why not start it at once?

One reason was certainly that the three cardinals of the curia who had briefed their peers on the Holy See's economic resources and commitments simply didn't know everything. The three were Caprio; Egidio Cardinal Vagnozzi, a former apostolic delegate in Washington who at the time was serving as a papal comptroller of sorts; and Casaroli, the secretary of state. Casaroli had just launched a curial drive to whittle away the autonomy of the Vatican bank, but had not made much headway. Before him Benelli, Paul VI's chief of staff, also had tried hard to bring the Institute for the Works of Religion under his control, but had failed.

John Paul II attended some of the cardinals' debates but was not able to shed much light on the Vatican's finances. As archbishop of Krakow he had not been an outstanding administrator. Mainly interested in philosophy and pastoral activities, he preferred to work on doctrinal papers to be used at the Bishops' Synod in Rome or as lectures around the world rather than to go over the accounts of his archdiocese. Donations from sympathizers in America and elsewhere helped pay off the debts of the church in Krakow. The Polish pope's absence from some of the cardinals' discussions was a gesture implying that they had full liberty to speak their minds on the Holy See's money matters. Of course, John Paul II later received exhaustive reports on the debates.

Like the pope himself, many of the cardinals who attended the plenary session of the sacred college in November 1979 had little experience in international finance and were baffled by the conundrum of the Holy See's economics. They had no way of verifying what the curia officials chose to tell them. The cardinals were simply informed that the Holy See's expenditures were ballooning because of inflation in Italy and in other countries, because of the pay demands of Vatican workers who were for the first time organizing themselves into what resembled a labor union, and because of the new tasks confronting the church's central government as a result of Vatican II. Some of the participants in the cardinals' gathering candidly said afterward that they weren't much wiser than they had been before. However, the cardinals as a body had at last started to ask questions about the Vatican's finances.

PENCE AND PROPERTIES

Eighteen months after the inconclusive session of the sacred college in November 1979, John Paul II named a "council" of fifteen cardinals, each a residential archbishop somewhere in the world, for overseeing the Holy See's finances. The pontiff was at the time recovering from the wounds he'd suffered in the attack on him in St. Peter's Square in May 1981, but Vatican officials explained that he had planned to set up a special cardinals' committee in charge of money matters long before the attempt on his life.

The group of fifteen included Cardinal Cooke of New York and Cardinal Krol of Philadelphia besides colleagues from Argentina, Australia, Brazil, Canada, France, West Germany, India, Kenya, Mexico, Pakistan, the Philippines, Spain, and Upper Volta. It was immediately noted that there was no Italian in the new watchdog committee, but the Vatican pointed out that the group was to cooperate closely with Italian cardinals of the curia—the secretary of state, Casaroli, and Caprio, who had meanwhile succeeded Vagnozzi as president of the Prefecture of the Economic Affairs of the Holy See, a supervisory agency that so far had had little success in efforts to clear up Vatican money mysteries. John Paul II's new fifteen-man body included three cardinals who had early supported his election in 1978, Krol of Philadelphia, Joseph Cardinal Hoeffner of Cologne, and Narciso Cardinal Jubany Arnau of Barcelona. Three of the fifteen were representatives from two nations where the Roman Catholic Church is rich and has always contributed much money to the Vatican—the United States and West Germany. The remaining members of the cardinals' committee had been chosen from predominantly Roman Catholic areas in the West, and from Third World countries where the local church relies on material aid from Rome and from church organizations elsewhere.

It had already become plain during the 1979 plenary session of the sacred college that the Polish pope and his advisers expected Roman Catholics in the United States, West Germany, and other industrial nations to step up their money contributions to help close the Vatican's budget gap. The fifteen cardinals who were named joint supervisors of the Holy See's economic affairs soon realized that, although they were still not being given much hard information, they were mainly supposed to raise new funds for the Vatican. In other words, Rome wanted more money from the world's affluent dioceses, a boost in the yield of the age-old periodic bounty for the papal treasury, the Peter's Pence. The Holy See expected Roman Catholics in rich nations to find new ways of increasing this bounty.

The tradition of annual collections for the pope in Roman Catholic churches all over the world goes back to the early Middle Ages, and is believed to have started in England before the Norman Conquest. The stream of pennies and other small coins, then already known as Peter's Pence, donated by millions of faithful throughout Europe and sent to Rome, became a mere trickle after the Protestant Reformation, and eventually dried out completely. (This does not mean, however, that all other financial contributions to the Vatican from church bodies at large were halted too.) The Peter's Pence, mobilizing individual Roman Catholics for the material support of the papacy, was revived in France in the second half of the nineteenth century.

After unified Italy had taken Rome in 1870, putting an end to the States of the Church, the contributions from abroad for the pope, now "the prisoner in the Vatican," soared. In several countries regular collections "for the Holy Father" have been held every June 29 ever since, on the feast of Saint Peter and

168

Saint Paul. How much the annual Peter's Pence drive brought in was a Vatican secret until very recently. The funds were transferred to Rome, often through the banking channels of the Institute for the Works of Religion, and were administered by a special office in the Secretariat of State that reported directly to the pontiff. The periodic church collections were a kind of world-wide papal popularity poll. Under the beloved John XXIII, the Peter's Pence reportedly reached $13 million to $14 million in some years; during the uninspiring pontificate of Paul VI, the annual amount sagged to $4 million and below; John Paul II's warm personality and activism caused it to go up again.

Facing growing deficits, in 1981 the Vatican suggested to the bishops throughout the world that they solicit donations "for the Holy Father" twice a year—on June 29, the traditional date, and at the beginning of Advent, in December. The two collections raised $15,350,375.44, as the Vatican later stated. Another $6 million were said to have been received in the form of "donations without a specific objective," or cash contributions from wealthy dioceses. The money went a long way toward covering the Vatican deficit. The remaining gap was bridged by a subsidy from the Vatican bank, following a practice that had started earlier when the bottom line on the accounts of the church's administrative center had first shown red figures. Theoretically, the profits of the Vatican bank were income of the Holy See like the Peter's Pence; practically, the bank had always disposed of its earnings at will. To the outsider, the Vatican bank's subsidies to the central government of the church must appear as bookkeeping jugglery.

In meetings held in 1981 and 1982 the fifteen-man cardinals' committee agreed it would make efforts further to increase the revenue from the Peter's Pence—on condition that the curia contained its expenses. It might be argued that for a church claiming 800 million members in all continents an amount of little more than $20 million annually in contributions from the rank and file to the center is small potatoes—the equivalent of three cents a head, much less than the value of a penny in medieval England. The Peter's Pence income also compared poorly with the funds that the 12 million Jews outside Israel were raising for that country year after year. However, it ought to be pointed out that the world's Roman Catholics in some of the years since World War II have given as much as ten times the amount of Peter's Pence for their church's proselytizing activities. The funds collected by the Vatican's missionary arm, the Sacred Congregation for the Evangelization of the Peoples, are being managed independently of the curia. Furthermore, church organizations in the United States, West Germany, and other nations regularly send sizable amounts of money directly to poor dioceses in the Third World, although the Vatican would like to insert itself into such bilateral aid programs.

The curia, on being earnestly admonished by the committee of the fifteen cardinals to cut out extravagance and waste, reacted predictably. The cardinal secretary of state and other department heads of the papal bureaucracy issued a new set of directives to reduce expenditures. Another one of the recurrent Vatican economy drives was on, as familiar to the clerical and lay personnel of the Holy See as they are to the office staffs of multinational corporations and other large business enterprises. Vatican officials were again warned that they could not put the cost of so-called "working dinners" in Rome restaurants on expense accounts, and that they would need very good reason for being authorized to travel on church business. The curia's office workers were once more told they mustn't buy pens by the package, should save reusable envelopes and writing paper, and ought to make every effort to reduce outgoing mail.

To avoid overtime payments for pontifical security officers, John Paul II rescheduled for the morning hours some general audiences in St. Peter's Square that in earlier years he had held late in the afternoon. The secretariats for ecumenical dialogue, for contacts with non-Christians and nonbelievers, and for anti-war and civil rights affairs, which had been set up in the wake of Vatican II, found their budgets sharply cut. They were all ordered to weed out conferences, symposiums, visits, and other activities that were regarded as too costly in proportion with their results. The Secretariat of State also used the austerity drive to tighten its control over the young agencies as well as to save money. Old curialists who remembered similar economy waves from the days of Pius XII again grumbled about the Holy See's penny-wise-and-pound-foolish policy.

The Vatican economy wave seemed to be contrary to what most Romans know, or think they know, about the Holy See's wealth, so visible and tangible in the Italian capital. For one thing, the Vatican is the direct proprietor of some five thousand apartments in buildings scattered all over Rome. Granted, most of them are let to priests and lay employees of church bodies at

170

rentals that are sometimes below the rent-control ceilings provided by Italian legislation. Lenient though the Holy See may be as a landlord, it is free to sell some or all of its five thousand apartments, or convert them into office space—for which there is no rent control in Italy—if it is strapped for cash. Actually, quite a number of Vatican-owned buildings, including some historic palaces in central Rome, have been on the market since World War II, and have been purchased by investors, developers, and organizations that needed large premises. Thus ANSA, the leading Italian news agency, bought the Palace of the Datary in 1973 for around $2.5 million, and installed its teletype machines in the frescoed halls of the curia's long-defunct datary, the office for ecclesiastical appointments and benefices (matters now handled by other Vatican departments). A confederation of Roman Catholic cooperatives bought the sixteenth-century Palazzo Altemps in the Piazza Navona in 1981 for close to $5 million. Similar deals were completed or are envisaged by the Vatican with regard to other old Roman properties.

In addition to these assets, an impressive array of other real estate in the Italian capital is also church-owned. The title holders are monks' and nuns' orders, ecclesiastical colleges and academies, confraternities and parishes, and a dazzling mosaic of other religious bodies.

When I once was about to rent a small apartment in the Via Sistina, an elegant street near the Spanish Steps, I found to my surprise that the landlord was a community of Maronites from Lebanon, one of the Eastern-rite groups of Christians that are in communion with the pope. To sign the lease I had to see a bearded Arab ecclesiastic in a convent close to the Church of St. Peter in Shackles, which contains Michelangelo's statue of Moses, in a distant part of the city, near the Colosseum. Later I learned that the Maronites owned much property in that neighborhood too. Any house hunter in Rome is likely to make similar discoveries.

Property experts estimate that the church owns between one-fifth and one-fourth of all the land and buildings within city limits. The value of all this real estate surely amounts to many billions of dollars, although nobody knows just how many. The left-wing parties that control City Hall repeatedly toy with the idea of a general census of church properties in Rome, but have never followed through, because the Italian Communists don't want to seem anticlerical. Even more astonishing, it is quite improbable that anyone in the Vatican has a map of all church-owned real estate in Rome.

How did the Vatican and the dependent church bodies acquire so much property? Most of it is a legacy from the many centuries when the pope was also temporal ruler of Rome and of vast domains all over central Italy—the States of the Church—and when wealthy cardinals and their relatives bought or occupied land and built palaces. Other real estate was donated or bequeathed to the church by benefactors, or set up as endowment for religious foundations. The building boom in and around the Italian capital after World War II enabled ecclesiastical groups to pull off very profitable deals.

A member of a large religious men's order who holds an important Vatican job told me of one such transaction: "Have you seen our new college and headquarters far out in the Val Melaina district [on Rome's northern outskirts]? We didn't own the land, but the contractors who did gave it to us for free on condition that we build our order's new complex there. Of course we accepted, and the construction work didn't really cost much." The trick was that once the prestigious religious community had decided to install itself on that peripheral site, the city authorities felt obliged to build streets and sewers, and to provide water, electricity, and other services. Such infrastructure in a formerly rural area caused real estate values over a wide radius to soar, bringing considerable gains to the developers who had earlier bought up the vacant land for a song.

Other Roman Catholic groups riding Rome's real estate boom turned over convents for which they could no longer find enough novices to architects, who transformed the properties into hotels and fancy apartment houses. Such practices raised protests in the Italian press and in the national parliament, but *L'Osservatore Romano* disclaimed any Vatican responsibility for the wealth and the real estate deals of religious orders in Rome. "To attribute their holdings to the Holy See and call them a 'Vatican empire' in the material sense of property is an expression of either ignorance or bad faith," the pontifical newspaper sniffed. "The owner of a property may dispose of it, whereas the Holy See does not dispose of properties owned by other bodies, even though they may be ecclesiastical. To deny this would be like asserting that the properties of individual Italians residing abroad belong to the Italian state, representing wealth of which the Italian state could freely dispose."

The Vatican daily pointed out that the pontifical yearbook listed 221 religious communities of men and 1,173 communities of women, the majority of these orders having their headquarters in Rome. "All these institutions are on the level of ownership substantially autonomous of the Holy See," *L'Osservatore Romano* stated. In its haste to whitewash the Vatican and refute the charges of real estate speculation by religious bodies, the papal newspaper forgot a provision of the church's own law, canon 1518 of the 1917 Code of Canon Law: "The Roman Pontiff is the supreme administrator and manager ["dispensator" in the Latin original] of all ecclesiastical properties."

In 1978 the Roman Catholic Church's supreme court, the Tribunal of the Apostolic Signature, then headed by Cardinal Felici, ruled that any church property anywhere in the world could be disposed of only with the pontiff's consent. The decision was prompted by a dispute over church possessions between the bishop of Lérida, Spain, and the chapter of his cathedral; it upheld the old principle of papal stewardship regarding all church wealth. The landmark sentence that grew out of that clerical dispute weakened the curial thesis that the Vatican was innocent when religious institutions were making a killing in the Rome real estate market.

In practice, the doctrine of papal stewardship concerning all church property was very rarely invoked either before or after 1978. It would probably be unenforceable anyway if powerful dioceses or religious orders were involved—another example of the chasms between what canon law says and what actually happens.

PONTIFICAL PORTFOLIO

While the Holy See has always been reluctant to discuss its vast real estate holdings in Rome and elsewhere, it was—and is—even more secretive about its other assets. The only unquestionable figure is the amount of money that the Vatican received from Italy in 1929, about $80 million at the then-prevailing dollar-lira rate of 1 to 19. The sum represents the actual value of 750 million lire in cash and a billion lire in 5-percent Italian government bonds (worth about 800 million lire at the time) collected by the Holy See under a financial convention that was a part of the Lateran Treaties between Pope Pius XI and Mussolini. The accord defined the payment as an indemnity for the property losses sustained by the Holy See in the process of Italy's unification in the nineteenth century when the papal state was occupied by the new national government, and many church possessions were seized. In the preamble to the financial convention the Holy See put on record that the sum it was receiving was far below the value of its former properties, and was the minimum it could accept in the way of compensation. In truth, the $80 million in 1929 dollars was the largest chunk of cash the papal treasurers had seen in a long time.

Pius XI, who was thinking big, used a part of the money—between a quarter and a third—for a vast building program in the Vatican and on other church-owned sites in Rome and elsewhere in Italy. The structures that went up in subsequent years included the government headquarters (Governatorato) of the new State of Vatican City in the gardens behind St. Peter's, a new home for the old Pontifical Gregorian University on the Piazza della Pilotta in downtown Rome, and other constructions to house offices of the curia and provide apartments for cardinals and archbishops. The new buildings were mostly in an eclectic neo-Renaissance style with massive walls, cheerless courtyards, and frowning facades. They were well finished and carefully maintained, quite unlike the Fascist regime's modern architecture, which was showy at the time of inauguration, and a few years later was disfigured by cracks and peeling plaster.

To manage the funds that the Vatican received from Italy, Pius XI set up a Special Administration of the Holy See. The pontiff, who had relatives in banking, called a well-qualified layman, Bernardino Nogara, into Vatican service and put him in charge of the new economic body as its "delegate." Nogara, who had an engineering degree, had been an executive of one of Italy's biggest financial institutions, the Milan-based Banca Commerciale Italiana; he had served as its agent in Istanbul and had specialized in the international gold trade.

Nogara's money management job in the Vatican was unique in several ways. He was responsible only to the pope, and enjoyed the esteem and authority of a sort of lay cardinal. He was surrounded by ecclesiastical bureaucrats who may have had a keen appreciation of money but did not know much about investment strategies and banking techniques. Nogara was able to use the official apparatus of a sovereign entity, the newly established

State of Vatican City, for the transfer and placement of funds, unhampered by Italian laws, currency restrictions, and taxes. He received valuable information through the Holy See's worldwide network of nuncios, bishops, and other church sources. No accounts or balance sheets had to be published, and no auditor ever asked to see the Special Administration's books. Nogara was publicity-shy and as secretive as the curia, which was quite all right with his employer.

As time went by, the bearded banker proved to be shrewd, cautious, and honest. There was never any suggestion that he had used his privileged position for personal gain. As a prudent administrator of church funds, he invested about a third of the capital entrusted to him in real estate, another third in gold, and the remaining third in securities. He bought heavily into Italian financial institutions and industrial corporations and, through banking connections in Switzerland and elsewhere, also built a portfolio of blue chip stocks and bonds that were traded internationally.

Under Pius XII, that pontiff's three nephews and his close associate, Count Galeazzi, were collaborating with Nogara in the management of the Vatican's growing financial interests. As has been noted earlier, the three Princes Pacelli and Count Galeazzi started serving on the boards of various Italian companies. Since the names of board members had to be published, some clues to the ramifications of Vatican partnerships in Italian enterprises became visible.

At the end of World War II the Vatican was deeply entrenched in Italian business, but the nation's economy was in ruins. It was at this juncture that the archbishop of New York, Cardinal Spellman, got into the act. He not only contributed much money to the Vatican but also offered expert advice on how to diversify its assets by investing in Wall Street. As Nogara grew older, the three papal nephews and Count Galeazzi, aided with funds and counsel by Cardinal Spellman, increasingly took control of the Holy See's finances. Nogara officially went into retirement in 1954, but remained as a consultant until his death in 1958. His post as delegate of the Special Administration of the Holy See was taken up by a Swiss banker, Henri de Maillardoz, who served the Vatican as a discreet adviser rather than an active manager until 1969.

By that time Pope Paul VI had combined the Special Administration of the Holy See with a much older agency, the Administration of the Properties of the Holy See, which had been mainly managing the Vatican's real estate holdings. The body that resulted from the merger, decreed in 1967, was called the Administration of the Patrimony of the Apostolic See, and was usually referred to by the acronym of its Italian name, APSA. Under the supervision of a cardinal as its president and four other members of the sacred college, APSA was divided into an ordinary and an extraordinary section; they continued doing what the Administration of the Properties of the Holy See and the Special Administration of the Holy See had, respectively, been doing. The staffs also remained the same, with the tensions that seem unavoidable when two bureaucratic organizations are unified.

"Ordinary" and "extraordinary" are terms that may be encountered in various areas of the papal bureaucracy. Often they have lost any meaning they might have originally had. In the case of APSA, the ordinary section was to manage mostly real estate and other tangible assets, the extraordinary section financial investments and interests.

The investment portfolio that the extraordinary section of APSA had inherited from the former Special Administration at the time was estimated to be worth between $120 million and $500 million. The wide difference was due to the Vatican's stonewalling whenever its finances were discussed. While curia officials adamantly refused to supply any specific figure, they dropped little hints that seemed to confirm the low estimate. Financial analysts using conservative methods of extrapolation, or educated guessing, became convinced that APSA's investment principal was rather in the neighborhood of half a billion dollars, which appears to be a more realistic figure. Periodically, the press in various countries came up with much higher estimates, which were always dismissed by the Vatican as "fantastic" and "wild."

At the beginning of Paul VI's pontificate the bulk of the funds managed first by the Special Administration and then by APSA's extraordinary section was still tied up in Italian enterprises. Among them were some national and regional financial institutions, like the important, state-controlled Banco di Roma, the Banco Ambrosiano of Milan, and other banks operating mainly in northern Italy. The Vatican also owned a sizable interest in Società Generale Immobiliare, a real estate and contracting giant that had branched out internationally with the

Watergate complex in Washington, D.C., the Pan American building on the Champs-Elysées in Paris, the Hilton Hotel in Rome, and other prestige projects; it was eventually caught in a cash squeeze and had to sell many properties. The Holy See also was a partner in smaller Italian businesses, including a money-losing pasta company, Pantanella, whose disgruntled workers had a habit of parading in Rome's streets carrying signs with anti-Vatican slogans.

Paul VI was embarrassed by press reports that the Holy See was also a stockholder of the Istituto Farmacologico Serono, an Italian producer of contraceptive pills, the birth-control device that the pope condemned as sinful. Moreover, there were unverified rumors that the Vatican's investment portfolio had, at one time or another, held securities of corporations operating the Monte Carlo gambling casino, or manufacturing defoliants used by United States forces in the Vietnam War. Vatican officials bitterly resented such allegations. However, the only effective method of dispelling all suspicion of financial shenanigans with papal money would have been to publish a complete list of investments the way many nonprofit institutions and foundations do. This the Holy See had consistently avoided, laying itself open to criticism, gossip, and innuendo. It was hardly convincing when Paul VI would defensively remark on occasion that the church was poor and "must also appear poor," meaning it should avoid both the trappings of opulence and an image as a financial power.

When Paul VI reorganized the curia in 1967, without really achieving a thorough reform of the Vatican bureaucracy, he not only merged two financial bodies into a new agency, APSA, but also established a new Prefecture of the Economic Affairs of the Holy See as a supervisory department. What the pope had in mind was a supreme planning and controlling authority, a branch of the church's central administration to combine the tasks that in the United States government are performed by the Office of Management and Budget and the General Accounting Office. However, the new prefecture was hamstrung from the beginning by the papal decision to keep the Vatican bank outside its control.

Cardinal Vagnozzi became the first head of the watchdog body; Cardinals Cody of Chicago and Höffner of Cologne were to assist him. Vagnozzi had relatives who were running an old chinaware business in the center of Rome, and his name was something of a local household word; as apostolic delegate in Washington he had known about the Vatican's financial interests in the United States and had been instrumental in some transactions. Yet despite such familiarity with money matters, Vagnozzi lacked specific experience in budget planning and accounting.

Cody and Höffner were successful managers of church money at home, but as absentee members of the new supervisory group they had little impact in the Vatican. Vagnozzi soon found that the financial units he was supposed to control were withholding information from him and showing themselves uncooperative in other ways. Only the pope might have forced them to be more forthcoming with Vagnozzi, but Paul VI was all too often busy with other things and failed to give Vagnozzi the support he needed to assert himself. In his twelve years as head of the prefecture, the cardinal never succeeded in submitting to Paul VI or his successors a comprehensive balance sheet of the tangle of financial departments—not including the Vatican bank—that had been placed under his supervision. From time to time there were rumors that he wanted to resign.

The web of the Holy See's money affairs might have disheartened a well-trained and highly experienced professional auditor. The Administration of the Patrimony of the Apostolic See (APSA), with its ordinary and extraordinary sections hardly on speaking terms, continued to operate side by side, or sometimes in competition or even in conflict with, the government of the State of Vatican City. That legal entity had a financial system and a budget of its own, with separate revenue and expenditures. There was also a jumble of other bodies, all jealously clinging to their own funds—the Reverend Fabric of St. Peter's, in charge of the great basilica's upkeep; the Sacred Congregation for the Evangelization of the Peoples; the supersecret office of the Peter's Pence; the Palatine Administrations, including such units as the papal newspaper, *L'Osservatore Romano;* and others.

Vagnozzi's death in December 1980, at the age of 74 years, offered Cardinal Casaroli, the secretary of state, a chance for pulling off what amounted to a bureaucratic coup. He managed to persuade Pope John Paul II to shift Caprio from the Administration of the Patrimony of the Apostolic See to the post that Vagnozzi had held, chief of the Prefecture for the Economic Affairs of the Holy See, and to appoint himself, Casaroli,

178

as the new head of APSA. The Vatican's ranking expert on canon law, Cardinal Felici, who was no friend of Casaroli's, had been asked for an opinion on such a shuffle, and had advised that the secretary of state should not at the same time be in control of APSA. However, John Paul II overruled Felici. The cardinal secretary of state emerged strengthened from the bureaucratic maneuver because he was now in charge of a broad segment of the Holy See's finances, although other money matters had remained outside his jurisdiction. Even before Casaroli, the Secretariat of State had consistently tried to control all papal money matters; now these old efforts had achieved an important step forward.

The Vatican's economic situation was then characterized, as has been mentioned earlier, by rising expenditures and deficits. Up to then they had been covered with receipts from the sale of Vatican properties and with Peter's Pence money, although the latter traditionally had been considered a papal reserve fund for emergencies. New financial alarm signals were flashing as the government of the State of Vatican City, which had long been able to balance its independent budget, started operating in the red.

Since its establishment in 1929, the pontifical state had developed its own sources of revenue that permitted it to thrive without resorting to direct taxation. The few hundred citizens of the State of Vatican City have never paid any income tax. The state's earnings from its mail stamps and coins, the money that tourists paid for admission to the Vatican museums, and the substantial profits from its duty-free commissary and its three service stations for motorists were for a long time sufficient to cover all expenditures. These included wages and salaries for the state's security forces, drivers, gardeners, and other lay workers (around eighteen hundred in all); the maintenance of art collections and buildings; and the operation of its motor pool, of its autonomous oil-fueled power plant, and of Vatican Radio.

When the new committee of fifteen cardinals began to tackle the job of bringing order into the Holy See's economic affairs, there were still no overall balance sheet and no general inventory of marketable and income-producing Vatican assets. Above all, nobody seemed to know what the Vatican bank was earning, how and with whom it was doing business, and in what way it was using its profits besides plugging the worst holes in the Vatican coffers.

A BULWARK BANK

The bank that hid behind the pious name, Institute for the Works of Religion, one of the most secretive financial institutions in the world, was appropriately hard to find. Outside clients entered the State of Vatican City through the Gate of St. Anne, past Swiss Guards and pontifical vigilance officers, turned left into the small Courtyard of the Triangle, which is oppressively enclosed by high walls, and ascended to the upper level of a five-hundred-year-old bulwark that was built under Pope Nicholas V in the fifteenth century.

No mistake, the well-lit office was a bank. It might look a little old-fashioned with marble floors and glass partitions, tellers in correct civilian suits, and customers—priests, nuns, a few laymen, hardly ever a laywoman—making deposits or withdrawals. The atmosphere was almost that of a church; loud words were seldom heard, and a crucifix hung on the wall. The mother superior of some order, flanked by another elderly nun, probably their community's treasurer, shoved a bundle of checks across the marble counter; at the next window a young priest looking like a junior curialist counted the dollar bills he had just received. A gray-haired civilian, perhaps a diplomat or a corporation lawyer, clutched an elegant attaché case and waited for his turn at a considerate distance.

Yet, since the 1970s the dignified, discreet agency has been embroiled in a congeries of scandals that landed some of its executives and associates in prison amid rumors of murderous plots, badly tarnished the image of the Holy See, and, no less painful, caused it huge financial losses.

To put things into perspective, the Institute for the Works of Religion was not one of the world's great financial organizations. It didn't publish the amount of its deposits, but analysts believed they totaled around $2 billion, which would have placed the institution in the Bastion of Nicholas V in the company of, say, regional banks in Columbus, Ohio, or San Juan, Puerto Rico. But there were important differences. The Institute for the Works of Religion was about the only bank on earth not subject to the normal regulatory agencies of the state in which it was based. The Prefecture of the Economic Affairs of the Holy See, the pope's supreme financial control authority, was expressly forbidden to look into the Vatican bank's affairs.

Nominally, a committee of five cardinals exercised "vigilance" over the Institute for the Works of Religion. But the group met rarely. For a long time the routine was that the five cardinals, when they did gather, were given a concise statement on the bank's financial situation and business activities, but were not supposed to take their copy of the document with them. As a token of appreciation for their restraint, they usually found an envelope attached to the statement; inside was a check, perhaps for the equivalent of $5,000, "for Your Eminence's personal charities." Practically, the top officers of the Vatican bank were responsible solely to the pope. Like other Vatican bodies that dealt with money, the Institute for the Works of Religion published no balance sheet, did not disclose details of its assets and business operations, and had at its disposal the international facilities of a sovereign power, the State of Vatican City. Bankers from Zurich to New York, from Chicago to Singapore and Hong Kong were eager to do business with the pontifical agency.

The Bastion of Nicholas V was linked with Wall Street by direct wire, and was in touch daily with other centers of international finance. Although most of the Vatican bank's assets were invested in blue-chip securities abroad, it had considerable interests in Italy. It owned stock in the Fiat Motor Company and other industrial groups, and in some banks. It controlled a financial institution specializing in Italian-Swiss business, the Banco di Roma per la Svizzera, which was founded in 1947 in partnership with the Banco di Roma, owned by the Italian government. A nephew of Pius XII, Prince Marcantonio Pacelli, for many years served as president of the Italian-Swiss subsidiary.

The depositors of the Vatican bank totaled nearly nine thousand. One of them was the supreme pontiff; Pius XII had account number 16/16, but his successors were assigned less conspicuous code numbers. Religious orders, ecclesiastical colleges, dioceses, parishes, and other institutions and legal entities made up the bulk of the clients. Individuals maintaining accounts with the Institute for the Works of Religion included cardinals, other high prelates, diplomats who were accredited to the Holy See, and a select group of lay people of various nationalities, Italians among them. To be permitted, as a lay person, to do one's banking in the Tower of Nicholas V (as the bastion is also called), one must be baptized—though not necessarily in the Roman Catholic faith, any baptismal certificate would do—and one must pledge to turn over at least a part of one's funds, right away or at some future time, for good works. This meant in practice that the Vatican bank would withhold a portion of the funds in a private account when the owner wanted to close it, or died.

Nevertheless it seemed to pay to be a client. To have an account with the Institute for the Works of Religion was a much-coveted, though never publicized, privilege. Above all, the money entrusted to the Vatican bank was safe from Italy's stringent, confusing, and often outright vexatory fiscal and currency regulations. A resident of Rome might on any business day walk through the Gate of St. Anne into the pontifical enclave with a satchel full of 100,000-lire bills and deposit them at the Institute for the Works of Religion if he (or she) had an account there. He could expect to get interest on the money that he wouldn't have to report on his Italian income tax return, or he might transfer funds to Switzerland, Luxembourg, or the Bahamas. In the early 1980s the Vatican bank promised the Rome government, at the latter's urging, that it would observe Italian fiscal laws in its dealings with Italian clients. However, to circumvent these laws, it was sufficient to know somebody with a foreign passport who maintained an account at the Institute for the Works of Religion and would accommodate an Italian friend.

Getting capital out of the country had long been a major concern of rich Italians. In the 1950s a good-looking young archivist in Pius XII's Secretariat of State, Msgr. Edoardo Prettner Cippico, was found to be mixed up in illegal foreign currency deals and harebrained film projects. Among other things, it seemed, he had helped some wealthy people to transfer money abroad. When the scandal came out in the open, Vatican authorities had the monsignor detained in the old Tower of Winds, near the Apostolic Library, pending an investigation. Monsignor Prettner Cippico adventurously escaped after locking his guard, a Vatican gendarme, into his own prison cell, and vanished into the city outside the Vatican walls.

Italian police tracked the monsignor down in the apartment of a friend, the widow of a Fascist general, in the fashionable Parioli district. Prettner Cippico was unfrocked by the church, and tried on fraud charges by the Italian state. A Roman court sentenced him to nine years' imprisonment, but an appeals court later cleared him on the ground that he had had no intention of swindling anybody and had acted only out of inexperience and self-importance. The Vatican allowed the former monsignor to keep his church-owned apartment, and saw to it that he didn't starve. After eking out a meager living for several years with translation jobs and other occasional work, Prettner Cippico was eventually reinstated into the priesthood, although he did not regain his old title of monsignor. "Ah, Cippico," an old Roman priest, who was not particularly fond of the Vatican, once said to me. "He was the fall guy. He had to cover up for people much better known than he was, people close to Pope Pacelli—you know what I mean. But he behaved all right, never talked, and in the end was rehabilitated." I heard similar remarks from others, the kind of gossip that was always drifting around the Vatican and its bank, and which could almost never be substantiated.

The Holy See and its Institute for the Works of Religion as a haven for tax evaders and a conduit for money traffic was a constant anticlerical theme. I once asked the governor of the Bank of Italy, Guido Carli, about the often-heard allegation that wealthy Italians were illegally transferring billions of lire abroad through the Vatican. "There are thousands of ways to do this," the central bank chief replied wearily. "You really don't need the Vatican." (Carli was not considered favorable to the church; when Peyrefitte was in trouble in Italy for disrespectful comments about the pope, Carli publicly expressed sympathy for the French author.)

An Italian tycoon who wanted to send funds to another country could, for instance, turn to one of several illegal rings that were carrying out such transfers reliably and for a consideration. Or he could produce inflated invoices for metals or hides that he had bought abroad for industrial purposes in Italy; the government would allocate the necessary foreign currency to him, and the importer would pay off his foreign supplier and deposit the surplus in his own Swiss bank account. People in the import-export business and big-time operators with associates in Wall Street, London, and Zurich didn't need the Institute for the Works of Religion to spirit money out of Italy. Neither did the Mafia: it had its own channels for laundering the billions of lire it was netting from narcotics traffic and extorting from the families of kidnap victims.

The Vatican bank could be a convenience for members of the Roman uppercrust who didn't have much international experience—noblemen who had made a bundle by selling their land to real estate speculators, or corrupt officeholders with unconfessed income, and the like. But it could also help those on a lower social level: a Roman with the proverbial uncle in America who was naive enough to send a $10 bill in an ordinary letter might turn to a friendly priest and say, "Father, can't you get me a good rate of exchange in the Vatican?" The priest usually could.

For the religious orders and other church institutions the bank in the Bastion of Nicholas V rendered precious services. Many of these organizations receive contributions from abroad and want to send money to their affiliates in other countries. The Roman mother house of some nuns' order will get monetary gifts from its branch in West Germany, and will have to send funds to its missionary sisters in West Africa. Theoretically, the nuns could turn to an Italian bank, but they would find themselves engulfed in a baroque bureaucracy with innumerable complicated forms to fill in and long waiting periods. The Institute for the Works of Religion enables the nuns to operate like a multinational corporation, shifting resources to where they are needed with a telephone call or a telex message. The Vatican bank would also pay the nuns a good return on the balance in their account.

From the viewpoint of the host country, Italy, the money affairs of most of the Vatican bank's clients fall into a gray zone —they neither conform strictly with the nation's muddled financial laws nor are they outright outlaws. The Italian authorities had been tolerant toward the Vatican's money operations, but their attitude began changing toward the end of the 1970s. At one time the Italian fiscal police even raised a question about a dollar deposit that Mother Teresa of Calcutta had made. The money had been donated by Americans, and the nun who had won the Nobel Peace Prize and happened to be in Rome had simply meant to transfer the dollars to India.

A government less friendly to the Holy See might tighten the rules and make it very difficult for church bodies to transfer money abroad. Even under existing laws the local authorities might determine that the mother house of the nuns' order is an Italian-based institution and therefore subject to currency restrictions. The result would probably be that the West German nuns would send their subsidies directly to West Africa, and that the mother house would sooner or later move to Switzerland or some other country that is more accommodating in money matters. High churchmen on occasion have hinted in talks with

Italian officials that rigorous enforcement of the host country's fiscal and currency regulations with regard to church bodies would have unpleasant consequences for the Roman economy. The implication is that church institutions that are clients of the Vatican bank do, after all, spend some money locally, and that it would be bad for business if they were forced to relocate.

The Vatican's traditional reticence regarding its banking operations was mirrored in the pontifical yearbook. Year after year this guide to the intricacies of the Vatican administration, in its explanatory notes, would devote exactly eight lines to the Institute for the Works of Religion, five lines fewer, for example, than to such a marginal unit as the Holy See's Institute for Arab Studies. Laconically, the yearbook said that the Vatican bank (it did not use the word "bank") was established in Vatican City by a "venerated chirographic document," or handwritten declaration, from Pius XII in 1942 as a juridical entity of its own, and had absorbed the Administration of the Works of Religion that Leo XIII had set up in 1887. "The purpose of the Institute is to safeguard and administer the capitals destined for works of religion," the yearbook concluded with a terse tautology.

Pius XII created the bank at the height of World War II as a mechanism to facilitate the movement of funds owned or collected by church bodies in various parts of a violently fractured world. The institute's charter provided that any profit from its operations would be turned over to the pontiff. In the postwar years the Vatican bank started ploughing money back and investing in other financial institutions and in business ventures the way the Special Administration of the Holy See was doing. The papal bank also offered technical assistance in transferring Peter's Pence funds to Rome. Some people believed that the Banco di Santo Spirito (Bank of the Holy Ghost) too was a Vatican bank; this was no longer true. The old Roman institution—it was founded by Pope Paul V in 1605 to serve the financial needs of the States of the Church—has long been controlled by the Italian state.

Hair-splitting canon lawyers would insist that the Institute for the Works of Religion was a juridical unit *"in* Vatican City but not *of* the Vatican." This nice distinction might mean, if anything, that the Holy See intended to wash its corporate hands if anything untoward, like insolvency, were to happen to the Vatican bank. However, when the Institute for the Works of

185

Religion was caught in the bankruptcy of an associate, the Banco Ambrosiano of Milan, in 1982, the Vatican found to its dismay it could not actually shirk its responsibility.

Just about a score of people, a few ecclesiastics, a handful of laymen with degrees in law or accounting, and some subalterns used to make up the entire staff of the Institute for the Works of Religion. Its civilian employees, like most Italian bank workers (a privileged caste), would receive sixteen monthly salaries every year, and were therefore greatly envied by other Vatican personnel who weren't treated with such largess. (The four extra monthly salary payments grew out of an initial "thirteenth month" bonus just before Christmas. A fourteenth, fifteenth, and sixteenth installment, due at various times in the year, were later added.)

The men behind the glass partition in the Bastion of Nicholas V are polite, reserved, and taciturn. Only two or three top executives in the back rooms are really in the know. There have been murmurs about the mysteries of the Institute for the Works of Religion ever since its foundation, but never as many as since 1969 when an American, Bishop Marcinkus, joined the bank.

THE POPE'S "GORILLA"

Ambiguity had been built into the Vatican bank from its beginning; but the choice of the American bishop Paul Marcinkus as its executive seemed a deliberate invitation to controversy and gossip. The athletic prelate, standing six feet three inches tall, possessed the tact of a trailer truck. He had few friends in the Vatican—but those he had counted. He didn't care what the local and international press wrote about him, and did not pretend to like journalists or hold them in high regard. He seemed to enjoy adverse publicity.

"I'm from the place where Al Capone came from," Marcinkus would occasionally remark. He was born in Cicero, Illinois, an ethnic suburb of Chicago, in 1922, one of five children—four sons and a daughter—of a Lithuanian immigrant who made his living as a window washer. The youngest Marcinkus boy, Paul Casimir, studied for the priesthood and was ordained when he was 25 years old. His archbishop sent him to Rome for postgrad-

186

uate studies, and he specialized in canon law at the Pontifical Gregorian University. After some pastoral work at home and a stint in Chicago's archdiocesan tribunal, he was reassigned to Rome and joined the Vatican bureaucracy. The Secretariat of State sent him as an aide to the papal missions in Bolivia and Canada, and then recalled him for service at its English-language desk.

The strapping American, who had meanwhile reached the rank of monsignor, became a familiar figure at the Acqua Santa (Holy Water) golf links between the Ancient and the New Appian Ways. Despite its devotional name, the rolling golf course with its cozy clubhouse and its swimming pool had long been the habitat of a frivolous and snobbish set; Count Galeazzo Ciano, Mussolini's fatuous son-in-law and foreign minister, used to carry on his dalliances with Roman princesses there. After the downfall of fascism the Acqua Santa Club tried to strike a balance between old nobility and the newly rich in its membership. When the Società Generale Immobiliare, then controlled by the Vatican, built another golf course in a deluxe development in the Olgiata district on the northern outskirts of Rome, closer to St. Peter's than the Acqua Santa, Marcinkus became a habitué there too. He also took to patronizing dolce vita restaurants in Trastevere and other neighborhoods near the Vatican.

The role and importance of the sports-loving, bon vivant American in the Vatican changed dramatically with the pontificate of Paul VI. One of the new pope's first moves was to announce an unprecedented papal pilgrimage to the Holy Land. For the trip, the curia needed an advance man and travel manager who spoke English, had more experience with practical things than most Vatican bureaucrats did, and was physically equipped for tackling such a responsible and demanding task. Marcinkus was an obvious choice. To prepare the papal journey, he surveyed beforehand all the places in Jordan and Israel that Paul VI would visit, and made the necessary arrangements. During the papal trip, he was a key member of Paul VI's party, and with his robust frame shielded the frail pontiff from the crush of people at the Mandelbaum Gate that then led into the Old City of Jerusalem. He never left the pope's side during Paul VI's public appearances in the Holy Land.

The pontiff appreciated Marcinkus's services as a papal tour director, and relied on him again when he visited India in 1965, and in all his later journeys outside Italy. The tall, baldish ecclesiastic who was always seen at the pope's elbow, dealing with local prelates, authorities, and security officers in a no-nonsense manner, became familiar to television audiences all over the world. Wherever Paul VI went, Marcinkus had been before. As yet another papal journey was being prepared, the Chicagoan would inspect all the sites to be visited some weeks ahead; he would case the neighborhoods through which the papal motorcade would pass, discuss security problems with police experts, and ask to be shown the room where Paul VI would spend the night and the sacristy where he would change into liturgical vestments for some scheduled ceremony. Marcinkus displayed uncommon attention to detail when he worked out routes and timetables, and unflagging watchfulness when he was around the traveling pontiff.

In the Vatican, the towering American soon became known as "the gorilla." The epithet betrayed a mixture of malevolence, envy, and admiration; copying American and French gangster parlance, the Italians called the bodyguards of powerful personages—government ministers, big businessmen, or Mafia dons— "gorillas." Soon Marcinkus found himself inducted into Paul VI's Milan mafia, the papal entourage that tended to bypass the curia bureaucrats.

During the preparations for Paul VI's journeys, and in their course, Marcinkus had to keep in constant touch with the pope's secretary, Monsignor Macchi. The two became fast friends. The practical-minded American, a Roman by adoption, soon acted as a kind of guide to the convivial delights of the city for the intellectual from northern Italy; in turn Marcinkus got interested in modern art through Macchi. It was through the Milan mafia that Marcinkus was introduced to Sindona. When Paul VI needed a new ecclesiastical executive for the Vatican bank, it took little effort for his coterie to persuade him that Marcinkus was the right man. Actually, the American prelate lacked almost all qualifications for the job of managing a bank, especially a bank that would require difficult decisions based on expertise in the field of international finance. Marcinkus said he had attended business administration classes at Harvard University, but did not claim to have any experience in banking. Sindona would say later, in prison interviews, that Marcinkus was a financial amateur. His promotion to the post at the Vatican bank caused more surprise among members of the Italian financial community than among churchmen. Yet, even with his sketchy background, financiers thought the American monsignor seemed better prepared for his new job than most other ecclesiastics in the curia, with their theological, legal, and diplomatic training.

A condition for the appointment to the Institute for the Works of Religion was that the Chicagoan would continue to organize papal trips; this was all right with Marcinkus. He was 46 years old when late in 1968 Paul VI made him titular bishop of Horta, Italianized as Orta, a long-obliterated see in North Africa, and named him delegate, or chief administrator, of the Institute for the Works of Religion. In 1969 Marcinkus was promoted to president of the Vatican bank.

When the American prelate took command in the pope's financial bulwark, Sindona already had excellent contacts with the Holy See. The Sicilian financier had first gained an entree into the Vatican by, characteristically, mobilizing family connections. A distant relative of his wife, Msgr. Amleto Tondini, who was a renowned Latinist, happened to hold various posts in the curia, and Sindona turned to him. The learned churchman introduced his protégé to a Vatican lay official, who at the time was administrative secretary of the Institute for the Works of Religion, Massimo Spada. A papal chamberlain with a claim to titles of nobility, Spada also did many other things besides.

Spada helped raise funds for the construction of new churches on Rome's outskirts and, in a more mundane capacity, was president, director, or member of the board of a string of banks and insurance companies in Rome and northern Italy. When Sindona's star was shining bright, Spada became his partner in various business ventures, and was a director of a Sindona bank when Marcinkus joined the Institute for the Works of Religion. Spada had been pensioned off by the Vatican in 1963, only 58 years old. This had caused many rumors in the curial bureaucracy, where early retirement is rare; it was said he had been caught in conflicts of interest. At any rate, Spada continued making much money outside the Vatican.

Meanwhile, Sindona had established other useful church ties. In the early 1960s he had helped finance a pet project, an old people's home, of the archbishop of Milan, Cardinal Montini, and had become friendly with his secretary, Macchi. After Cardinal Montini was elected pope, Sindona had easy access to the Apostolic Palace. In 1969 Paul VI made a momentous decision. After his habitual long agonizing he came to the conclusion that most Vatican financial interests in Italy should be unloaded, and new profitable investment opportunities in the United States, West Germany, Switzerland, and other countries be found. Several reasons prompted this move. One was the bad performance of such groups as Società Generale Immobiliare and the pasta firm, Pantanella, and the resulting troubles with their labor force. Another reason was the realization that the "Italian miracle" of rapid industrial development and economic growth of the 1950s and 1960s was over. Paul VI also seemed to fear that Italy was drifting toward the left, maybe toward communism. The center-left governments that had lately succeeded one another in Rome were questioning the Vatican's claim to being exempt from all Italian financial laws, and had started collecting taxes on dividends that domestic enterprises were paying to the Holy See.

The Milan mafia recommended the seemingly successful financier, Sindona, as the business genius who could help the Holy See disengage itself from its Italian economic ventures and funnel the money that would thus become available into promising investments in other countries. Sindona was eager to be of service.

How Paul VI and high Vatican prelates could fall for a financier who was, even then, the target of criticisms in the Italian business community and eventually turned out to be a crook is hard to explain. Maybe one reason was that Sindona didn't look the part; he did not fit the cliché of the fiery or sinister Sicilian lawbreaker either. He was a mousy man who seemed timid and might have been a monsignor wearing a dark business suit.

At his tidy desk in a Milan office building Sindona mechanically folded innumerable origami paper boats while talking softly to a visitor about Liechtenstein-registered holding companies and transatlantic money deals. He had married his schooldays sweetheart, Caterina, and spent weekends with his family in an unassuming villa near Milan. Sundays they went to mass. There was nothing of the adventurer about him; he was no Cagliostro; he lacked the glamor of Ivar Kreuger, the Swedish match king and master swindler, or the flamboyance of Serge Alexandre Stavisky, whose financial capers rocked France in the early 1930s.

Sindona was born in 1922 in Patti, a town west of Messina, into the family of the secretary of a farming cooperative. He studied law at Messina University, and while still working for his degree earned some money, like other Sicilians in those days, trafficking in United States military supplies. In 1947, again like many other southerners, he moved to Milan where he became a tax consultant. Displaying an uncommon talent for making friends who could help him, he was soon an intimate of business leaders, and started wheeling and dealing on his own. In 1959 he was able to buy into a private bank. He specialized in picking up ailing enterprises and selling them again, some to American groups. A few of the purchasers later discovered that Sindona had palmed corporate lemons off to them, and the first unfavorable appraisals of his methods made the rounds. Some people in Italy's business-financial establishment never warmed up to him. Sindona nevertheless managed to build an international conglomerate of interlocking banks and business corporations that at one point comprised 146 companies in eleven countries.

I once saw Sindona during one of his rare public triumphs. He was not a great party giver, but he did appear as the self-satisfied host at a reception offered at Rome's Grand Hotel—the place that Cardinal Spellman had favored—one evening in September 1971. The occasion was Sindona's purchase of the Rome *Daily American,* an English-language newspaper. It was whispered that the financier from Patti, Sicily, had picked up the money-losing operation, small beer for him at that stage of his career, to do influential American groups a favor by running the daily as an organ of propaganda for U.S. policies and business. Graham A. Martin, then the United States ambassador in Rome (he was later to be the last United States ambassador in Saigon) was present at the Sindona party. Another guest who vigorously shook the hand of the new owner of the *Daily American* and talked at length to him was Bishop Marcinkus. When I asked Sindona why he had bought the English-language daily, he said with a thin smile that he had always liked the American press.

Sindona was then near the peak of his fame and power. He had taken over the Vatican's interests in Società Generale Immobiliare and, in part, managed to fob them off on other purchasers, his favorite technique. He had helped finance Italy's dominant political force, the Christian Democratic party. He was doing business with the Swiss Bank Corporation, Hambros Bank of London, and other internationally respected financial institutions. In 1972 he started his campaign for the takeover of the Franklin National Bank, the nineteenth largest bank in the United States, using funds, it was later found, that he had looted from his Italian companies. In 1974 Sindona's sprawling house of cards caved in, and the Franklin National was bankrupt, the largest bank failure in United States history.

The Federal Reserve Bank of New York had advanced more than $1.7 billion to Franklin National in unsuccessful efforts to stave off insolvency. Sindona, who had owned a 21 percent interest in the bank, had publicly vowed until the end that he would "save" the institution. After the Franklin National bankruptcy, investigators brought out that the bank, which had originally been based in Long Island, New York, had been poorly managed under Sindona and had suffered huge losses in disastrous foreign currency speculations. Sindona had assumed that the United States dollar would rise against the French franc and other currencies, but had been wrong. The insolvent institution was immediately taken over by a new group, the European American Bank and Trust Company, under an agreement that guaranteed Franklin National depositors they would not suffer any losses.

Sindona's many other enterprises in various countries were in deep trouble too, and the Holy See, which had been a silent partner in some of them, was in a financial squeeze.

In January 1975 the Vatican officially admitted that it had suffered "some losses" in the Sindona insolvency, but insisted that the damage was much less than the $100 million figure suggested by the Italian press. How much, the Vatican never said. Sindona himself, in a statement written in jail six years later, would assert that the Holy See had lost no money at all in his bankruptcy, having managed to pass the debits on to him. The Institute for the Works of Religion actually succeeded in recovering some deposits from Sindona-owned banks that technically were already insolvent.

Italy demanded the Sicilian financier's extradition from the United States, but the request could not be granted pending federal proceedings against him in connection with the Franklin National collapse. While Sindona was free on bail awaiting trial, he disappeared from New York from August to October 1979. He asserted later he had been kidnaped. United States officials testified that he had flown to Europe under a false name; it seems he was in Vienna and Athens, and also slipped into Italy, finding a hideout in Sicily. After he had eventually surfaced again in New York, his delayed trial was held in federal district court in Manhattan in the spring of 1980; he was found guilty of fraud and sentenced to 25 years in prison. The seven-week court proceedings focused on the National Bank failure and left many Sindona mysteries unsolved.

During the trial, counsel for Sindona asked the court to hear the testimony of three Vatican officials as character witnesses. The three were Sergio Cardinal Guerri, who was then acting president of the cardinals' commission for the State of Vatican City and in the past had had many dealings with Sindona; Cardinal Caprio; and Bishop Marcinkus. The three prelates had agreed to make their depositions on videotape in Rome, and the necessary arrangements had been completed at the United States embassy on the Via Veneto. But when the defendant's counsel, former federal judge Marvin Frankel, flew to Rome to obtain the testimony, he was told that Cardinal Casaroli, the secretary of state, had forbidden the two fellow cardinals and Marcinkus to testify in Sindona's favor. Casaroli clearly did not want the Holy See to become even more implicated in the unsavory affair by coming to the support of a financial adventurer. Ostensibly, Casaroli vetoed the proposed depositions by the three prelates on the grounds that they would be tantamount to acknowledging the jurisdiction of a secular court over cardinals and thus would create a precedent detrimental to the church. This argument did not seem to take into account that Marcinkus was no cardinal, and that he was an American citizen (even though he might carry a Holy See passport).

Casaroli's decision to bar the Vatican's three money managers from saying a good word for Sindona to a United States court was widely interpreted as a backhanded slap at the three would-be witnesses, and as a move designed to strengthen the cardinal secretary of state's strategy to gain control of the entire system of Vatican finances, including the Institute for the Works of Religion. The secretary of state had doubtless secured Pope John Paul II's go-ahead before he pulled rank on two cardinals and a bishop. From his prison cell Sindona bitterly complained about being let down by the Vatican.

As for Marcinkus, he later appeared to be playing down his ties with Sindona. American friends of the Chicagoan said he was loyally taking the rap for mistakes committed by others— Paul VI and Macchi—who had allowed Sindona to invest Vatican money in shaky banks and other dubious enterprises. The nature of the Sindona-Marcinkus relationship has remained enigmatic; clues to solving the mystery may be buried in the Vatican's Secret Archives.

Although the Sindona affair, with its Vatican ramifications, disturbed many high churchmen at large and prompted them to ask embarrassing questions whenever they visited Rome, it did not do any harm to Marcinkus's standing with the pontiff. After Paul VI died, there was much speculation that whoever succeeded him would oust the American bishop from the Vatican bank. The Italian press, emboldened by leaks from Marcinkus's many enemies in the curia, represented him as a major culprit in the Vatican's brush with the Sindona disaster. It cannot be guessed what John Paul I would have done, although there is some evidence that he was shocked by what he had read and was being told about the Holy See's money deals. His successor, John Paul II, took to Marcinkus at once. He liked the way the American organized his visit to Mexico, the first of many overseas journeys by the Polish pope; he appreciated Marcinkus as a congenial outdoors type who enjoyed physical exercise; and he showed an undisguised ethnic solidarity with the Lithuanian-descended churchman who was being sniped at by the Italians in the curia.

As tour manager for John Paul II, Marcinkus spoke "with authority," as an American diplomat remarked to me. He probably meant to say that the prelate from Chicago was throwing his weight around. During a meeting in New York preparatory to John Paul II's visit to the United States in September 1979, there was a question about whether on arrival the pontiff should first visit United Nations headquarters or St. Patrick's Cathedral. Marcinkus cut the debate short by declaring that "the United Nations doesn't count anything in the world." An international civil servant got up and stalked out of the room. In other countries where Marcinkus made arrangements for a papal trip, his bluntness riled some local officials and papal envoys. Apostolic nuncios reported to the Vatican that the pope's advance man had made decisions touching on political matters, inducing Cardinal Casaroli to issue special instructions to make clear that Marcinkus's job was exclusively technical—the logistics of papal journeys—and that politics remained the prerogative of the Secretariat of State. Such incidents further cooled the relationship between Marcinkus and Casaroli, which had never been cordial.

But Marcinkus appeared to go from strength to strength. He not only continued in his post as president of the Vatican bank; in 1981 John Paul II promoted the Chicagoan to the rank of titular archbishop of Horta and made him acting chief of the

State of Vatican City administration while instructing him to continue serving, for the time being, as president of the Institute for the Works of Religion. That one official should simultaneously hold two such important posts was quite unusual.

The Vatican bank had meanwhile been buffeted by other storms. In the wake of the Sindona scandal Italian authorities had opened a series of inquiries into the activities of financial institutions and tightened government surveillance of banks. The highest-ranking lay executive in the Institute for the Works of Religion, Luigi Mennini, was arrested on a charge of having been an accessory in Sindona's fraudulent bankruptcy, and spent 40 days in prison.

Mennini, at the time 70 years old, a timid-looking father of fourteen children including a priest and a nun, had been with the Vatican bank since its foundation in 1942 and had eventually become its highest lay official. A predecessor of Mennini in that post, Massimo Spada—the protean financier who had been one of Sindona's first Vatican contacts—was also arrested on similar charges. Spada had resigned long before from the Vatican bank, but had remained very active in Italian business and finance. While the Italian inquiry into the Sindona case was slowly proceeding, new trouble was brewing for Mennini, Marcinkus, and the Vatican bank.

GOD'S BANKER

As the Holy See was licking its wounds from the Sindona debacle, another financial scandal came into the open that was to hurt the reputation and credibility of the pope's money managers even more painfully. It centered on the Banco Ambrosiano of Milan, a credit institution that had always enjoyed church support, and was now to drag the Vatican into a sequence of sinister, and even tragic, events.

Named after the heavenly patron of the city of Milan, its fourth-century bishop, Saint Ambrose, the Banco Ambrosiano was founded in 1896 as a vehicle for the financial dealings of wealthy Roman Catholic families and interest groups in Lombardy, then as now among Italy's most dynamic regions. The bank's bylaws stated expressly that only baptized persons could become shareholders and members of its board. While this rule permitted the participation of Protestants (of whom there are few in Italy) it barred Jewish interests, then noteworthy in northern Italy. The archdiocese of Milan owned stock in the bank. After World War I a nephew of Pius XI, Franco Ratti, for years served as top executive of the Banco Ambrosiano, and many thousands of small savers, following the advice from their parish priests, kept their nest eggs in the institution, "the Catholic bank," or purchased a few shares. After the Institute for the Works of Religion was established, during World War II, it too became a stockholder in the Milan bank. When the scandal broke in 1981 the direct interest of the Holy See in the Banco Ambrosiano amounted, according to official data, to a modest 1.59 percent of its capital; however, there were rumors that the Vatican had invested much additional money in the Milan institution through companies that it was wholly or in part controlling, so as to become, in effect, its unacknowledged main stockholder.

At the beginning of the 1970s, when Sindona was riding high, the Banco Ambrosiano was still a regional concern, influential in Milan and the province around it but hardly known outside Italy. After a decade of spectacular growth it was Italy's largest private bank, a financial power center that controlled other credit institutions and sundry enterprises at home, and had far-flung interests abroad, especially in the western hemisphere. The architect of this expansion was Roberto Calvi, the martinet son of a Milan banking executive; the younger Calvi had joined the Banco Ambrosiano as a clerk in 1947 and had doggedly worked his way up to become its president. A prematurely bald, mustached loner who spent endless hours at his desk in the bank's Milan headquarters, he was described as an exceptionally cold fish by those who worked under him. Over the years Calvi had built a reputation for reliability and financial savvy. It didn't seem to matter that he had been an ally of Sindona in some deals. The two men had first met in the late 1960s and had stayed in touch. From the Sicilian financier Calvi had apparently learned to juggle funds and shares through elusive companies based in international tax havens.

One of the partly owned affiliates of the Banco Ambrosiano was the Cisalpine Overseas Bank, Ltd. of Nassau, the Bahamas. (The word *cisalpine* means "south of the Alps," including Lombardy. The institution later changed its name to Banco Ambrosiano Overseas.) The board of directors of this offshore venture, which met infrequently, counted among its members Calvi and a "Mr. Paul Marcinkus," who was the American bishop all right, although the bank listing had omitted the customary "The Most Reverend." The unusual presence of an already controversial member of the Roman Catholic hierarchy on the board of a bank known to engage in freewheeling deals was one of the few outward signs of Holy See involvement in Banco Ambrosiano business.

Actually, the Vatican, and especially its Institute for the Works of Religion, had turned to the Milan bank as a partner in its international financial operations right after the Sindona calamity. In statements made in prison, Sindona would later claim that it was he who introduced Calvi to Marcinkus in 1971. However, the American bishop would have met the chief of the church-backed Banco Ambrosiano at any event, rather sooner than later. Marcinkus and Calvi hit it off personally. Early in 1982, when Calvi was already in bad trouble, Marcinkus went out of his way in a talk with an Italian journalist to emphasize his Milan friend's respectability and competence. The Italian press had by then labeled Calvi "God's banker" in a sarcastic allusion to his association with the Holy See.

Italian financial authorities since the Sindona scandal had felt growing misgivings about some activities of the Banco Ambrosiano and its subsidiaries. In a report on an investigation of the Milan institution, Banca d'Italia (Bank of Italy) characterized Banco Ambrosiano's outpost in the Bahamas as a secretive unit operating on behalf of clients "who cannot be identified," and noted the Vatican connection. In the Italian system, the central bank exercises surveillance of all credit institutions in the country. However, when the leadership of the Bank of Italy wanted to tighten control over Banco Ambrosiano it found that the Milan bank was protected by powerful factions within the governing Christian Democratic party and other political forces. Top officials of the Bank of Italy suffered harassment and were pushed out of their posts in what seemed a vendetta for their probes into Banco Ambrosiano affairs.

Calvi, meanwhile, had sought to strengthen his position and please his political backers by acquiring the controlling interest in the Italian newspaper with the largest circulation, *Corriere della Sera* of Milan, one of the nation's leading opinion makers. At this point he suddenly found himself embroiled in another one of Italy's baroque scandals, which are often the only scenes the public sees during murky power plays between political factions, the nation's feuding secret services, economic interest groups, and individual adventurers. Calvi was found to have been a member—together with Sindona and some one thousand other Italians in influential positions—of a secret Masonic lodge that was exposed as an association for mutual support and as a right-wing pressure group. Politicians, diplomats, generals, secret service chiefs, magistrates, civil servants, journalists, bankers, and businessmen had belonged to the high-level network, which called itself "P. 2" (P incongruously stood for "propaganda," although the lodge had shunned any publicity). Some, but by no means all, of the alleged P. 2 Masonic brethren were disciplined or dismissed from their state posts, although it was hard to prove that mere membership in the lodge was a criminal offense.

The Roman Catholic Church had never lifted its centuries-old ban of Freemasonry, and the discovery that "God's banker," Calvi, had belonged to the mysterious lodge caused uneasiness in the Vatican, and hastened his downfall. The Bank of Italy continued to probe the affairs of Banco Ambrosiano, and the judiciary arm of government joined in the investigation. Calvi was arrested on charges of having violated Italy's currency laws by illegally transferring large funds out of the country. In 1981 he was sentenced to four years' imprisonment, but obtained release from jail pending an appeal. The inquiries of the central bank had meanwhile zeroed in on some questionable loans, amounting to $1.4 billion (including interests due until then), that Calvi-controlled banks had granted to hazy companies, most of them registered in Panama. The funds for this lending program had mostly been raised in the volatile Eurodollar market.

The Bank of Italy investigators became convinced that both Calvi and the Vatican owned sizable interests in the exotic companies, which bore such names as Astolfine, Bellatrix, Erin Co., Manic, and World-Wide Trading 33, Inc., and that some of the money borrowed by these corporate phantoms had been used for buying up shares in Banco Ambrosiano, and probably also in other groups, in a design to exercise hidden control. The probe by the Italian central bank also brought out that the Institute for the Works of Religion had issued statements, technically known as "letters of comfort," or "letters of patronage," that—in rather vague language, it is true—declared its interest in the letterhead companies and its awareness of their indebtedness.

The documents could be interpreted as Vatican guarantee of the obscure borrowers' creditworthiness. The letters were apparently used to overcome the quite understandable reluctance of some officials in Calvi-controlled institutions and their creditors to lend large sums to companies about which they knew very little.

A dramatic chain of events started when "God's banker" disappeared after having last been seen in an apartment in downtown Rome, close to the Pontifical Capranica College, that he had been maintaining and intermittently using during stealthy visits to the Italian capital. As a court hearing on Calvi's appeal against the 1981 sentence was approaching, it was thought that the Milan banker, fearing he would have to go back to jail, had decided to skip. Five days after Calvi had vanished, his personal secretary for nine years, Graziella Teresa Corrocher, 55 years old, jumped or fell to her death from a fifth-floor window of the Banco Ambrosiano headquarters in Milan. She left a note cursing Calvi for the disgrace he had brought on the bank and its staff. Some Italian newspapers voiced the suspicion that there had been foul play, but the authorities found that Miss Corrocher had committed suicide.

On June 18, 1982, Calvi's body was found hanging from a scaffolding under Blackfriars Bridge in London, near that square mile of financial institutions, the City. The Italian police established that the banker, who was 61 years old when he died, had reached England traveling on a false passport over a roundabout route by way of Venice, Trieste, and Austria.

To Italians, long inured to Mafia executions, political skulduggery, and terrorism, there was no doubt "God's banker" had been assassinated in a conspiracy of malign forces. Almost all of Italy's information media espoused this plot theory, and the judiciary also suspected that a crime had been committed. Some fans of murder mysteries detected a clue or message even in the circumstance that Calvi's body had been dangling from Blackfriars Bridge: the old name of the London landmark recalled the Dominican Order, hence the banker's death must have had something to do with his church ties. Other amateur detectives suggested that Calvi had been killed just as he was about to seek new loans in the City of London in a desperate attempt to recoup his losses. When a jury at the London coroner's court, following an inquest, decided in a majority verdict that Calvi had killed himself, the Italian public, press, and judiciary reacted with skepticism, if not with derision, of English naiveté. Calvi's widow and son, then in the United States, declared they were convinced that the banker had not committed suicide, and that he had been murdered to prevent him from making disclosures that would have been damaging to the Vatican and internationally known personages in politics and finance. In March 1983 three High Court judges in London overturned the coroner's suicide verdict of the year before, agreeing with the Calvi family that the earlier inquest had been a miscarriage of justice.

At the end of another inquest in London coroner's court in June 1983, during which many new witnesses were heard, a nine-member jury returned an open verdict. This meant that it had found no conclusive evidence of either suicide or murder.

The outcome of the second inquest appeared to strengthen the claims of Calvi's heirs to the $3-million life insurance money. The banker's insurance policy had excluded payment in case of suicide.

Calvi's death and the revelations about his business practices set off a financial panic. A run on Banco Ambrosiano by frightened depositors brought the institution to its knees. Under strong Italian government prodding a consortium of Italian state-controlled and private banks came up with urgently needed funds. Eventually the government liquidated the Calvi bank; its domestic assets and liabilities were taken over by a successor institution, Nuovo Banco Ambrosiano, that was owned by the rescue consortium. The shareholders of the original, now bankrupt, Banco Ambrosiano, including the Vatican, had to pay for the salvage operation with heavy losses.

Many of the foreign subsidiaries of the Calvi bank were also in difficulties. A Luxembourg affiliate, Banco Ambrosiano Holdings, defaulted on $400 million in loans, and was placed in receivership. The international banking community, already jittery because of the inability of several Third World borrowers to service the huge loans they had received while the going was good, feared that the havoc wrought by Calvi's rogue bank might worsen an incipient crisis of confidence in financial institutions everywhere. Italian government officials, in contacts with the Vatican, urged the papal money men to help ward off a scandal that might prove harmful both to Italy's international credit rating and to the prestige of the Holy See. According to the Italian government, the Vatican's liabilities in the Ambrosiano affair amounted to at least $1.3 billion.

Treasury Minister Beniamino Andreatta told the Chamber of Deputies in Rome during a debate on the Calvi affair that the Italian government hoped the Institute for the Works of Religion and the Holy See would shoulder their responsibility for acquiescing in Calvi's manipulations. The minister also declared that the Vatican bank "in some operations with the Banco Ambrosiano appears to have acted as a de facto partner." No government member of the Italian Republic had ever spoken so bluntly in public about the Holy See's financial dealings; Andreatta's remarks also carried particular weight because he was a Christian Democrat, one of the top economic experts of the Roman Catholic party. His firm stand in the contacts with the Vatican eventually induced it to seek a compromise with the Italian government, at least tacitly conceding its responsibility in some of Calvi's manipulations.

But first there was a shocker: the Italian officials who were trying to make sense of the Banco Ambrosiano tangle were stunned when the Vatican bank produced a letter, signed by Calvi and dated September 1, 1981, clearing the Institute for the Works of Religion of all legal and financial responsibilities for the loans to the phantom companies. This "counter-letter," apparently written at Marcinkus's request, seemed to void the endorsements, or "letters of comfort," from the Vatican bank.

The fact that the document absolving the Institute for the Works of Religion of all obligations concerning the unsecured loans had been kept secret by Calvi and the Vatican bank prompted Italian newspapers to charge chicanery and fraud, and to predict that Marcinkus would be replaced. News reporters beleaguered the Vatican with requests for a clarification, but for some time ran into a wall of peevish silence. Archbishop Marcinkus told an American priest-journalist: "I have never done anything that can be considered a fraud; I am still here and I am not aware of any plan to remove me." He turned down all other demands for press interviews. However, Cardinal Casaroli, the secretary of state whose relations with Marcinkus had become even chillier than they were before the Calvi affair, persuaded John Paul II that something had to be done to placate the outrage of many churchmen and of public opinion in general.

The pope authorized Casaroli to set up an international commission of three financial experts, all laymen, to examine the Vatican bank's position with regard to Banco Ambrosiano. The three wise men picked by Casaroli were Joseph Brennan, a former chairman of the Emigrant Savings Bank of New York; Philippe de Weck, a former president of the Union Bank of Switzerland; and Carlo Cerutti, an official of an Italian state-controlled communications concern. At the insistence of the West German bishops, an expert from their country, Hermann J. Abs, a former chief executive of the Deutsche Bank, was later added to the group. However, the choice of Abs proved unfortunate. Jewish groups in the United States urged the Holy See to disassociate itself from the aged German banker on the ground that he shared responsibility for the anti-Jewish persecution in Poland during World War II.

Until Casaroli's intervention, *L'Osservatore Romano* had, characteristically, ignored the Calvi scandal and its Vatican ramifications. Now the pontifical newspaper asserted in an editorial that the Holy See wanted to "shed all possible light on alleged involvements and responsibilities" in the Banco Ambrosiano case. Under the headline MENDACIOUS MEDIA, the comment by *L'Osservatore Romano* also angrily protested the attitude of the press, charging that its reports on the Calvi affair had violated professional ethics by maliciously misrepresenting the "intricate and complex" relationship between the troubled Milan bank and the Institute for the Works of Religion. The Vatican daily also lambasted Italian newspapers for "provincial gossip aimed at hitting [ecclesiastical] persons and institutions, and putting them up one against the other."

Obviously the American archbishop, the Polish pope, and the Italians in the curia were meant. For the Italian press it was easy to retort that the Holy See had nobody but itself to blame for the bad publicity. After all, it had first ventured into the jungle of international finances in ambiguous company, and then stubbornly withheld any information on the "intricate and complex" nature of that partnership.

Cardinal Benelli of Florence commented in an interview that in all his years as a close aide to Paul VI he had never seen a balance sheet of the Institute for the Works of Religion. This seemed to imply that under that pontiff the Vatican bank had virtually been free to do what it wanted. Referring to its management team, and clearly alluding to Marcinkus (whom he had never liked), Cardinal Benelli remarked: "If there was any imprudence, it was because of incompetence and lack of experience."

The investigating magistrates in Milan who were probing the

conundrum of the Calvi empire decided that certain aspects of the dealings between the Banco Ambrosiano and the Institute for the Works of Religion might have been criminal. The magistrates officially named Marcinkus, Mennini, and Pellegrino de Strobel, the Vatican bank's 70-year-old chief accountant, as potential suspects in an inquiry into a case of possible aggravated fraud. Under Italian law any person who may face penal charges in a judicial inquiry must be formally notified, and the Milan court proceeded to do so with regard to the leading trio of the Vatican bank. Marcinkus, Mennini, and de Strobel refused to accept the communications from the Milan magistrates, sent to them by registered letters. The Holy See stiffly informed the Rome government that papal officials could take into consideration any messages from Italian authorities only if these were forwarded through diplomatic channels—by the Italian embassy at the Holy See or by the apostolic nunciature in Rome.

However, Marcinkus, Mennini, and de Strobel took no chances. They abandoned their Rome apartments and went to live in the pontifical state where they were safe from Italian summons servers and possible arrest warrants. They were new "prisoners in the Vatican," though for different reasons from those that prompted Pius IX never again to leave his walled sanctuary after Italian troops entered Rome in 1870. Marcinkus, asked why he had chosen to move from his accommodation in the Villa Stritch to Vatican City, explained that, being the official directly in charge of the Vatican state, his presence around the clock was advisable. "The apartment goes with the job," he said, pointing out that he was taking advantage of the chance to avoid the Rome traffic battle four times a day (he used to leave the Vatican for lunch and possibly a siesta).

When John Paul II visited Spain in November 1982, Marcinkus stayed behind. The director general of Vatican Radio, the Reverend Roberto Tucci, who had accompanied the pontiff on earlier trips to coordinate the broadcasting services, took over the function of tour manager. However, Tucci remained in the background during this and later papal journeys, as if he had no ambition to become another "gorilla."

Meanwhile, the banking experts called in by the cardinal secretary of state tried to sort out the labyrinthine dealings between the Institute for the Works of Religion and the Banco Ambrosiano and its exotic subsidiaries. The wise men betrayed their puzzlement concerning the letters of comfort that the Vatican bank had issued, but eventually upheld its thesis that it had no liabilities toward the phantom companies. However, the experts—all four of them Roman Catholics who were known to be favorable to the Vatican—also suggested "collaboration" between the Holy See and Italy on the basis of the documents in the hands of either part "to draw the conclusions that will appear legitimate." The implication was that the Vatican bank might to some extent be morally responsible for the Banco Ambrosiano failure, and that a compromise was in order.

The Holy See confidentially advised the Italian government that it was ready to negotiate amid expectations that the pope's money managers would come up with at least a fraction of the missing funds.

This strategy was endorsed by the commission of fifteen cardinals in charge of supervising Vatican finances when it met to examine the Banco Ambrosiano affair. Some of the group's members were known to have been harshly critical of the Vatican bank's management and operations. However, the commission agreed, for the sake of the Holy See's image, to stick to the version that Marcinkus and his aides had fallen victims to Calvi's ruses, and had been unaware that the Milan banker had maneuvered his own institution and its allies into a financial quagmire. This was also the story that was told to the other cardinals when the sacred college held its second plenary "consultation" in November 1982. In the debates behind closed doors there was more criticism of the way the Vatican had mismanaged its money affairs. Many cardinals repeated earlier recommendations that the Holy See should at last stop any adventures in international finance, and publish its budget figures. If it were to do so, various members of the sacred college pointed out, donations from all over the world would doubtless increase so as to enable the Vatican to balance its budget.

At the end of the four-day meeting of the cardinals the Vatican, for the first time in history, released some data concerning its revenue and expenditures. It appeared that the Holy See and the State of Vatican City in 1981 had had an income of about $70 million (including Peter's Pence) and outlays of about $68.5 million, 58 percent of which were for salaries and pensions. After all the talk of growing deficits, the papal administration was, after all, breaking even.

"Some fathers [cardinals] pointed out that this [Vatican] budget is clearly smaller than that of some large dioceses," an official statement said, "not to speak of public and private institutions with a much more limited scope of action than that of the Holy See."

As far as the Institute for the Works of Religion was concerned, the statement insisted that it was "not a bank in the common sense of the term," but asserted that as a depository of funds destined for religious activities everywhere it "must also use the necessary banking services." The Vatican declaration also stated that the Institute for the Works of Religion had "naturally maintained contacts and relations with banking institutions in various parts of the world and, obviously, also in Italy," and that the Banco Ambrosiano had been "traditionally considered a Catholic bank with a reputation for seriousness." When the Banco Ambrosiano had failed, the Vatican statement went on, the Institute for the Works of Religion had realized that its trust had been betrayed, and that its name had been misused for carrying out "an occult project" whereby it came, without its knowledge, to be in legal control of ten companies. In a particularly tortuous passage the Vatican claimed that despite the letters of comfort the Institute for the Works of Religion "in conformity with common doctrine and the usual banking practice" had assumed no legal obligations concerning the indebtedness of the phantom companies that it had been controlling.

The Vatican explanations, in labored curial language, betrayed deep embarrassment. The Holy See promised publicly that it would reorganize the Institute for the Works of Religion to make it more efficient, and would continue to call on the four lay experts—Abs, Brennan, Cerutti and de Weck—as consultants. Obviously responding to private pressures from the cardinals, John Paul II stressed in various addresses and public remarks that the Holy See in the future must count on the Peter's Pence to a greater extent than it had done in the past, and must administer the funds thus collected with "meticulous" thrift. In a letter to Casaroli, the pontiff declared that "the Apostolic See can and must use the spontaneous contributions of the faithful and of other persons of goodwill without taking recourse to other means that might appear to be less respectful of its particular character." In other words, no more "bankers of God."

In the confidential talks between the Vatican and Italy a silent agreement was reached that if the Holy See payed for some of the damage in the Banco Ambrosiano collapse the Italian courts would not press their criminal cases against papal personnel. Marcinkus, Mennini, and de Strobel began to make cautious sorties from their Vatican sanctuary but continued to live in the pontifical state.

Marcinkus's ecclesiastical career suffered. When he was made acting chief of the Vatican City administration in 1981 it seemed a foregone conclusion that the pope would give him the red hat on the next suitable occasion. Yet when John Paul II created eighteen new cardinals in February 1983 Marcinkus was not among them. However, as if to show that the prelate from Cicero, Illinois, still enjoyed his confidence, the pontiff soon granted him a formal audience, and had *L'Osservatore Romano* report about it with Marcinkus's full titles—pro-president of the Pontifical Commission for the State of Vatican City and president of the Institute for the Works of Religion.

About that time the image of the Vatican bank was further blackened by another scandal, apparently unrelated with the Banco Ambrosiano case. The secretary of the Institute for the Works of Religion, Msgr. Donato de Bonis, was formally named by Italian investigators as a suspect in a tax-fraud conspiracy involving oil company executives, officers of the Finance Guard (the nation's fiscal police), and churchmen. Influential ecclesiastics—Monsignor de Bonis among them—were said to have been instrumental in placing conniving police officers into key positions.

The scandals enveloping the Vatican bank had been many years in the making, and their origin went back long before John Paul II was elected. That they came to light in his pontificate, with inestimable harm to the prestige of the papacy, was a source of much irritation to the Polish pontiff.

However, despite rearguard actions by reluctant papal bureaucrats, the Sindona and Calvi cases made a thorough reform of the Vatican's bizarre financial system seem a possibility at long last.

Several cardinals at large suggested that the bishops' conferences in wealthy nations might be amenable to pledging fixed yearly contributions to the Holy See's budget. The condition would be, it was pointed out, that the Vatican bank must halt its wheeling and dealing, and that the papal administration provide much more financial information than it had done so far.

Cardinal Höffner of Cologne, a member of the fifteen-man cardinals' committee in charge of supervising Vatican finances, recommended publicly the appointment of competent lay administrators to the Institute for the Works of Religion. The cardinal also demanded that the operations of the Vatican bank must be periodically audited by independent financial experts, and that any "speculations" with church money be curbed. Cardinal Höffner noted in an interview that the yearly budget of his archdiocese of Cologne was nearly four times the $70 million the Holy See had reported as its income in 1981. The financial muscle of the Roman Catholic Church in West Germany lent authority to the cardinal's views.

As investigators in various countries still grappled with the many mysteries and unanswered questions of the financial affairs that implicated the Holy See, the Vatican seemed to be assuming a new trend. The age-old secretiveness surrounding the Vatican's money matters would be loosened and there would be a stronger reliance on voluntary contributions from the rank and file rather than on questionable investment strategies and irresponsible adventures.

CHAPTER 7

°LOBBYING °IN °THE °SACRED °PALACES

FACTIONALISM SEEMS INEVITABLE in any large organization, and it would be surprising if it were absent from such a vast, complex body as the central government of the Roman Catholic Church. In the Vatican, cardinals and lesser prelates are constantly jostling for direct access to the pope, and scheming for more power; their maneuvers and intrigues in all epochs account for a good deal of church history.

In addition, the Holy See, like the governments and legislatures of the world's territorial states, has always been subject to outside pressures. These may come from secular powers and such ideological movements as Marxism, or from forces in the church at large. Among the latter, the religious orders have always been most tenacious in seeking to increase their influence in the Vatican, often acting as veritable pressure groups.

Since the thirteenth century, two orders of friars—the Dominicans and the Franciscans—have especially competed with each other for favor or power in the papal court. Sharing a bent for asceticism, the first group stressed dogmatic rigor, the second absolute poverty; over the centuries both spiritual families have stood for austerity in faith and morals. Up to this day the pope's theologian, a member of his official household, is always a Dominican. The Franciscans, among other things, have remained the instruments of a vaguely defined papal guardianship of the Holy Land.

The papacy has often used the mendicant ("begging") orders, mainly the Dominicans and Franciscans, as its thought police. Dominicans played a prominent part in the Inquisition, and still are conspicuous among the officials and consultants of its successor agency, the Sacred Congregation for the Discipline of the Faith. (However, lately the Dominican order has also produced outstanding liberal thinkers, and has engaged in the worker-priest movement, a pastoral experiment on the shop floor of industrial enterprises in France and elsewhere, on which the Roman Curia has long frowned.) The Franciscans, split into various subgroups, have often denounced alleged moral laxity and deviations from orthodox faith in the church, and for some time had a reputation for zealotry. As scholars, thinkers, and educated persons in general were rediscovering the art, literature, history, philosophy, and mythology of classical antiquity, first in Italy and then in other European countries, Franciscans and Dominicans were in the forefront of those excoriating the spread of what they called "epicureanism," or worldliness. These peevish denunciations were met with scorn by Italian writers, who at the end of the Middle Ages and the beginning of the Renaissance inveighed against monks and, especially, friars, accusing them of hypocrisy.

The Roman Catholic Church's all-out effort to halt the spread of Protestantism—indeed to root it out—brought new forces to the front line, particularly the Jesuits. A large part of the present chapter is devoted to that order and the vicissitudes of its relations with the Vatican in our time. Another section of the chapter deals with a new type of "secular" organization within the church, Opus Dei.

Such groupings within the clergy and the rank and file of Roman Catholics today are still vying for power and influence as they have been doing for centuries; they might be compared to the mighty lobbies in Washington and other world capitals. In the Vatican, ecclesiastical lobbies always seek to have the ear of the pontiff and to have a say in his decisions and the preparation of his public pronouncements. Also at stake in the continual infighting between clerical pressure groups are issues of theology and church discipline; the staffing of key posts in the curia, Roman Catholic universities, and seminaries; and the appointment of bishops. Missionary activities and, always, finances are other bones of contention. The biggest coup an ecclesiastical lobby can achieve is to have one of its own elected to the papacy —or at least an enemy of a rival group.

THE EMBATTLED "FIRST LEGION"

Conspiracy theories have ever been popular, but few have proved as durable as the belief in the secret and sinister influence of the Jesuits. For four centuries the view has been widespread that this elite order, founded by Saint Ignatius of Loyola and bound to the pope by a special oath of fealty, was the real power behind the pontifical throne. Even today people who are not particularly interested in organized religion tend to equate the Society of Jesus with the Roman Catholic Church, or at least with its clergy.

The old perception that the followers of Saint Ignatius are unscrupulous plotters at the service of the pope in Rome has become a part of idiom. Look up *Jesuit* in the dictionary, and you find the word's definition—a member of a Roman Catholic religious order devoted to missionary and educational work— coupled with a second meaning: "a crafty schemer, cunning dissembler." In other languages too "Jesuit" carries overtones suggesting intrigue, lusting for power, deviousness, and hypocrisy. In the past, many devout Roman Catholics shared such distrust. The Jansenists, those religious purists of eighteenth-century France, were so insistent in accusing the Jesuits of doctrinal and moral laxity and of a penchant for meddling in worldly affairs that Pope Clement XIV, also under pressure from secular anti-Jesuit forces in Spain and Portugal, suppressed the order in 1773. Some Jesuits went underground, and it took their society 41 years to become legal again within the church.

Ignatius of Loyola, the Spanish nobleman and former soldier, founded the Society of Jesus in 1540 as a militant body from which the pope could expect blind obedience. "If the church hierarchy tells me that white is black, it is black," Saint Ignatius said. The order quickly became the cutting edge of the Church of Rome in its struggle against the forces of the Reformation, started by Martin Luther and continued by other Protestant leaders. As forceful preachers, Jesuits defended Rome's dogmas and traditions from Protestant criticism; as educators they instilled the Roman doctrines into the minds of young people; as theologians and writers they became the papacy's chief apologists; and as advisers to royalty and princes they counseled ruthlessness in dealing with "heretics."

As thoroughly trained spiritual fighters, Jesuits have always used and invited military metaphors: "the Company"; "the pope's vanguard"; "the first legion"; "the long black line."

Carrying out the commands of the pope and of the order's own top leader, the general (a military-sounding abbreviation of "superior general"), a Jesuit was expected to be obedient *perinde ac cadaver* (roughly, having no more will of his own than a corpse). At the same time the Society of Jesus always showed itself highly adaptable, and since the Roman Catholic Counter-Reformation has gained a reputation for resourcefulness. Over the centuries Jesuits have been confessors and confidants of European monarchs, educators of princes, proselytizers in the Indies (like Saint Francis Xavier), builders of fortresslike cathedrals throughout the Western Hemisphere, and respected scholars at the court of the emperor of China. Jesuits were among the first Westerners in Japan, and established and ran unique autonomous communities of Christianized Indians, the Reductions, in Paraguay. When Clement XIV suppressed the order, Catherine the Great of Russia refused to permit the papal decree to be enforced in the Roman Catholic areas of her domains, essentially Russian Poland, and thus helped the company to survive. Other Jesuits, under cover, also kept their traditions alive in scattered communities elsewhere. When Pope Pius VII restored the order in 1814, because he had come to the conclusion he needed its experience, there were enough trained Jesuits for a new official start of the company.

Before and after its disbandment by Clement XIV, the Jesuit order had difficulties with the Holy See, and was expelled from a number of countries. In the so-called rites controversy in the second half of the seventeenth century, the toleration of some Confucian ceremonies by Jesuit missionaries in China was bitterly attacked by rival religious orders. In 1704 Pope Clement XI eventually banned the Jesuit-approved rites of traditional ancestor worship among Chinese converts to Roman Catholicism —a historic blunder that all but wiped out 120 years of evangelizing efforts and caused the Church of Rome to "lose China."

Later the Society of Jesus had to face such adversaries as the authoritarian marquess of Pombal in Portugal and other powerful figures in the Age of Enlightenment. In the nineteenth century Bismarck expelled the order from his new German Reich. It took Switzerland 125 years to repeal a constitutional ban on Jesuit activities in the confederation; a 1973 referendum showed only a slim majority for readmittance of the order.

The resilient Jesuits have made many comebacks. But they have never forgotten the dire times when a pontiff left them naked to their enemies. Few members of the company ever enter the Church of the Most Holy Apostles at the center of Rome, which is entrusted to the Conventual Franciscans, an order to which Clement XIV belonged before his elevation to the papacy. The sumptuous church contains a marble monument by Antonio Canova to the Franciscan pontiff who banned the Jesuits. In an exceptional admission that popes may be fallible, John Paul II, during an audience with the Jesuit leadership in 1982, spoke about the company as the group "that the enemies of Christ persecuted until they obtained its suppression, but which the church has made to rise again, realizing the need for such valiant and devoted sons."

The ban by Clement XIV was only the most telling example of the difficulties that have arisen between the head of the church and the militant elite that—in a vow prescribed by Saint Ignatius—commits itself to absolute obedience. In what may seem intellectual arrogance, Jesuits have occasionally suggested that whatever they were doing was justified and in keeping with their vow of loyalty to the pope, because it would in the end be for the good of the papacy. Such an attitude of "we know best what benefits the pontiff" explains the broad range of Jesuit postures over the years.

In the twentieth century Jesuit personalities have ranged from Pierre Teilhard de Chardin, the French thinker who sought to conciliate evolutionism with Christian revelation (and for that reason had trouble with the inquisitors of the Vatican's Holy Office), to the Reverend Robert Drinan, president of Americans for Democratic Action. As a member of the United States House of Representatives Father Drinan opposed the Vietnam War, and urged President Nixon's impeachment; later he obeyed John Paul II's blanket prohibition for priests to hold elective political office.

As an intellectual and organizational force, in Rome and in

the Vatican, the Jesuit presence has been formidable for centuries. One of the company's citadels is still the Pontifical Gregorian University, the church's foremost institution of higher learning. Founded by Saint Ignatius as the Roman College in 1551, and endowed with a monumental building by Pope Gregory XIII (after whom it is named) in 1582, this bulwark of clerical scholarship has been the alma mater of eight canonized saints; sixteen popes; and thousands of cardinals, archbishops, and bishops. (John Paul II was not an alumnus. After his studies in the clandestine seminary of the archbishop of Krakow during World War II, young Father Wojtyla did postgraduate work in Rome at the Angelicum, now the Pontifical University of St. Thomas Aquinas, which is operated by the Dominican order. When the future pope attended it, the Angelicum was considered particularly conservative, even by Vatican standards.)

Nowadays, about three-fourths of the Gregorian University's faculty are still Jesuits, but the vast majority of its more than two thousand students are unaffiliated with the company. Americans, to whom the university is "the Greg," are the second strongest group, next to the Italians, in the cosmopolitan student body. The institution on the Piazza della Pilotta (a stone's throw from the church with Clement XIV's tomb and monument) has gone coeducational since Vatican II. Women students, most (but not all) of them nuns, were soon accounting for one-fourth of the total enrollment. Elderly churchmen are still apt to shake their heads when they see a seminarian and a member of a female religious order, neither wearing clerical garb, wander off together after a class in moral theology. The Gregorian University system offers not only the traditional curriculum of church colleges but also includes departments of psychology and social sciences, the widely renowned Pontifical Bible Institute, an Oriental Institute, and an Institute for Marxist Studies that is the only Roman Catholic center of its kind in Rome. The Society of Jesus is also operating residences for seminarians from Brazil, other Latin American nations, the German-speaking countries, Hungarians, Poles, and others in Rome.

Jesuit astronomers man the Vatican observatory in the pontifical hillside estate at Castel Gandolfo, and do work in scientific centers in the United States. The Jesuit stargazers exchange data with colleagues in many countries including the Soviet

Union. Another autonomous unit in Rome's sprawling Jesuit establishment is the semimonthly magazine *Civiltà Cattolica,* a journal of religious thought closely supervised by the Holy See. It is considered the most authoritative Roman Catholic periodical in the world; galley proofs of each issue are routinely submitted to the Vatican's Secretariat of State and are often examined by the pope himself. Old galleys with handwritten corrections by Pope Leo XIII are treasured in the magazine's archives. The editors and staff writers of *Civiltà Cattolica* live in a pleasant building in a park, the Villa Malta, in a choice neighborhood adjoining the Borghese Gardens. One of them, an American historian, the Reverend Robert A. Graham, could be seen there, writing at his stand-up desk like a medieval monk whenever he was not poring over source material in the National Archives in Washington or elsewhere in the world.

Jesuits have been in charge of the Holy See's broadcasts ever since Guglielmo Marconi, the inventor of wireless communications, built Vatican Radio for Pope Pius XI in 1931. Since then the Vatican broadcasting station has grown into an operation with programs in 34 languages around the clock. To the Jesuit order, Vatican Radio, although supervised by the Secretariat of State, is an important instrument of worldwide influence. Toward the end of the 1970s rumors cropped up that the company might have to give it up, and that the Vatican's broadcasting services might be taken over by Opus Dei. The ambitious and wealthy movement, it was suggested, was willing to bear the entire operating costs of Vatican Radio, which to this day are covered by the hard-pressed administration of the pontifical state. Nothing came of the rumors, but it was known that Archbishop Marcinkus and the other Vatican money men were looking for new sources of financing for the broadcasts. The speculation about Opus Dei voices for the Holy See's microphones was characteristic of the jockeying between that organization and the Jesuit order at the beginning of John Paul II's pontificate.

In addition to all the strategic positions in ecclesiastical Rome that the company traditionally has occupied, it usually has been well represented in the curia itself. For generations hundreds of Jesuits have at one time or another served in the departments of the church's central administration as officials, permanent advisers, or experts on call. The "first legion" wouldn't make much fuss about it but was known to value highly every foothold in the Vatican. In recent times Jesuit leverage in the Apostolic

214

Palace has never been stronger than under Pius XII. That pope's confessor, secretary, and closest scholarly advisers were all German members of the company, as will be recalled. Mother Pasqualina was impressed by Jesuit discipline and learning, and favored Pius XII's reliance on the order. At the time, Jesuits controlled much of the curial apparatus. A Jesuit was the postulator, or official advocate of sainthood, in the proceedings for Pius XII's beatification and canonization.

Under Pius XII the general of the Society of Jesus, first a Pole and then a Belgian, really was "the black pope." In his black habit the head of the company commanded thousands of obedient militants all over the earth, and wielded so much influence at the center of the church that he was considered second in power only to the white-clad pontiff.

In accordance with the Constitutions of Saint Ignatius, the Society of Jesus with a present membership of 26,000 has a monarchical and highly centralized structure with the general as the key figure. The company's legislative body is the General Congregation, an assembly of more than two hundred Jesuits from all continents, some attending by force of their office, others elected by the rank and file. The General Congregation chooses the Jesuit general, and can amend the rules laid down by the founder. The 32nd General Congregation, held in Rome during 1974–75, in a departure from the Constitutions of Saint Ignatius, decided that the general, up to then elected for life, may resign. At that time the company was headed by the Very Reverend Pedro Arrupe y Gondra, a Basque like the founder. Six years later he invoked the faculty given the general by the 32nd General Congregation and announced that he planned to resign in due course. His decision was the prelude to a Roman drama.

A GENTLE GENERAL

Father Arrupe was elected the 28th successor to Saint Ignatius in 1965 when the Second Vatican Council was about to end. To thousands of Jesuits he embodied the spirit of Vatican II, and he became the company's best-loved general in a long time.

In the Society of Jesus the great church gathering held from 1962 to 1965 had unleashed liberal forces, as it had done in other church groups and among Roman Catholics in general. Many members of the company had helped prepare the council from the moment the idea of summoning the supreme church assembly had been announced by John XXIII in the Basilica of St. Paul Outside the Walls in 1959. After the pontiff had placed Cardinal Bea, the Jesuit Bible scholar, in charge of the crucial Secretariat for the Promotion of Christian Unity, that body had quickly become a rallying point for avant-garde theologians and committed ecumenists. Throughout Vatican II renowned Jesuit scholars, like John Courtney Murray, Henri de Lubac, and Gustave Weigel, had served as advisers and exercised much influence as liberal lobbyists.

The intellectual stir caused by these scholars continued within the company longer than it did in other church organizations. Jesuits, especially in the United States and in Western Europe, started causing dismay in the Vatican by questioning papal pronouncements. Some of these progressives criticized the rule of priestly celibacy, called for the admission of women to holy orders, and, as mentioned before, opposed Paul VI's ban on chemical or physical methods of birth control.

An increasing number of Jesuits asked their superiors for release from their vows, or abandoned their order and the priesthood without waiting for such an authorization. When Father Arrupe was elected general, the company's membership was at an all-time high of 36,000. At the time of his resignation it counted 27,000 members and was still shrinking. However, since other religious communities were also retrenching, the Society of Jesus was still the strongest Roman Catholic order, followed by the Franciscans.

Father Arrupe showed much understanding for the personal problems of his priests and lay brothers. A Jesuit educator who was in Japan at the same time as the future general told me that the strongest expression of displeasure over somebody's conduct ever heard from the provincial superior, Arrupe, was "We all need the grace of God." Arrupe was an uncommon churchman with exceptional achievements. A native of Bilbao, in northern Spain, who had started medical school before deciding to enter the priesthood and the company, he spent 27 years in Japan. He learned to speak Japanese fluently, wrote books in that language, and earned the nickname of "Shinto priest." When American war planes dropped an atomic bomb on Hiroshima in 1945, he was at his order's novitiate at Nagatsuka on the outskirts of the doomed city. He and his fellow Jesuits are credited

216

with saving many lives by treating survivors of the blast at the order's residence, which had also been damaged.

By the time he became head of all Jesuits the sharp-featured Arrupe had a reputation for being something of a liberal. As superior general he repeatedly called on the company to step up its work among the poor and phase out activities that seemed to identify it with the well-to-do. He wanted his order's educators to go into the ghettoes to teach the disadvantaged. In India, now the company's second strongest assistancy (regional branch) after the United States, Jesuit institutions moved from the cool, isolated places in the hills to teeming urban areas of Delhi and Madras.

As Arrupe was exhorting his order to strengthen its social commitment worldwide, a posture opposed by conservatives, he himself became the target of criticism from traditionalists within the church; they charged him with permissiveness and a lack of administrative efficiency. His predecessor, the Very Reverend Jan B. Janssens, a Flemish Belgian and a disciplinarian who headed the company from 1946 to 1964, had seldom left his headquarters in Rome. Laying himself open to charges of inefficiency in the order's government, Arrupe, on the other hand, visited almost every country in the world including the United States—the first time a Jesuit general had ever done so—to maintain personal contacts with his forces in the field. Many with whom he talked wanted to be released from the order, and his response was often sympathetic. He was also compassionate toward the Reverend Daniel Berrigan, and visited the antiwar activist in the federal prison where he was being held after participating in the destruction of draft-board records. "He is a Jesuit in trouble," was the general's explanation for the jail encounter.

There were also Jesuits in trouble in Latin America, where the order is deeply entrenched, and in other countries of the Third World. Members of the company had been active in revolutionary movements in Guatemala, Nicaragua, El Salvador, Chile, the Philippines, and elsewhere, attracting the enmity of anti-Marxists. Arrupe, in one of his rare public statements, told Italian journalists in 1979: "We [Jesuits] are often accused of being Communists. Of course we are not. But the fact is that people want a testimony of life, not words alone. This is even more true in Latin America where, for instance, sugarcane cutters are forced to live in huts like animals, and are fed only to the extent

217

that their strength as laborers is maintained." Referring to Marxism, Arrupe observed that "one cannot neglect a culture, an anthropology, that today is so influential and widespread." The Jesuit general remarked that "the possibility of a certain dialogue and also of a critical collaboration with Marxist-inspired groups and movements cannot a priori be ruled out." Nevertheless, he added, "we cannot accept the commitment of [pro-Marxist] Jesuits. . . . This should not prevent us from taking a deep interest in Marxism because many elements of that ideology are in the air that we breathe. We must learn to know the Marxists well. I continually ask the Jesuits to study them thoroughly. . . . Many Marxist views are mistaken and dangerous, but it is no less true that they are often inspired by a profound sense of the injustices they want to combat."

Such opinions provided fresh ammunition for conservatives who had been denouncing all along the Jesuit general's alleged indulgence of deviations from Roman Catholic orthodoxy. His lenient attitude toward Jesuits who wanted to leave the order—curialists called them "defectors"—also scandalized many in the Vatican.

Within the company one blandly spoke of departing rather than of defecting or deserting members. Some of them managed to stay in fields in which they had been working as Jesuits. In the Netherlands, with the support of liberal bishops, educators who had left the Society of Jesus taught in seminaries until the Vatican called a halt to the practice. Other Jesuit dropouts became marriage counselors, welfare workers, or publishing assistants.

Quite a few former Jesuits kept in touch with the company. They had all been formed in the same intellectual mold, would lace their conversation in various languages with Latin quotations and puns, and chuckle at the same clerical jokes. At the order's headquarters in Rome, I asked one resident priest about an English writer who had once been a well-known Jesuit and later abandoned the order, got married, and became the father of two children. "Oh, he comes to see us every time he visits Rome," was the answer. "He is a friend, you know."

Despite the decline in the company's membership, one out of every twenty Roman Catholic priests in the world was still a Jesuit. Nearly one thousand men were novices, although it was by no means sure that they all would stay in the company. A candidate for the Society of Jesus spends two years as a novice, taking his first vows of poverty, chastity, and obedience at the end of this period. After ordination to the priesthood Jesuits do postgraduate work in philosophy and theology as "scholastics," and are encouraged to start specialized studies. When this training has been completed, a Jesuit reconfirms his earlier three vows and is called a "spiritual coadjutor." Lay brothers take the first three vows and wear the Jesuits' black habit but are not ordained; they usually do subaltern chores in Jesuit residences.

The top class in the company is represented by the "professed" Jesuits. It takes at least eight years, but sometimes as many as seventeen years, to join this elite-within-an-elite group. Professed members again take the three vows of poverty, chastity, and obedience, and a fourth solemn vow of special obedience to the pope from which other Jesuits are barred. The solemnity of this ultimate vow makes it very difficult to obtain release. Only the professed members of the company, who recently accounted for about two-thirds of all Jesuits, are eligible for leadership positions in it. Younger Jesuits critical of the two-tier system agitated in the early 1970s for everyone in the company to be admitted to the "fourth vow." But Paul VI prohibited the proposed change in the rules. The papal veto was prompted by the fear that young, liberal Jesuits might quickly gain leading positions in the order if it were made too easy for them to become professed members.

By that time, Paul VI was already deeply worried about the mood among many Jesuits. A number of incidents added to his irritation. A Spanish member of the order and of the Gregorian University's faculty, the Reverend José Maria Diez-Alegria, caused an ecclesiastical scandal in 1972 with a book, published without authorization from his order's superiors, in which he showed left-wing sympathies and criticized the Vatican's wealth. In the slender volume, entitled *I Believe in Hope,* the Jesuit scholar also admitted that he had been able to remain celibate only by resorting to masturbation. Diez-Alegria eventually left the order. Another member of the company, the Reverend Peter Hebblethwaite, formerly editor of the British Jesuit magazine *The Month,* in 1973 scathingly portrayed Archbishop Benelli, then Paul VI's chief of staff, as a power-obsessed old-style bureaucrat in an article written for a secular newspaper, *The Observer.* The Jesuit general personally apologized to Benelli for the attack from Hebblethwaite, who soon afterward departed from the order and the priesthood.

219

While instances of unrest and malaise in the Jesuit ranks became increasingly numerous, some members of the company still clung to the old ways. They lamented that the order's cohesion was weakening, and declared themselves outraged by the conduct and views of their liberal-minded fellow Jesuits. The Society of Jesus no longer appeared as a solid phalanx of faith but rather as a loose network of priestly intellectuals who had saved a certain esprit de corps but were in open disagreement on many things, even fundamentals. To conservative Roman Catholics and to diehards in the Roman Curia such ferment and fractures within the company suggested an army whose assault forces—the crack units, the marines or paratroopers of the church militant—were suffering from sagging morale, factionalism, and desertion.

In 1974 Paul VI wrote to the order that in some of its branches he had noted "certain tendencies of an intellectual and disciplinary nature that, if encouraged, would introduce very serious and perhaps incurable changes in your essential structures." A little later the same pontiff alluded to unconventional attitudes of some Jesuits who had been in the news, and deplored them as "painful facts that make the very essence of belonging to the company questionable, and that are occurring all too often."

Paul VI's successor, John Paul I, was considering another pontifical reproof to the Jesuits before he died. According to the presumed draft that was later circulated, he had intended to put the order formally on its guard against "secularizing influences," meaning that many members were betraying an unseemly worldliness.

A solemn reprimand to the Jesuits came from John Paul II in an audience for Arrupe and the general's top aides in the Vatican's Throne Hall in September 1979, especially arranged for a dressing-down from the company's commander-in-chief. The head of the church sternly declared that a religious crisis in the contemporary world was affecting the Society of Jesus, "causing bewilderment among the Christian people and concern to the church, to the hierarchy, and personally to the pope who is speaking to you." John Paul II was understood to be voicing worries that present-day agnosticism and secularism were making inroads on the Jesuit order.

The Polish pope had been following the developments in the company. When he was a seminarian in Krakow, a Pole, the

Very Reverend Wladimir Ledóchowski, was the order's general, and Jesuits were very influential in his nation's church. As archbishop the future pope had a conflict with the Society of Jesus because of its insistence on controlling the theological faculty of Krakow University. Archbishop Wojtyla, backed up for once by the Communist state authorities, successfully asserted his personal responsibility for the theology department. John Paul II was to prove later that he did not bear any grudge against the company as such, that he was distinguishing between Jesuit and Jesuit. He caused astonishment in the curia in 1980 when, in a thoroughly personal decision, he named the rector (president) of the Gregorian University, the Reverend Carlo Maria Martini, archbishop of Milan, Italy's wealthy second city. A Jesuit biblical scholar and an expert on the Middle East, Martini thus was —to his own surprise—assigned to the much-coveted see that almost automatically brings the red hat to its incumbent. What's more, two twentieth-century popes, Pius XI and Paul VI, had been archbishops of Milan before their elevation.

A little later, John Paul II appointed another Jesuit, the Reverend Roger Heckel, as bishop of Strasbourg, France, a city that is host to the European Parliament and a site of ecumenical contacts between Roman Catholics and Protestants.

A Jesuit—like a member of any other religious order—whom the head of the church picks as bishop, archbishop, or cardinal, is legally, though not always emotionally, separated from his former group. Monks and friars who are assigned to a parish or some other pastoral work in a diocese are answerable both to the local bishop and their own superiors. Members of religious orders who serve in the Roman Curia also owe dual loyalty—to their own organization and to the Vatican leadership.

The sacred college of cardinals usually includes at least one Jesuit; at the beginning of John Paul II's pontificate three cardinals—an Ecuadorian, an Indian, and a Malagasy—were Jesuits. He added two more, Martini and de Lubac, the French theologian. This was a triumph for the Society of Jesus in a period of great tribulation.

A few weeks after John Paul II's tense encounter with the company's leadership in September 1979 every Jesuit community on earth received a photograph of the superior general kneeling before the pontiff, who was making the gesture of blessing. In an earnest message accompanying the picture and the text of the pope's address, Arrupe urged every Jesuit to engage in self-criticism and help bring about the "necessary changes." The general nevertheless conceded "the delicate nature of personal problems, the difficulty of new, ambiguous, conflictual situations." Arrupe requested all Jesuit communities to report to him in writing whether they were aware of any members of the order leading less than austere lives, being slack in their religious practices, seeking independence of their superiors, maintaining "relations full of ambiguity with other persons," or otherwise failing in the observance of their vows.

In 1981 Arrupe announced that he intended to step down. He cited reasons of age; the general was then 74 years old. He meant to complete his gradual withdrawal from the top post in the company by 1983 when he would be beyond the statutory 75-year retirement age for bishops. His implication was that the head of an order should not have to serve longer. John Paul II asked Arrupe to stay in office for the time being, and made his request public. It was a signal that the pontiff wanted more time to think about the Jesuits' status and future in the church.

IGNATIAN OBEDIENCE

Soon after having been ordered by the pope to remain at his post, the Jesuit general went on yet another trip, this time to visit communities of his order in his beloved east Asia. Returning to Rome after a tiring flight, Arrupe found at Fiumicino airport that his right hand would not obey when he wanted to lift his battered suitcase from the baggage carousel. His early medical training permitted him to diagnose what was happening to him—a brain hemorrhage. Unable to speak, his right side paralyzed, the head of the Jesuit order was taken to Salvator Mundi hospital on the Janiculum hill. During the following months he regained some of his impaired faculties.

Soon after he was stricken Arrupe indicated that one of his four general assistants (principal aides), the Reverend Vincent T. O'Keefe, should serve as vicar general, or interim head, of the order. Many Jesuits thought that the tall, genial Father O'-Keefe, a polyglot New Yorker who once was president of Fordham University, might eventually succeed Arrupe to become the company's first American general.

One day in October 1981 the pope's secretary of state, Cardinal Casaroli, walked from the Vatican to Jesuit world headquarters, a nineteenth-century reconstruction-Renaissance building with twentieth-century annexes in the Borgo Santo Spirito, a few hundred yards from St. Peter's Square. Casaroli was without any of the insignia of his rank; the tourists and passersby who saw the slight, short churchman in black could not have guessed that history was being made.

At the Jesuit center Casaroli asked to be shown upstairs to the infirmary where Arrupe was recuperating from his stroke since his dismissal from Salvator Mundi hospital. The secretary of state made sure that the patient was lucid and understood him, and slowly read to him a letter from Pope John Paul II. In the message the pontiff notified the Society of Jesus that he had named a personal delegate and a deputy delegate for the order. In effect, John Paul II had displaced Arrupe and O'Keefe as, respectively, the nominal and acting leaders of the Jesuit order. The general indicated that he accepted the pontiff's decision.

The pope's new personal delegate for the Society of Jesus was an Italian, the Reverend Paolo Dezza, then 79 years old and afflicted with poor eyesight. A scholar who had begun his career as a professor of philosophy at the Gregorian University, he had held various administrative positions in the company and had been superior of its Italian province. He had had personal contacts with six popes, had been confessor to Paul VI and John Paul I, and had served in half a dozen curia departments. He had been rector of the Gregorian University, and for ten years acted as one of the four top advisers to Arrupe. In his long black cassock and ascetic ways, and with his Vatican experience, Dezza was a traditional Jesuit after John Paul II's heart.

The pontiff's letter hinted that Dezza would not be the company's next general, and in a matter-of-fact sentence ordered that if Dezza were to die before the order had elected a new leader, the Reverend Giuseppe Pittau should succeed him as John Paul II's personal delegate. The deputy delegate, Father Pittau, a Sardinian who had attended Harvard University, had lived in Japan for seventeen years. He had been president of Tokyo's Sophia University, a prestigious Jesuit institution, and head of the order's Japanese province. When John Paul II visited Japan in 1981 he was impressed by Pittau, then 52 years old, a discovery to be kept in mind for future assignments.

The new Dezza-Pittau team took over the offices at Jesuit headquarters that had been Arrupe's. Soon afterward Dezza stated publicly that he had been instructed by the pope not to convene a General Congregation for the election of a new general right away but to see to it that such a session would be carefully prepared "according to the directives from the Holy Father." It was easy to understand the meaning: the pontiff wanted the electors of the next Jesuit general to be thoroughly vetted, and personally to sift likely candidates for the job that meant so much to the entire church. Pittau was at once tipped as John Paul II's favorite.

Although the papal intervention in the life of the company was in effect a demotion of the general and of the vicar general, Arrupe continued being referred to as the superior general, and O'Keefe was politely told by the pontiff's delegate, Dezza, to offer his advice to the new top leadership in the same manner as he had been doing to Arrupe. But the pope's move was correctly interpreted as a disavowal of the American. Conservatives in the Vatican and John Paul II himself had long been distrustful of liberal currents among Jesuits in the Western Hemisphere, and O'Keefe had been suspected of sympathizing with those liberals in some measure. Furthermore, the former head of Fordham University was regarded as being too media-conscious by curialists. O'Keefe had always been friendly with journalists, and had on occasion appeared as a religious-affairs commentator on American network television. His critics in the curia were afraid that as vicar general he might orchestrate a public relations campaign for the Jesuit order rather than restore the old discipline.

The Polish pope's decision to impose a leader of his own choice on the company, though legitimate from the standpoint of church law, shocked and angered many Jesuits. Hundreds of the order's members expressed their solidarity with Arrupe and O'-Keefe in personal letters to them, or wrote directly to John Paul II to register their disagreement. One of the weightiest protests to the pontiff was signed by the Reverend Karl Rahner, one of the world's most respected Roman Catholic theologians, and by seventeen other Jesuits in West Germany. The letter noted that in the entire history of the order no pope had ever named a personal delegate for it, and said that the signers were unable "to recognize the finger of God in this administrative measure." John Paul II's action, the message went on, "is causing noteworthy problems of conscience to not a few among us," and pleaded: "Holy Father, permit us to elect our future superior general in the freedom that, from the beginnings of the church, has always represented one of the basic rules of all orders."

Pittau, the deputy of the pope's new delegate for the Society of Jesus, commented later: "Saint Ignatius has taught us to tell our superiors of our difficulties, and then to obey. The eighteen German Jesuits did not mean to perform a gesture of rebellion." The letter from Rahner and his companions, and similar messages, nevertheless prompted the new leaders of the order to seek ways to get the rank and file better in hand. Dezza and Pittau, after consulting with the pope who had appointed them, called a meeting of the heads of all 86 Jesuit provinces in the world to discuss what had happened and what the prospects of the order were.

As a momentous year in the company's history was closing, John Paul II sang again the traditional Te Deum in the main church of the order, the Gesù at the center of Rome, which holds the monumental tomb of Saint Ignatius and a relic (an arm) of Saint Francis Xavier. A solemn papal rite in the Gesù every December 31 enjoyed a long tradition but in recent years it had been abandoned. The Polish pope had revived it from the start of his pontificate, greatly pleasing the Society of Jesus. He had let it be known he didn't want to see any Jesuit in secular dress at the ceremony; nor did he.

On the last evening of 1981 John Paul II not only officiated in the Church of the Gesù but also paid an exceptional papal visit to the headquarters of the company after the Te Deum. When he arrived at the center the first thing he did was embrace and bless Arrupe. The white-faced general was sitting in an easy chair but insisted on getting up as well as he could, and managed to stammer a few words of thanks to the pontiff. Then John Paul II shared dinner with the nearly one hundred priests and lay brothers who at the time resided at the Jesuit center. "The Holy Father was very kind to us," one of the priests who were in the refectory on that New Year's Eve told me. "But he gave us absolutely no hint as to the future of the company."

Eight weeks later the 86 Jesuit provincials and the members of the headquarters staff met with their new leaders, Dezza and Pittau, for a soul-searching session. The ten-day meeting was held in the Villa Cavalletti, a seventeenth-century building in pseudo-Renaissance style with a garden near Grottaferrata amid the vineyards and olive groves south of Rome. The property had once been the country residence of a noble family; its last private owners had bequeathed it to the Society of Jesus, which had adapted it as a center for spiritual retreats. Behind closed doors the provincials from all continents reported to the pope's delegate and deputy delegate that there were deep misgivings about their appointment in some parts of the rank and file. Jesuits in Western Europe and in the Western Hemisphere were said to be particularly upset. However, the provincials promised, there would be no rebellion if the order was allowed to choose its next general reasonably soon and in keeping with its constitutional procedures. Dezza and Pittau informed the pope of this.

After the fourth day of the discussions in the Villa Cavalletti John Paul II received all participants in the Vatican. Arrupe, in a wheelchair, was also present, although his condition had not permitted him to attend the Grottaferrata meetings. The pontiff kept the Jesuit leaders, more than one hundred of them, waiting for over an hour while flustered Vatican aides scurried back and forth to reassure the Jesuits that the pope was not snubbing them but was being delayed by an audience with President François Mitterand of France that was lasting much longer than scheduled.

At last John Paul II appeared. His personal delegate for the Society of Jesus, Dezza, read an address pledging the company's loyalty and obedience to the head of the church. The pope replied with a lengthy address, acknowledging the international character of the Jesuit order by reading various sections in different languages. He expressed "recognition and gratitude" for what he described as the Jesuits' historic contributions to the church over the centuries. John Paul II had affectionate words for "the very dear Father Arrupe," calling him the superior general, and conceded that his decision to appoint a personal delegate as acting head of the company was "doubtless singular and exceptional." The pontiff noted "with deep emotion" that his intervention had been received by the order's membership "in a genuinely Ignatian spirit," meaning obedience. In an allusion to widespread speculation about a possible crisis in the order, maybe a revolt or a split, John Paul II said: "Public opinion, perhaps, expected from the Jesuits a gesture dictated solely by human logic, but it received with admiration a reply dictated instead by the spirit of the Gospel."

The tone of the pope's remarks conveyed a sense of relief; the Jesuits, on the whole, seemed to have submitted to his decisions. The head of the church assigned to the order a task for the future—help the church carry out the resolutions of Vatican II, especially those regarding ecumenism, the improvement of relations between the church and non-Christian faiths, and research into the "disturbing phenomenon of atheism." Following a strong recommendation from the curial bureaucracy, John Paul II also urged the Jesuits to cooperate closely with all departments of the church's central government. At the end of his speech the pope voiced his hope that the General Congregation could be summoned within the current year.

Father Pittau, the deputy to the pope's personal delegate for the Jesuit order, told reporters later: "Once the Jesuits were the church's light cavalry and were riding out front; now we are asked to dismount and to advance jointly with everybody else." Another Jesuit military image. It meant that the Polish pope had ordered the company not to consider itself the avant garde of the church any longer but to keep in step with the bulk of its forces. Pittau also confided that "the Holy Father deemed that some deficiencies had to be corrected at once" before a new general might be chosen. While Pittau started a series of field trips, beginning with visits to Latin America, to make sure that the rank and file understood what was expected of them, the papal delegate, Dezza, made plain in a circular what the pope wanted: "The company must not fail in its traditional faithfulness to the magisterium [teaching authority] of the church." According to Roman Catholic doctrine, the magisterium of the supreme pontiff is not only exercised in the rare dogmatic pronouncements that—since 1870—are regarded as infallible, but in other statements, like encyclicals. If a Jesuit disagreed with such papal teachings, Dezza said in his message, he must not say so "outside scientific circles to avoid confusion in the minds of the faithful." Criticism of pontifical teachings must in any case shun aggressiveness or lack of respect, publicity, or contestation, Dezza warned.

In other words, John Paul II, notoriously thin skinned, did not want to be sniped at by the members of the first legion. The papal delegate also quoted the general, Arrupe, as having said to the pope: "I love the company, and for it I joyfully offer my life and my silence." Silence, if nothing else, was what the Polish pope and the Vatican desired from the liberal Jesuits who had lately been so vocal.

Nine months later Dezza informed the superiors of all Jesuit provinces that he had been authorized by the pope to summon the order's 33rd General Congregation for the election of a new general, to open on September 2, 1983. In his circular to all communities of the Society of Jesus around the world, the papal delegate earnestly admonished them to choose representatives for the Rome meeting "capable of promoting the renewal of the company in accordance with the thinking of the Holy Father."

The first pontiff in history to do so, John Paul II personally opened the 33rd General Congregation in the order's general house in the Borgo Spirito on September 2, 1983. Two hundred eleven delegates from Jesuit provinces all over the world—except those in Czechoslovakia, Rumania, and Soviet Lithuania—were present. The outgoing general, Father Arrupe, was seated near the altar of the chapel at Jesuit headquarters when the pope was concelebrating mass with Fathers Dezza and Pittau and, symbolically, with all other Jesuits in the congregation. In an address in Italian, French, English, and Spanish, the pope praised Arrupe, urged the Society of Jesus to maintain "total faithfulness" to the church and the pontiff, and remarked that the order was playing an "avant-garde role," an acknowledgment that pleased his listeners. Father Arrupe, in a farewell message that was read to the delegates, implicitly defended his achievements as superior general by affirming that the order had made "progress" during recent years.

On September 13, while the pope was winding up a visit to Austria, the General Congregation, on the first ballot, elected a Dutchman, the Reverend Peter-Hans Kolvenbach, as the 29th successor to St. Ignatius. (Another Dutchman, the Most Reverend Johannes Philipp Roothaan, headed the order from 1829 to 1853.)

During the informal consultations before the vote, known in quaint Jesuit parlance as the "murmurings," a near consensus on the seeming outsider's name had quickly been reached. A vast majority of the delegates had agreed to bypass the pope's apparent candidate, Father Pittau, to stress the order's residual autonomy in a dignified way, and to elevate a moderate who would not displease John Paul II.

Father Kolvenbach, 54 years old, had joined the Society of Jesus in 1948 in Mariendaal, the Netherlands, and was transferred in 1959 to the order's vice province of the Middle East. He studied theology at the University of St. Joseph in Beirut, a Jesuit institution founded in 1881, and was ordained to the priesthood in 1962. After studies in philosophy and oriental lan-

228

guages in Paris and The Hague, he returned to the Middle East and, in 1974, became superior of the order's Middle Eastern vice province. Early in his priestly career he shifted from the mainstream Latin rite to the Armenian rite, one of the small eastern Christian communities that recognize the pope as their supreme head but are jealous of their own traditions and liturgy. In 1981 he was named rector of the Pontifical Oriental Institute in Rome, a Jesuit-run research center that is a part of the Gregorian University complex.

The tall, bearded Father Kolvenbach, who was apt to dart ironical glances through horn-rimmed glasses, had a reputation for asceticism. He often slept on the floor, habitually was up before 5:00 A.M., and made a point of walking long distances instead of using public transport. He spoke Dutch, English, German, French, Spanish, Italian, Russian, and Armenian; his main interest was Armenian language and history. After an expert on Japan "the company" now had as its head a specialist in Armenian and Middle Eastern affairs who had taken part in ecumenical talks with leaders of the Orthodox churches.

By electing a superior general who had chosen to join a minority Christian community rather than stay in the dominant Latin rite into which he had been born in the town of Druten near Nijmegen, the Jesuit order expressed its determination to stress interfaith efforts.

Pope John Paul II was informed of the outcome of the Jesuit balloting in Vienna. On his flight back to Rome the same day, reporters asked him for a comment. The pontiff said he was not sure whether he knew Father Kolvenbach personally, but was happy that the Society of Jesus had a new leader. "I had no favorite," John Paul II remarked.

GOD'S OCTOPUS

In the early 1960s I was stationed in Madrid, and became friendly with the new apostolic nuncio to Spain, Archbishop Antonio Ribeiro (who was later to become a cardinal). The prelate, of northern Italian stock, had been a papal envoy in China and had become somewhat Confucian; also, he passionately loved classical music, and was a pungent conversationalist.

When he first asked me to dinner at the nunciature, I found

the archbishop dressed in a black silk blouse with a mandarin collar; with him was an aide in a regular cassock. As the three of us sat down at table we started talking about Spanish politics. The door behind the nuncio opened, and a nun carrying a tureen entered the room. Unseen by her, the archbishop put a finger across his lips with a meaningful look at me. I didn't finish what I had begun saying. When the nun had left again, the nuncio whispered: "Be careful! She is Opus."

I needed no further explanation. In the Spain of those days Opus Dei (God's Work), the association of Roman Catholic ecclesiastics and members of the laity, had a reputation as a shadowy, pervasive force. At least three members of Generalissimo Francisco Franco's government were known to belong to the movement, and other ministers were believed to be sympathizers, maybe secret "cooperators." Franco's wife, Carmen, was said to be strongly influenced by the group, and Prince Juan Carlos, the future king, had Opus Dei tutors. Opus Dei "technocrats," competent managerial types, held key posts in government departments, banks, and big business. They played into one another's hands and had informers everywhere, it was believed. Archbishop Ribeiro confided to me later that he had already got rid of the Opus Dei nuns who were staffing the nunciature's switchboard when he arrived in Madrid; they had probably been listening to his telephone conversations, including those with the Vatican. He was waiting for an excuse to replace the nun in the nunciature's kitchen and the driver. The Opus Dei spies in nuns' garb and the driver were a legacy from the nuncio's predecessor, who was now a member of the sacred college, Ildebrando Cardinal Antoniutti. During his term in Madrid, Antoniutti had become an admirer of the semisecret society, and was now one of its chief advocates in the Roman Curia.

I don't know whether Archbishop Riberi's suspicions were all justified, but such was the atmosphere in Spain during the later years of the Franco regime that they sounded quite plausible. That aura of mystery, intrigue, and skulduggery followed Opus Dei to Rome, and has stubbornly clung to the elusive group. Its enemies call it "Octopus Dei," or the "holy mafia," and characterize it as a "white freemasonry." In the Vatican, an Opus Dei faction has gained ground since the late 1970s, especially after the election of the Polish pope. John Paul II had been seen praying at the tomb of the founder of Opus Dei, the Very Reverend José Maria Escrivá de Balaguer y Albás, in August 1978, shortly before ascending the throne of Saint Peter. Later he had appointed notorious Opus Dei backers to high curia posts—Cardinal Oddi as head of the Sacred Congregation for the Clergy, and Pietro Cardinal Palazzini as head of the Sacred Congregation for the Causes of Saints.

John Paul II was impressed by the doctrinal conservatism of Opus Dei, similar to his own brand of theology, and by its managerial efficiency in getting things done. His predecessor, John Paul I, had also been an admirer of Opus Dei; several cardinals of the Roman Curia beside Oddi and Palazzini were known to be its supporters, maybe even its secret members. The Polish pope's decision to assert his full authority over the Society of Jesus was inevitably put into the context of the well-known rivalry between the old order and the young association. It all seemed a modern revival of ancient Vatican power plays in which the Dominicans or the Franciscans had been the Jesuits' antagonists.

Within the church much of the fault finding with Jesuits had come from Opus Dei members and sympathizers. The rapidly growing new movement, sometimes described by outsiders as a lay order, stressed bedrock orthodoxy and unblinking loyalty to the pope, as if in tacit polemics with the Jesuits. Opus Dei too had its ecclesiastical enemies—Jesuits, not surprisingly, but also members of the episcopacy and the clergy, theologians, and lay people who characterized the movement as a "church within a church" or a "parallel church." Things were being said about the group that echoed the charges of an earlier age that had been leveled at the Jesuits: secretiveness, greed for corporate wealth and power, elitism, and propensity for manipulation.

While the hard-pressed Society of Jesus had to bow to John Paul II's will and surrender a part of its autonomy, the society that Escrivá had created was pushing for more independence from the traditional church structures. If the Polish pontiff's intervention in the internal affairs of the Jesuit order was without any precedent in church history, so was what Opus Dei wanted. Speaking the arid language of canon law, the group was asking officially to be regarded as a "personal prelacy." This meant that the more than seventy thousand members (including one thousand five hundred priests) in 87 countries then claimed by Opus Dei should no longer depend, in spiritual matters, on their local bishops as did other Roman Catholics, but should be placed under the authority of the movement's leader, the president general. Opus Dei asserted that it represented a "pastoral, organic, and indivisible unity" and ought to be recognized as such by the Holy See. Members and supporters of the movement pointed to what they said was a similar situation: the Roman Catholic armed forces personnel of several countries, wherever they are sent, depend on a military vicar and his chaplains in religious affairs rather than on their home bishop and his clergy. True, Cardinal Cooke of New York, for instance, in his capacity as military vicar of all United States armed forces, wielded ecclesiastical authority in South Korea, West Germany, and all other areas in the world where American service personnel were stationed, but the Roman Catholics whose spiritual leader he was would eventually return to their home dioceses when they became civilians again. Opus Dei really wanted something else, a worldwide, permanent superdiocese.

To an outsider, such jurisdictional distinctions may seem trifling; in the Roman Catholic Church with its intricate structure and legalistic approach to matters of faith and conscience the lines of ecclesiastical command are of paramount importance.

Cardinal Benelli, then archbishop of Florence and no friend of Opus Dei, thus explained to me what was at issue: "Some of my priests are Opus, although they won't say so. I tell them to take a new assignment, and, would you believe it, they reply they'll think it over for a few days. I know, of course, that they ask their Opus Dei superior whether they should obey me, their archbishop! Now, imagine if Opus Dei were to get what it wants! This would undermine the authority of all bishops everywhere and create a church within the church." The trouble was, the cardinal added after a pause, that John Paul II was "not unsympathetic" toward the idea of a special jurisdiction tailormade for the movement. In an address to Opus Dei members in 1979, the Polish pope had indeed lauded the group for having, from its beginning, "anticipated the theology of the laity" that was to characterize the church during Vatican II and afterward, meaning a broadened role of lay people in ecclesiastical affairs. Such papal praise seemed to imply recognition of a special status.

The organization's founder, Escrivá, during the years before his death in 1975, had petitioned two popes, John XXIII and Paul VI, to declare Opus Dei a self-contained international entity subject solely to the Holy See. Both pontiffs declined. The papacy at that time tended to tighten control of the traditional

232

religious orders, as the Jesuits were beginning to notice; the Opus Dei demands for more autonomy received short shrift. The founder nevertheless kept emphasizing that his group was not an order but something different and unique.

Escrivá, a native of Spain's northeastern region of Aragon, was a 26-year-old pastor in Madrid when he first gathered a group of well-educated laymen around him in 1928. A women's branch of his new movement, completely separated from its men, was set up in 1930. Later some priests also joined, and Escrivá named his organization "Sacerdotal Society of the Holy Cross (Opus Dei)." A churchman who knew Escrivá well and was an admirer of his movement told me: "A measure of secrecy was in the nature of Opus Dei from the start. One must have known the cultural and political climate in Spain in the late 1920s and early 1930s. The schools, the universities, the arts, the press, were all in the hands of anticlericals and freemasons. Escrivá decided they had to be fought by infiltrating the educational system and other structures of Spanish society with Catholic intellectuals who would help one another."

In 1934 Escrivá set out his philosophy in a volume, *Spiritual Considerations,* which was aimed at theologically untrained lay people. In a great many reprints under a new title, *Camino* (The Way), and translations into 33 languages, it became the little white book of Opus Dei, disseminated all over the world in, the movement claims, 3 million copies. The religious best seller exhorts readers in 999 inspirational maxims to strive for perfection in whatever they do, practice austerity, take care of their own person, and be humble, but at the same time consider themselves "leaders." The author's message: You can and should attain saintliness in your profession and amid the seeming banalities of everyday life.

Although *Camino* said that everyone was born a leader, Escrivá's movement was elitist from the start. One did not apply for membership, one was observed, tested, tapped, and coopted. The top category of lay members, the numeraries, took vows of poverty, chastity, and obedience like monks and nuns, and lived in residences that looked like very comfortable monasteries, while continuing their normal activities as doctors, educators, civil servants, or bankers. Many numeraries studied theology on the side, and quite a few eventually abandoned their civilian jobs to become priests. Opus Dei says that during the founder's lifetime about one thousand lay members, some of them middle-aged, took holy orders. Numeraries were pledged to rigorous discipline including "mortification," or self-inflicted pain, like flagellation by one's own hand, a few days every week. Thus Opus Dei revived penitential practices that once were common in many monks' and nuns' orders but have recently become rare. A subaltern class of the organization's members, the oblates (later renamed "associates") also lived in the residences, but were not bound by vows and mainly did household work.

The bulk of Opus Dei members was made up of supernumeraries. They took no vows, lived in their own private homes, and could be married. They promised to follow the instructions of the organization's leaders and to observe certain rules in their personal lives. To them, Opus Dei discipline might mean sleeping on the floor once a week. The movement was flanked by associations of cooperators who played no active role in Opus Dei, but supported it in various ways and wanted to be linked with it for reasons of their own. Cooperators did not have to be Roman Catholics or even Christians, provided they were useful to the movement. In practice, almost anyone could become a secret cooperator of Opus Dei by shelling out money. Active membership entailed heavier financial burdens. "The Opus squeezes you out like a tube of toothpaste," an Italian numerary told me with seeming pride.

Many of the Opus Dei members I have met in Spain, Italy, and other countries had some traits in common. They had a better-than-average education, were well groomed, excelled in their profession, and tended to be aloof, if not arrogant. The Opus Dei residences I have seen were elegantly appointed, like exclusive clubs. When questioned about the inner workings of Opus Dei, adherents always became evasive. They did not advertise their belonging to the movement but would not deny that they were members when asked directly. Escrivá always insisted that Opus Dei was operating in broad daylight, had no part in any political or business affairs, and was ready to supply exhaustive information regarding its activities to anyone who wished to learn more about them. But, for instance, when I asked the official spokesman for the president general who the leader of the movement's female branch was, he said he didn't know.

Opus Dei headquarters in Rome and spokesmen for the movement in all countries where it operates will, as a matter of policy, send denials to any newspaper, magazine, or broadcasting organization that has alleged the group's involvement in political, cultural, financial, or business affairs. Yet Opus Dei keeps insisting publicly that its members are completely free to do what they like in their professional and political activities.

However, having observed the movement in Spain and Italy—still its main bases—for many years, I share the opinion of critics who charge it with a certain conspiratorial mentality. Opus Dei members often appear intent on establishing confidential, religious-oriented networks in institutions of higher learning, the media, banks, government offices, and business organizations. Such networks may simply function as mutual-aid societies, or may be used for church strategy. Hard though it may be to prove, I am convinced that Opus Dei has a propensity for penetrating the structures of secular society or, to quote again the churchman who knew its founder, to "infiltrate" them.

APOSTOLATE OF PENETRATION

As is usual whenever a new Roman Catholic Church movement is born, the Vatican was in no hurry to take official note of Opus Dei. Only after Escrivá had moved permanently to Rome in 1946 did his organization gain formal approval by the Holy See. It was remarkable that in 1950 the Vatican also accepted Escrivá's idea that non-Catholics and non-Christians could become members of the cooperators' associations supporting Opus Dei. Those were the days when the pontifical newspaper, *L'Osservatore Romano,* if it could not help mentioning the primate of the Church of England, referred to him as the "archbishop" of Canterbury, with quotation marks, to brand him as illegitimate; quotation marks, and often lower case, were used for the titles of all other non-Catholic churchmen too, as if they were all impostors and frauds. Opus Dei would later claim that by admitting Protestants and Jews as cooperators it anticipated the ecumenical spirit of Vatican II. Actually, Escrivá opened the ranks of his movement to them because he wanted their financial contributions, a strategy for which the Vatican showed full understanding.

To classify Escrivá's organization, the Roman Curia's law experts invented a new category of religious association, the secular institutes. *Secular,* in this parlance of canon law, denotes a member of the church, priest, or lay person, not committed to monastic life. A secular priest is not unfrocked, but one who does not belong to any religious order.

As if to make things even more complicated, Opus Dei, though placed in the new category of secular institutes, was bunched together with the traditional orders and subjected to the supervision of the curia's department in charge of monks, friars, and nuns (today called the Sacred Congregation for Religious and for Secular Institutes). Opus Dei never really liked being defined as a secular institute although the Vatican would always refer to it as such in its yearbook and in official documents. In the late 1970s, Opus Dei started describing itself instead as an international association of Catholics, without making any formal announcement of the change in its styling. Every three years or so, the Roman Curia promoted a conference of the leaders of the church's secular institutes, but Opus Dei always strayed away, as if to make a point.

Before Escrivá's residency in Rome, he had founded various Opus Dei outposts in Spain; one of them, the Estudio General of Pamplona, grew into a highly regarded institution of higher learning, the University of Navarre. From Rome, the movement's founder and first president general promoted the creation of colleges, student residences, and other educational and social centers in many countries. Opus Dei thus encroached on the turf in which the Jesuits had been prominent during centuries.

Adherents of Opus Dei referred to Escrivá as "the Father" almost from the beginning—and still do. The organization has always had a paternalistic, authoritarian character. Former members in some countries have publicly charged that they were subject to strong pressure not to "desert" when they said they wanted to leave the organization. There were complaints to church authorities by Roman Catholic parents that Opus Dei was unduly influencing their sons and daughters. Some of these stories sounded as though young people were in the clutches of a sect bent on mind control—youths to be deprogrammed. A former Opus Dei member, Dr. John Roche of Oxford University, gave documents to the *Times* of London purporting to prove that "Opus Dei is a church within a church ultimately loyal only to itself and psychologically dangerous to its own members." George Basil Cardinal Hume, archbishop of Westminster and a former Benedictine monk, declared in 1981 that no one under the age of eighteen years should take a vow or make a long-term commitment to Opus Dei. (By that time Opus Dei had ceased to speak of vows taken by members; the term "commitment" was preferred.)

During his lifetime, Escrivá had put in time traveling, especially in Latin America, to visit Opus Dei centers and win new followers. In lectures and addresses in rapid-fire Spanish he would plug a rather unsophisticated Roman Catholic fundamentalism, stressing his theme of sanctity in everyday life, and occasionally clowning a little. After a good line he would, like a consummate performer, wait for the applause while his vivid eyes seemed to watch everyone in the audience.

The rather simple religious teachings of Escrivá still permeate the curriculum in Opus Dei schools and colleges, although their medical or business administration departments may draw on advanced knowledge and research. The religious fundamentalism of Opus Dei contrasts with the intellectualism of many Jesuit institutions today, adding to the rivalry between the two church groups.

After Escrivá's death of heart failure at the age of 73, his close associate of 40 years, the Reverend Alvaro del Portillo y Diez de Sollano, then 62 years old, became his successor. He looked remarkably like "the Father," with similar horn-rimmed eyeglasses and graying hair parted at the left side as Escrivá had done. The election of the new president general by some three hundred Opus Dei leaders was said to have been unanimous.

Escrivá is buried in an underground crypt at the Opus Dei center in Rome. The marble slab covering his tomb bears only two Spanish words: *El Padre* (The Father). Every day at least one mass is offered by an Opus Dei priest at the altar in the crypt. The organization's world headquarters above the tomb, on the Viale Bruno Buozzi in the affluent Parioli district in north Rome, from the outside looks like one of the more luxurious apartment houses in the neighborhood. Inside there is a large chapel on ground level and a profusion of marble and fresh flowers in the vault with the founder's tomb. Everything looks rich, polished, and rather asceptic; the contrast to the cluttered yet Spartan surroundings of Jesuit headquarters in the Borgo Santo Spirito is striking.

Early in 1981 the Vatican's Sacred Congregation for the Causes of Saints opened formal proceedings for the beatification and canonization of the founder of Opus Dei. Sixty-nine cardinals—more than half of the sacred college—and 1,300 bishops, representing almost a third of the church's hierarchy, had endorsed petitions asking the Vatican to proclaim Escrivá a saint. Pope John Paul II himself was known to be for it. The pontiff, who had occasionally commented favorably on the "power" of Opus Dei, asked its leaders to extend the organization's activities to his own homeland. In Escrivá's lifetime Opus Dei had kept out of Poland and other Communist-ruled countries because, its spokesmen explained, the founder did not want the movement to be active in societies where Roman Catholics were being discriminated against because of their faith. Another reason may have been that Escrivá, aware of the anti-Communist image of his organization, was afraid it would face great difficulties, maybe outright persecution, in Soviet-dominated nations. However, after Escrivá's death the movement offered the Vatican its manpower to infiltrate such hostile countries.

In the early 1980s Spaniards were still the largest national group within Opus Dei, accounting for about 40 percent of all members. Spanish was the prevailing language at Rome headquarters, and the correspondence between the center and branches of the organization was mostly in that language.

In Italy, Spain, and other countries Opus Dei was on good terms with grass-roots movements of young, neoconservative Roman Catholics that had recently sprung up, like Communion and Liberation, and the Focolari. A fundamentalist front within the church, led by Opus Dei, seemed to be emerging.

At the same time there was a tug of war between branches of the Roman Curia over the request by Opus Dei to be transformed into a "personal prelacy," independent of local bishops (particularly of unsympathetic ones like the archbishops of Westminster and Florence). Eduardo Cardinal Pironio, the head of the Sacred Congregation for Religious and for Secular Institutes, was opposed to such a change. An Argentine of Italian ancestry, a modern theologian and a liberal who had experienced difficulties with the Peronist party in his homeland, Pironio had been widely tipped as a frontrunner in the two papal elections of 1978. As chief of the Vatican department dealing with religious orders and the few secular institutes, he occupied a post held earlier by Cardinal Antoniutti, the archconservative who had saturated the nunciature in Madrid with Opus Dei personnel. As long as Antoniutti had been in charge at the curia, Escrivá had not minded being supervised by his department. The Argentine cardinal, however, was no friend of Opus Dei, and this was one of the reasons that the organization was pressing hard for a redefinition of its ecclesiastical status.

As head of a personal prelacy the president general of the movement would depend administratively on the Sacred Congregation of the Bishops. It so happened that the chief of this important curial office, which oversees the Roman Catholic hierarchy all over the world, Sebastiano Cardinal Baggio, was an old friend and admirer of Escrivá. Baggio had also been a favorite in the pontifical sweepstakes of 1978; his conciliatory personality, his diplomatic experience as a papal envoy in Canada and Latin America, and his administrative skills made him appear well equipped for the papacy.

Late in 1979 a leak from curia offices, patently engineered by an enemy of Opus Dei, led to the publication in Spain of confidential documents that showed how hard the movement was fighting for more autonomy in the church. It appeared that the president general of Opus Dei, del Portillo, in letters to Cardinal Baggio had insisted that John Paul II himself wanted the organization's status to be transformed into that of a personal prelacy, and had none too subtly implied that curial bureaucrats were sabotaging the fulfillment of the pontiff's desire. A report submitted to Baggio's department stressed that Opus Dei could place at the pope's disposal "a mobile corps of priests and laymen" for important and urgent missions. Such assignments, the text suggested, might be carried out as an "apostolate of penetration" under cover of normal professional activities "in countries under totalitarian regimes of an anti-Christian or atheistic nature, or characterized by extreme nationalism . . . preventing the action of missionaries and members of religious orders and an active and organized presence of the church."

What Opus Dei was offering to the papacy seemed a plan for organizing secret religious commandos and sending them (perhaps by parachute?) into hostile territories to link up with the underground of believers in God, Jesus Christ, and the Virgin Mary. It sounded quite romantic, and was possibly calculated to appeal particularly to a Polish pope. The idea of an "apostolate of penetration" was never explained in detail. It was left to the imagination of the readers in the Vatican to figure out how the secret operatives of Opus Dei would foil the police agencies of totalitarian countries. One was reminded of the clandestine masses offered in the homes of English recusant families who would not obey King Henry VIII's command to break with Rome, and of secret clergymen hiding in "the priest's hole."

In language that seemed to have been borrowed from the Jesuits of the Counter-Reformation, Opus Dei had in effect proposed to be the new adventurous vanguard of the pope, a new first legion not unlike the spiritual shock troops that Saint Ignatius had trained. Opus Dei did not deny that the documents were authentic, but stated that they were very incomplete, and refused further comments on the ground that the entire matter fell under the exclusive jurisdiction of the Holy See. The Vatican said nothing at all.

The leaked documents also contained some data that until then had not been generally known. A report to the Vatican claimed that Opus Dei members were active in 497 universities and colleges, 694 newspapers and magazines, 52 television and radio stations, 38 news agencies, and 12 motion picture companies in all continents. The figures did not mean that the Spanish-dominated movement was in full control of all these schools and information media, but indicated that it had managed to establish acknowledged or secret beachheads in them.

In Rome the group's institutions looked modest in comparison with the Gregorian University and the other units of the Jesuit establishment; Opus Dei was operating a vocational school complex and an international students' residence on the outskirts of the city. But the disclosures in Spain proved that the organization that Escrivá had founded wanted recognition as a world-wide force of Roman Catholic infiltration into hostile environments.

When the secret documents appeared in the press, John Paul II had already asked Cardinal Baggio to prepare the recognition of Opus Dei as the first personal prelacy in church history. Baggio named a commission of experts who, in 25 meetings from February 1980 to February 1981, examined the historic, legal, and pastoral aspects of the question, and drafted rules for the functioning of Opus Dei in its proposed new form. A special committee of cardinals, appointed in all secrecy by the pontiff, approved the recommendations of the experts' commission.

Soon afterward those archbishops and bishops around the world in whose dioceses Opus Dei was already operating received a confidential Vatican document with an outline of the personal prelacy project and a promise that any observation would be carefully considered. Some bishops, in letters to Rome, welcomed the fact that Opus Dei was about to get what it had wanted for so long; others didn't react, and yet others sent criticisms to the Sacred Congregation for the Bishops and to the pope personally. Several members of the Spanish hierarchy in particular warned that by assuming the unprecedented role of a personal prelacy Opus Dei would in their country gain, or regain, undue influence.

The Second Vatican Council, in a fleeting passage of its decree on the ministry and life of priests, had indeed foreseen the creation of "personal prelacies and other institutions" to which certain priests might be assigned to carry out "special pastoral projects for the benefit of different social groups in any region or among any race in any part of the world." This blanket authorization for the establishment of special clerical task forces had remained on paper for nearly seventeen years until 1982, when Opus Dei at last won its long battle for a privileged position within the church. Pope John Paul II overruled all objections by members of the Roman Curia and of the hierarchy at large who were hostile to the Spanish-controlled organization, and granted its status as the first personal prelacy in the Roman Catholic world—a signal victory in a twenty-year lobbying effort. Father del Portillo became the first prelate of Opus Dei. In this capacity he had, among other things, the right to ordain priests. The only concessions to the misgivings voiced by many members of the episcopacy were that del Portillo would have full and direct jurisdiction only over the priests who had come from the organization's own ranks (about one thousand two hundred in 1982), and that the opening of new Opus Dei centers anywhere needed the consent of the local bishop.

The papal document that gave Opus Dei almost everything it had ever wanted praised the group's firmness in matters of doctrine and discipline, and its "apostolic vigor." A numerary of Opus Dei who held a responsible position at the organization's world headquarters in Rome and who, at a mature age, was studying for the priesthood, told me with rather startling military imagery: "The providential decision by the Holy Father is like an atomic bomb. You have seen only the first flash, but wait for the fallout. Saint Francis had only a few companions when he started, and you know what he did for the church and the world. We have more than one thousand priests, poised to go into action anywhere. . . ." A churchman who taught at an ec-

241

clesiastical academy in Rome, and who made no secret of his reservations about Opus Dei, said to me: "The Polish pope envisions for the Spanish-led zealots a role similar to that which the Jesuits played during the Counter-Reformation. Opus Dei is now the first legion."

Combining religious fundamentalism with antiintellectual posturing, a propensity for undercover work, and a cult of managerial efficiency, the new first legion could be expected to make its influence felt especially in academic institutions, the media, and big business in Western nations. It remains to be seen whether Opus Dei will also follow through its plan to become the papacy's secret service in the East and in countries under "atheistic" regimes.

CHAPTER 8
PITFALLS OF VATICANOLOGY

FOR YEARS IT was an office joke that I worked on Propaganda Street, *Via di Propaganda.* The Rome Bureau of the *New York Times,* of which I was in charge, was then a tenant of the Italian news agency, ANSA, in its building on a street leading to the Spanish Square. Opposite was the rust-colored palace that was the headquarters of the Sacred Congregation *De Propaganda Fide* (Regarding the Propagation of the Faith). The Vatican missionary department has since changed its name to Sacred Congregation for the Evangelization of the Peoples, but the short street in downtown Rome where its administrative center sits retains the old title.

Since the seventeenth century, when Gregory XV set up the Sacred Congregation as the Vatican agency responsible for missionaries and the territories where they were active, the gerund of the Latin verb for "to propagate," *propagare,* has become a noun in modern languages, "propaganda." The term today suggests manipulation of public opinion, especially since Goebbels named his Nazi government department the Ministry for Popular Enlightenment and Propaganda. The unpleasant connotation that "propaganda" has acquired was doubtless the main reason the Vatican chose another name for its missionary agency. The trouble is that the Holy See's information policy, though it shuns the word, is to this day inspired by the concept of propaganda: it is forever seeking to put across its own—incomplete, distorted, or prettified—version of reality. As an adjunct to its dissemination of propaganda, the Vatican employs secrecy—so the Vatican version of things is put forward, and questions are rarely answered.

People who search for facts about the Vatican are all too often dismissed with generalities or inspirational rhetoric. More persistent inquiries are usually met with secretiveness or with exercises in apologetics, the branch of theology that specializes in the defense of religion and the church against critics. The Holy See's cult of secrecy may be justified as far as it is meant to protect matters of individual conscience, such as personal problems that have been revealed to a priest in confession, or submitted to the pope for a decision. But mystery envelops many other aspects of church activities too, such as finances.

Such reluctance to furnish straight information or to explain convincingly why many facts cannot be disclosed has contributed to the Vatican's old, and enduring, reputation for being mixed up in underhand dealings. It is also a reason that press coverage of the papacy is a frustrating business. The clumsy information policy of the Holy See fosters the widespread belief that many wicked mysteries are being harbored within the Vatican walls, and it may indirectly be responsible for continual attempts at worming those secrets out by illicit means.

The peevish reticence of the Roman Curia provides the climate for rumors—often quite unfounded—that are always rife in Rome. Whenever actual scandals occur, as they do in all institutions now and then, and they can no longer be hushed up, the belated explanations that the Vatican supplies meet with general disbelief even if it tries to stick to the truth. The Holy See still has to learn how to deal with international public opinion in an era of rapid global communications, inquisitive news reporting, and widespread disbelief in the wisdom—or even honesty—of people in power.

SPIES AROUND THE POPE

The taming of the Jesuit order by a strong-willed pope, the maneuvers of Opus Dei, and above all, the theories about an international plot behind the 1981 attempt on the life of John Paul II kept diplomats and intelligence agents well supplied with material for many months. "These things are a godsend," the counselor of a Western European embassy to the Holy See confided to me. "If we have nothing else for the weekly report to our foreign ministry when the courier leaves on Tuesday, we can always put in the latest twist in the Jesuit-Opus epic, or the speculation that a Bulgarian connection armed the would-be assassin of the pope."

What to tell headquarters in ciphered cables and lengthy analyses for the diplomatic pouch is a constant worry for the ambassadors accredited to the Holy See, for their aides, and for the spies who are assigned to ferret out the presumed secrets of the Vatican. Job conditions in Rome are pleasant; embassies have sumptuous premises, some of them surrounded by parks; diplomats and undercover agents enjoy the soft life of the city. They would like to stay where they have had the good fortune of being posted, and they are always afraid that their home authorities may find them not sufficiently productive, and shift them to some less desirable capital. In many years as a foreign correspondent in Rome I met plenty of diplomats and quite a number of opaque personages, probably spies, who would draw me into conversations about the Vatican to find out what I knew, and I was usually aware they were taking mental notes for their Tuesday (or Thursday, or Friday) report to their foreign department or mission control.

In a city of incessant gossip where everybody seems to know all there is to know about everyone else, it is remarkably difficult to gather confidential facts from the sacred palaces. Vaticanology is as frustrating and unreliable as Kremlinology, brilliant in hindsight and dicey in forecasts. Much of it is no more than guesswork by old hands. Practitioners of the art don't like to be reminded of the summer and autumn of 1978 when none of them, literally not one, was able to predict that the little-known patriarch of Venice, Luciani, and tne archbishop of Krakow, Wojtyla, would be raised to the papacy.

The enthronement of the dynamic churchman from Eastern Europe as the first non-Italian pontiff in the modern age prompted several governments—the Kremlin in particular—to reinforce the ranks of their Vatican watchers. John Paul II's continued interventions in the political and social developments in his native Poland, and his many travels, may well justify Moscow's heightened attention to Vatican activities. Papal diplomats in the world's capitals found themselves asked to Soviet embassy dinner parties; in Rome, Italian Communists who were obviously working for the Soviet embassy began cultivating old clerical contacts and trying to develop new ones. From many clues I gathered that several other governments—especially France, West Germany, Britain, and Israel—were stepping up efforts to tap the Vatican for information. The U. S. Department of State intensified its exchanges with John Paul II's aides while the Central Intelligence Agency, probably wisely, continued to cover Vatican affairs only marginally.

The heightened interest from the world powers and even from smaller nations in the papacy as a political-diplomatic center sprang from various sources. First, there was John Paul II's identification with Poland. Would the pontiff sponsor new anti-Communist crusades, or work for a new accommodation with the Kremlin? Then, the church's role in Latin America became a major topic of the ambassadors and intelligence community in Rome. Would John Paul II, who showed such concern for the countries in the Western Hemisphere, support social change or attempt to curb revolutionary movements there? The Middle East, the Third World, and the attitude of Roman Catholics toward the nuclear armaments race were other areas where the Vatican was felt to be able to play an important part. Not a few governments appeared to think they might use papal influence to boost their own policies; in other world capitals there seemed to be fears that such a highly visible pontiff might unleash popular movements that he himself could not foresee and control—for instance, in Eastern Europe. Each of the major nations monitored the Vatican in its own way and according to its own policy objectives.

France's diplomats and secret agents have kept the Holy See under close observation through the centuries, and were doing so with renewed zest under John Paul II. West Germany was betraying at least the same appetite for Vatican intelligence as did the Nazi Third Reich and the German governments between the two World Wars. With Bonn's sensitivity to events and trends in Eastern Europe, the election of the Polish pope only sharpened its desire to learn of every tiny detail of church action in that area. There were also signs that Britain was becoming much more alert to the papacy than it had been for a long time. Among smaller countries, Israel above all was carefully observing Vatican activities. Although officially unrepresented at the Holy See, Israel maintained a Vatican desk at its embassy to Italy, and experts had no doubt that it was flanked by a small but efficient intelligence network. One of its high-priority tasks was said to be surveillance of Christian Arabs in Rome. The most conspicuous of them, for a long time, was Archbishop Hilarion Capucci, a Syrian-born churchman who in effect was the representative of the Palestine Liberation Organization in the Roman Catholic hierarchy. His official title was that of apostolic visitor (papal inspector) to the Catholics of the Greek-Melchite rite in Europe; actually, he was maintaining a liaison between the Vatican and militant Palestinian groups. Capucci, a native of Aleppo, was found guilty of arms contraband by an Israeli court in 1974. Evidence was produced during his trial that, abusing his prerogatives as a Jerusalem-based auxiliary bishop of the Greek-Melchite patriarch, he had smuggled arms and explosives for Palestinian guerrillas in his car from Lebanon into the Israeli-occupied West Bank.

Capucci served three years of a twelve-year prison sentence, and was released in 1977 in an Israeli goodwill gesture toward the Holy See. The bishop, who had a thick police file in Jerusalem, was expelled from Israel the moment he left jail. Pope Paul VI relegated him to the Western Hemisphere, naming him apostolic visitor to the Greek-Melchite communities in Latin America, a rather shadowy church post. However, Capucci did not stay long in the field assigned to him, soon turned up in the Middle East again, and accepted honorary membership in the Palestine National Council, the 300-seat PLO "parliament." Eventually, responding to protests from Jerusalem, the Vatican gave Capucci the pro forma assignment in Western Europe, and informed Israel with a memorandum to its embassy in Rome that the Greek-Melchite bishop was under strict orders from Paul VI to keep out of the Middle East and to avoid any activities harmful to the Jewish state. Later, Capucci unsuccessfully tried his hand at obtaining the liberation of the hostages taken by Iranian "students" during their raid on the United States embassy in Teheran. When the Greek-Melchite bishop was not traveling in the Middle East (flouting Paul VI's ban) or in Western Europe, he lived in Rome, tailed by agents from Israeli intelligence, and presumably from other services as well.

Capucci was not the only churchman in Rome whose movements and contacts were under scrutiny by undercover operatives. Prelates, or even simple priests, from Poland and other Eastern European countries who visited the Vatican took the same precautions against informers and electronic surveillance as they used to do at home. A few of them told me they felt sure they were being shadowed in Rome by agents from their home governments.

Regardless of any foreign espionage efforts in Rome, the country that should know most about the Holy See is Italy. Between the Vatican and the surrounding city and nation the ties are innumerable; the atmosphere in the Roman Curia has remained essentially Italianate even under a "foreign" pontiff, as has been stressed earlier. Italian authorities and political factions have always kept a close watch on church affairs; conversely, the Vatican has often intervened in Italian domestic politics, quite overtly under Pius XII and Paul VI. For all these reasons the best channels of information on the Vatican ought to be Italian. The Italian intelligence agencies indeed have often used choice bits of their Vatican dossiers in tradeoffs for material they wanted from friendly services of other countries.

Yet over the years I have found on various occasions that high Italian officials, not to mention the average Italian newspaper readers, were full of curious misconceptions about what the Holy See was doing and collectively thinking. The public obtained a glimpse of the kind of information on church matters that the Rome government usually receives when a confidential report by the Italian ambassador to the Holy See, Vittorio Cordero di Montezemolo, was leaked to the press. The document, written after Paul VI's death, discussed in a highly speculative manner the possible outcome of the conclave for the election of a successor. His speculations were to prove wrong. Cordero di Montezemolo was an intelligent man and a successful diplomat in other posts; but at the Holy See he was uninformed.

One reason for the generally poor quality of Italian reporting on the Vatican is what seems an advantage, proximity. Italians are convinced they know a lot about the papacy, and they do— but most of this knowledge is gossip and trivial detail that hamper, instead of help, serious analysis. The abundance of rumor and the dearth of substantive information emanating from the Vatican are baffling to the diplomats and, presumably, to many intelligence agents posted in Rome. Much of their raw material is cocktail party conversation, guesswork by genuine or self-styled Vatican experts, or even outright invention. Whenever there is some verifiable fact, it is most likely linked with internal church affairs—such as the antagonism between Jesuits and Opus Dei— that may fascinate the specialist but seem irrelevant to the government offices that are concerned with secular power relations.

As has been noted before, the largest segment of the reports that flow into the Roman Curia from all parts of the world refers to the dioceses; the church hierarchy and finances; the religious orders and institutions; doctrinal conflicts; and the personal problems of priests, monks, and nuns. The universal church is highly self-absorbed; its head, the supreme pontiff must devote most of his time, attention, and energy to internal ecclesiastical matters. True, at times a papal decision in church affairs may have political and even international consequences. For instance, after the death of Stefan Cardinal Wyszynski, several governments were eager to know well in advance whom John Paul II would appoint as the new primate of Poland. (It seems the Communist authorities in Warsaw and Moscow were informed beforehand, maybe through telephone taps, that the post would go to Bishop Jozef Glemp of Warmia; Washington did not know.) However, many other developments in the Vatican to which churchmen and religious-affairs specialists attach great importance seem insignificant to the foreign departments of most governments.

An ambassador to the Holy See who is determined to make a success of his job will cultivate relationships with ecclesiastics from his nation who are on assignment in Rome because they are a prime source of information to him. Visiting prelates may also count on being asked to social functions at the embassy of their home country in the Italian capital, or maybe to a dinner party offered in their honor by some other diplomatic mission—not right on arrival but later when they have already seen curial officials, perhaps even the pope, and may be expected to possess fresh information. Several embassies dealing with the Holy See have on their staff some priest with the title "ecclesiastical counselor" whose task it is to promote such clerical contacts. Many churchmen and a few nuns in Vatican posts, Italians and non-Italians, keep in touch with diplomats or officials of their home governments, and are willing to tell them something, or much, of what they know. The State Archives of Venice contain evidence that the Venetian cardinals in Rome during the Middle Ages and the Renaissance regularly sent secret reports to the authorities of the Most Serene Republic on what was going on at the pontifical court. Churchmen from other parts of the world also have notoriously acted as Vatican informers to their governments over the centuries.

From the standpoint of the intelligence buyer, the trouble is that even a prelate holding down a permanent job in the Vatican who is amenable to cooperating with the government of his own (or another) country is not always a good source. He knows what is in the documents that pass across his desk and what he picks up during commission meetings and in the corridors, but may remain completely in the dark about papal moves and decisions in vital fields.

The pope's Secretariat of State is the keeper of most—though not all—Vatican secrets, but its members are of little help to diplomats, intelligence operatives, and news reporters. As an elite group in the pontifical bureaucracy, the officials of the Secretariat of State not only take a special vow to observe strictest secrecy under pain of excommunication that only the pope can lift, they also are often too busy for embassy receptions and small talk, and they are under constant surveillance by their superiors and by one another. As already mentioned, some secrets are shared by the head of the church only with the top officials of the Secretariat of State, and there are always matters that the supreme pontiff won't tell even his closest aides.

The policy of restricting sensitive knowledge to a very small number of highly motivated persons in modern times has assured that the Vatican's most vital secrets have, on the whole, been well kept. On the other hand, there are many signs that intelligence networks have managed to recruit paid informers among the lay and clerical employees of the papal state. The salaries in the Vatican are generally low, and some member of the staff may be tempted to pick up extra money by selling information to outsiders, perhaps even by copying some secret document. The lucrative commerce in data on the health of Pius XII organized by his archiater was a serious, but by no means unique, indiscretion. In later years I myself was approached by various persons claiming they could procure confidential material from the curia, at a price. I rejected all such offers, explaining that I was not in the business of checkbook journalism. (Much earlier, when I used to deliver the monthly pay envelope from the *New York Times* to Pius XII's doctor, I was convinced that what we were doing was not right. I was too junior a member of the Rome Bureau then to expect my scruples to be taken into consideration.)

Once a middleman, to show what his Vatican contact was able to deliver, gave me the galley proofs of an apostolic letter on important points of church doctrine that Paul VI would issue some days later; the text, which I did not use, soon proved to be authentic. If news reporters can, if they want, buy secret Vatican information, it may be supposed that intelligence networks with their large funds for bribery can do so even more easily.

In 1982, the left-wing magazine *Konkret* of Hamburg quoted a former officer of West Germany's Federal Information Service, Hans Langemann, as asserting that in the late 1950s and in the 1960s he had run a spy ring inside the Vatican. It seems that the Bonn authorities at that time were most eager to learn everything about the Holy See's Ostpolitik and about a possible Vatican role in contacts between Italian Communists, West German Social Democrats, and Eastern European governments. According to the disclosures in *Konkret,* the paid agents of the Bonn-directed network included a nobleman, a Jesuit, and an Italian prelate (code named "Bruno") later promoted to abbot, who produced valuable material not only from the curia but also from Italian government departments. At the time of the startling publication in the Hamburg magazine, Langemann had left West Germany's federal intelligence and was in the service of a security agency of the State of Bavaria. He was suspended, and an investigation was opened. As is usual in such cases, little was heard of its findings.

The affair also had repercussions in the Vatican. John Paul II's secretary of state, Cardinal Casaroli, was particularly upset by a report in the West German magazine *Stern* that copies of classified curia documents, stealthily taken from desk drawers in his own office, had been made for Langemann. The material was said to have included a memorandum to Casaroli preparatory to top-secret talks between him and a Communist emissary from East Germany. A very well-informed prelate told me that Casaroli ordered a thorough inquiry, which ascertained that ecclesiastics had indeed been spying for Bonn in Rome, and received payments for their undercover network. The espionage network was referred to in West German official reports as "Operation Eva." The Vatican investigators also found that most of the material procured by Langemann was based on hearsay, secondhand sources, and even newspaper clippings, while some of it was outright fakery. West Germany's Federal Information Service, in other words, may have paid good money for shoddy goods. The churchmen who had been found, or were suspected, to have collaborated with West German intelligence were removed from the Vatican, but no further punishments were imposed on them.

Apart from access to the Vatican's own secrets that a church job in Rome may provide or facilitate, it would seem that such a position might also serve as an excellent cover for espionage or undercover activities aimed at other targets. In the 1950s the British popular newspapers praised an Irish prelate of the curia's Supreme Sacred Congregation of the Holy Office (now the Sacred Congregation of the Discipline of the Faith), Msgr. Hugh O'Flaherty, as the "Scarlet Pimpernel of the Vatican." According to the press accounts, during World War II the monsignor had run a kind of underground railroad for Allied prisoners of war who had escaped from camps in Italy. O'Flaherty himself would not say much about his extracurricular wartime activities. Later, long after his death, O'Flaherty's clandestine role during World War II was fictionalized in a televsion film, *The Scarlet and the Black,* with Gregory Peck.

The Nazis also used the Vatican for secret operations. Many questions were raised by the activities of Bishop Alois Hudal, rector of the Teutonic College in Rome, during the years immediately after the end of World War II. The bishop, an Austrian from Graz whose pro-Nazi sympathies were already notorious during the 1930s, held a part-time post in the Vatican's Supreme Sacred Congregation of the Holy Office, and knew Monsignor O'Flaherty well. Whereas the Irishman was taking care of Allied prisoners of war, the Austrian looked after Nazis on the run. Italian and Western intelligence officers said later they were convinced that Hudal, who had meanwhile died, had been instrumental in the escape of war criminals. German and Austrian Nazis and pro-Nazi figures from German-occupied countries are known to have found a temporary refuge in 1945 and 1946 in ecclesiastical buildings in the Italian capital before they were supplied with false identity papers to go on to Latin America.

After the liberation of Rome in 1944 Allied counterintelligence discovered a Gestapo spy and sabotage center in a building on Rome's southwestern outskirts that belonged to the Holy See. The property had been bought by the curia's Sacred Congregation for the Eastern Churches in 1943 with funds generously provided by an "anonymous Georgian benefactor" for the establishment of a Georgian seminary in Rome. Six young men, supposed to hail from what was then the Georgian Soviet Republic, arrived by way of Germany, ostensibly to start studies for the Roman Catholic priesthood. Actually, all six and their burly housekeeper (and secret commander) were members of the S.S. Allied investigators found a clandestine radio transmitter and receiver in the basement of the presumed seminary; the building was meant as a base for a secret network of Nazi agents left behind in Rome after the retreat of the German armed forces.

Another piece of Roman real estate has aroused more recent suspicions in the Vatican and among local security experts. It is the old Villa Abamelek, a vast, walled estate at the beginning of the Ancient Aurelian Way, less than a mile south of St. Peter's Square. The Soviet embassy in Italy acquired the property, once owned by Russian nobility, after World War II—on a disputed title—as the residence for Moscow's ambassadors. Since then extensive construction work has been carried out on the estate to provide accommodations for other members of the embassy. People in the neighborhood have heard old stories that some caves in the gardens of the Villa Abamelek, like other holes in the tufa subsoil of the area, are part of a labyrinth of catacombs linked with the grottoes beneath St. Peter's. The Vatican does not seem to worry about the possibility of subterranean passages between the Soviet enclave, which is covered by diplomatic immunity, and the pontifical state. Security-minded curialists, however, are intrigued by reports that the extraterritorial Soviet complex is crammed with advanced electronic equipment. Several antennas are visible from the outside. Could the Villa Abamelek serve as a facility for listening in on Vatican telephone conversations?

The popes and their aides have known for a long time that secret business should be transacted without any risk of intrusion. Pius XI refused to touch the white telephone that had been installed in his study. Pius XII had been tipped off that Communist telephone workers were monitoring the lines between Castel Gandolfo and the Vatican; even for minor matters he would summon curial officials to his summer residence rather than consult them by telephone. The pope's Secretariat of State today is in frequent contact by telephone with papal envoys and members of the church hierarchy in distant parts of the world, but the party at either end is aware that somebody will in all likelihood be listening. Three or four different intelligence agencies were believed to be tapping the lines whenever one of John Paul II's aides called a member of the Roman Catholic hierarchy in Poland.

The Vatican itself is probably not above bugging its own telephones. I have no proof that such a practice actually exists, but over the years I have met quite a number of curialists and employees of the pontifical state who were sure it did, and who would take no chances with the Vatican communications network. Anyone who lingers long enough outside the Gate of St. Anne will sooner or later notice some priest or layman dashing to a pay telephone in the Italian state post office opposite the Vatican walls or in some nearby espresso bar to make a call that he thinks will be safe from papal eavesdroppers.

Telephone surveillance in the Vatican, if it really takes place, would be in the hands of a small intelligence unit within the Vigilance Office, a papal police body. Apart from this unit there is no institutionalized Vatican intelligence service. Instead, apostolic nuncios, bishops, religious orders, missionaries, and other groups and individuals keep the Holy See—and especially the Secretariat of State—constantly supplied with secret reports. The Jesuits and Opus Dei also participate in this vast information gathering.

The Vatican nevertheless lacked the instruments for carrying out its own investigation of the suspected international conspiracy that led to the attack on John Paul II in 1981, and had to rely on what Italian and other intelligence agencies told it.

INVENTED SECRETS

Facing the Vatican's wall of secrecy, news reporters are confronted with even more daunting challenges than are diplomats and spies. For one thing, the Vaticanology of journalists is immediately printed or broadcast, and thus liable to criticism and denials, whereas the reports by ambassadors and intelligence agents go into discreet files, and misinformation in them may never be exposed, or only by future historians. It is considered unethical for the press to bribe informers the way secret operatives do (although most news media lack the necessary funds in any case). Furthermore, the press does not have the institutionalized access to high Vatican officials that diplomats accredited to the Holy See automatically enjoy.

A place that journalists covering the Vatican may frequent, and where the Holy See occasionally issues what it regards as news, has existed for decades. It is now called the Press Room of the Holy See, and is located outside Vatican City, in one of the modern buildings off St. Peter's Square as if to emphasize its marginal nature. Although most journalists have to meet daily deadlines in the evening and during the night hours, the press center is normally open only from morning until the Roman lunch hour between 1:00 and 2:00 P.M. The Vatican officials dealing with the press are customarily uninformed, reticent, and sometimes dour; often they cannot be reached in the afternoon and evening, or even disappear for days. Journalists frequenting the press room receive official announcements from the Vatican, with little comment and with evasive answers to their questions.

The atmosphere is that of the information office of a touchy authoritarian government, tempered by the Roman cynicism—and the frequent profanities—of the habitues. The regulars in the Press Room of the Holy See are known as *Vaticanisti,* as they were called long before the term "Vaticanologist" became internationally current. The hard core of this group is made up of about a dozen Italians who not only serve as the accredited Vatican correspondents for information media in their country, but often do part-time work for foreign news organizations; one or the other of them may also act as informant to some embassy. The problem with the Vaticanisti is that they know little of the world, and even of the church, at large, although they may have traveled with the pope on some of his journeys. Few of them know any language besides Italian, and their ecclesiastical sources are almost exclusively Italians. This is a reason why so much of the news produced by the Vaticanisti has a provincial flavor even if it finds its way into international media.

The year of the three popes, 1978, brought out how little the Vaticanisti really know about the inner workings of the church. After Paul VI's death only one or two of the Italian journalists frequenting the Vatican press center gave the patriarch of Venice, Luciani, a remote chance to be elected pope. And two months later, in October 1978, none of the Vaticanisti as much as mentioned the archbishop of Krakow, Wojtyla, as a possible candidate for the papacy.

Unsatisfactory though the arrangements for reporting on the papacy are today, they must nevertheless be considered an improvement over the situation before the Second Vatican Council. At that time, there was no press service of the Holy See; nevertheless one of the earliest Vaticanisti was already practicing, holding a near monopoly of all journalistic reporting on the papacy. He was Msgr. Emilio Pucci, a dignified and erudite prelate who had once served in the Secretariat of State. For family reasons he needed more money than he was earning in his curia post, and he had found that the press was willing to pay. He had been allowed to use a hole-in-the-wall office off the Courtyard of St. Damasus where the official visitors to Pope Pius XI and, then, to Pius XII passed by, and he put out a daily bulletin with a list of papal audiences and such other Vatican news as he managed to pick up. Since at the time there was no other independent way for news organizations to secure regular information out of the Vatican, they all subscribed to Monsignor Pucci's services. The Pucci bulletins came on onionskin paper; an assistant would bang them out on a typewriter after having squeezed in as many thin sheets as possible. We paid little, and the copy that we received was one of the last, often barely legible, especially when tired carbon paper had once more been reused. The monsignor's assistant, a layman, would give news that he regarded as urgent to subscribers by phone, for an additional fee. The Pucci service was not consistently reliable. Once I was puzzled by an item stating that the archbishop of New York, Spellman (who wasn't a cardinal yet) would visit the Middle East. "That surely is news," I said to myself, and began to check out the information. It turned out that Spellman had announced he was going to make a trip to the Midwest of the United States, and that Monsignor Pucci, having read or heard of the archbishop's travel plans, in a linguistic-geographical misunderstanding had manufactured a piece of highly interesting, but unfortunately false, international news of them.

The acting chief of the *New York Times* bureau in Rome at the time was one of the most conscientious reporters I have ever known, Milton Bracker. He once complained to Monsignor Pucci that the onionskin bulletins were often inaccurate and hardly worth what little money we were paying for them. The white-haired prelate looked mysterious, and said that if we were prepared to spend more he would be happy to let us have his "special service," which was being distributed to only a select circle of subscribers. We declined the offer. A little later Monsignor Pucci found himself disgraced when the authorities of post-Fascist Italy discovered a list of paid informers of Mussolini's secret police, the Agency of Vigilance and Repression of

256

Anti-Fascists that had been known, and feared, by its Italian acronym, as OVRA. Pucci's name was on the list. I was convinced at the time, and still believe today, that the elderly monsignor was not an OVRA spy, but that he had just sold a subscription to his Vatican news bulletins—maybe the top onionskin—or his "special service" to the secret police.

Monsignor Pucci's assistant, Giulio Bartoloni, continued to put out daily Vatican news bulletins for some years. Even at the height of Monsignor Pucci's reputation as the top *Vaticanista,* some rivals had turned up in the Rome market for information on the pope and the central government of the church. One of them was Virgilio Scattolini, a one-time playwright and author of racy novels with such titles as *The Mrs. Who Never Was a Miss.* Later Scattolini had landed a part-time job as a film critic for *L'Osservatore Romano,* the pontifical newspaper. For some years he also issued a Vatican news letter to which journalists, banks, religious communities, embassies, political groups, and, as was eventually found, OVRA and various other secret services subscribed.

I once held a few samples of Scattolini's output in my hands while an associate of his made a sales pitch for a trial subscription from the *New York Times.* The sheets with the bland heading *Notiziario* (News Service) were original typescripts, not copies like the Pucci onionskins; later I learned that Scattolini typed out a special version of his news letter for each subscriber or prospect to create an impression of exclusivity and attention to individual requirements. The specimens I examined contained information about what had been said in private papal audiences with cardinals and ambassadors, about confidential reports from apostolic nuncios and apostolic administrators in the world capitals, and about debates during meetings of Vatican commissions. Scattolini's reports were detailed, all the names of the officials he mentioned were accurate, and the material was interesting. A pity, I said to myself and then reported to my bureau chief that it was all fakery. A minimum of experience in Vatican affairs and curial practices was sufficient to understand how Scattolini produced his news letters: he scanned *L'Osservatore Romano* for the official announcements of the pope's audiences and other activities of the Roman Curia, carefully read the Italian press to keep abreast of domestic and international affairs, picked the names of papal envoys out of the pontifical yearbook, figured out what they might have reported to the Holy See, and gave free rein to his imagination, speculating what the pope, high church-men, and diplomats might have discussed in meetings that had, or had not, taken place. We turned down the offer of a cut-rate trial subscription to Scattolini's news service although we sus-pected that some of our competitors were using material from it.

In the following months we recognized the brush style of this artist in several fanciful items of Vatican "news" that appeared in various United States and British publications. How widely Scattolini's fictions were disseminated is now known thanks to the detective work of Rev. Graham, the Jesuit historian. The American scholar has proved that Scattolini's fakes not only found their way into some of the world's most renowned newspa-pers and were bought by OVRA, the Fascist secret police, but that they were also taken at face value by Nazi Germany's intel-ligence networks. United States diplomats and intelligence ana-lysts saw the material too, but had their doubts about it or were uninterested. Father Graham suggested that the secret service of the Soviet Union was also, "probably," among Scattolini's cli-ents. I may add the fact that the person who, on Scattolini's behalf, gave us the sales talk for a trial subscription was an Ital-ian who for years had worked for the Soviet news agency, TASS, and perhaps at the time still did.

At the apex of his career as a tireless manufacturer of imagi-nary Vatican news, Scattolini must have earned good money. However, too much success was his undoing. Whether author-ized by him or not, a collection of his news letters came out in 1948 as an anonymous volume entitled *Secret Documents of the Vatican Diplomacy*. The Holy See presented a formal protest to Italy against what it termed a complete and malicious fabrica-tion. Scattolini, then 58 years old, was charged by a Rome mag-istrate with "hostile actions against a foreign state," Vatican City. During the pretrial investigation Scattolini admitted that he had invented all the details in his news letters, but in court he claimed to have had a secret informant in the Vatican whom he would not name. Scattolini was sentenced to seven months and four days in prison.

The Scattolini case might have brought home to the curia that its poor information policy was favoring rumors, gossip, and shady practices. Nevertheless there was hardly any change until Vatican II. Journalists who wanted to report on the papacy were still confined to the cramped ground-floor room in the building of *L'Osservatore Romano* where they were allowed to wait for official announcements or for the text of papal utterances. What was handed out to the press usually appeared in the pontifical newspaper a few hours later. The badly paid members of the editorial staff of *L'Osservatore Romano,* from the editor-in-chief down, gladly agreed to work as consultants or tipsters for foreign news agencies and newspapers, but such part-time collaboration usually proved frustrating for both sides. For example, the editor of *L'Osservatore Romano,* who received a monthly retainer from the Rome correspondent of some British news organization would, to his annoyance, receive late-night calls requesting an immediate "Vatican reaction" to something that had happened in Northern Ireland; or, worse, Fleet Street wanted an instant "papal comment" on birth control or divorce. American news correspondents would similarly be ordered by their home offices—usually after midnight, Rome time—to ask the Vatican at once what it thought about something the president of the United States had said or done, or whether it countenanced the remarks by some priest in Chicago or Minneapolis who was completely unknown to the Holy See. During many years as a foreign correspondent in Rome again and again I have tried to explain to my editors in New York that the Vatican was not the White House or the State Department, that there was no such person as a Vatican spokesman, and that nobody of the many hundreds of papal employees was willing, especially in the middle of the night, to make a statement for publication next morning, and possibly have his name used in the bargain.

For generations the representatives of international news media, harassed by their home offices, have delivered the requested statements and comments, attributing them to anonymous "Vatican sources." They still do, although the Holy See now does have an official spokesman for the press, and even deputy spokesmen. The favorite answer of these officials, whenever they are asked about anything, is "no comment," if they are available at all and are not playing hide-and-seek with the journalists. The "Vatican sources," like the mythical "diplomatic circles" who populate many news dispatches from the world's capitals, are often the correspondents themselves. They draw on their knowledge of the background and the precedents of the issue in question, and figure—not unlike Scattolini—what the pope and his aides might think or do. When the figuring is done by a clerical friend whom the journalist is fortunate enough to reach at home at a decent hour, the source is usually upgraded into a "high Vatican official."

When the Second Vatican Council opened in 1962, a new press center, later to be named the Press Room, was awaiting the twelve hundred journalists who had converged on Rome to report about the event. In the beginning, there seemed to be disappointingly little news. At the inauguration of the grand church assembly in St. Peter's the members of the press who had been admitted to the ceremony found themselves cooped up in enclosures in the north and south transepts where they could hardly see anything. The working sessions of Vatican II were closed to reporters, and the Vatican issued terse statements after each meeting with little more than a list of "council fathers" who had taken part in the debates.

However, the presence in Rome of hundreds of prelates from countries where the press enjoyed greater respect than it did in the Vatican brought about a quick change. Many bishops and theologians had no misgivings about being interviewed by journalists, and the delegations from the United States and other areas started organizing regular press briefings on issues being debated at the council. Members of the liberal-moderate majority of the bishops participating in Vatican II began using the information media, through press conferences and calculated leaks, to bring pressure on the conservative diehards. After Paul VI had succeeded John XXIII, the media pressure was also aimed at the new pope, who always seemed intent on reconciling the council majority with the conservative minority even at the risk of a stalemate. It is doubtful whether, without prodding by the international press, Vatican II would have gotten around to vote the Declaration on the Relation of the Church to Non-Christian Religions, with its condemnation of anti-Semitism, and its Declaration on Religious Liberty, shortly before the council's end in 1965. Paul VI obviously feared that the reaction in the media would be most unfavorable if the two documents— known as "Nostra Aetate" (In Our Age) and "Dignitatis Humanae" (Of Human Dignity)—were allowed to lapse.

After Vatican II was closed, its press center became what it is today, the Press Room of the Holy See. It is weighed down by a bureaucratic superstructure that Paul VI created in 1964 as an annex to the Secretariat of State, the Pontifical Commission for Social Communications. The name betrays how gingerly the curia views public information. The commission is theoretically in charge of all contacts between the Holy See and the informa-

260

tion media, but journalists and writers who focus on the Vatican tend to bypass the body and develop their own sources. In practice, the commission is useful mainly for photographers who want a permit to take pictures of some recess of Vatican City that is normally inaccessible to outsiders.

The Vatican has not won plaudits for its choice of spokesmen for day-to-day dealings with the press. One of them was a well-meaning ecclesiastic from the Aosta valley, the French-speaking region in northwestern Italy, Msgr. Fausto Vallainc. He was no success with the Roman Vaticanisti because in addition to being uninformed he was a bungler. He left soon and became, eventually, a bishop in Piedmont. His successor, Father Panciroli, was a member of Paul VI's "Milan mafia." The slight, blond priest, who belonged to an order specializing in missionary work in the Sudan and other African countries, the Combonian Fathers, soon earned a reputation among journalists as a humorless, remote functionary who might be an asset to the press department of, say, the Czechoslovak or the Paraguayan government. Whenever Panciroli was questioned on a development or event about which he had no instructions from his superiors, he would coldly say *"Non risulta"* (roughly, "We have no knowledge of this").

Panciroli's unhelpful attitude irked journalists, especially during emergencies that have occurred during John Paul II's pontificate. When the Polish pope was gravely wounded in the attempt on his life in May 1981, Panciroli had nothing to say to the tense reporters crowding the Press Room of the Holy See, although the Jesuits of Vatican Radio, on their own, had for hours been broadcasting many details of what had happened and of the pontiff's condition. Exactly a year later, during his pilgrimage to Fatima, Portugal, John Paul II escaped another attack, this time by a Spanish priest belonging to an extreme fringe of the traditionalist church movement who had rushed at him brandishing an army bayonet. For many hours journalists were unable to contact Panciroli, who had come to Portugal with the pontifical party. When he at last surfaced, he asserted that John Paul II had been unaware of anything untoward. Film footage shot by the cameramen of Portugal's national television network, but not immediately put on the air, proved later that the assailant had come dangerously close to the pope and that John Paul II had clearly realized the priest's hostile intent. Despite such embarrassments, Panciroli has remained at his post for liaison with the media.

Such lack of candor, and even outright misinformation dispensed by Vatican spokesmen, contrasts with the openness of the Polish pope whenever he is approached by reporters. Their questions are usually respectful, and the pontiff's answers are almost always given in good humor, and are often frank and to the point. Only on the flight back from his visit to eight countries in Central America in 1983 did John Paul II tell the reporters on the papal airliner, "No questions!" But everybody was dead tired then, and the pontiff understandably wanted to digest his impressions before commenting on them. On the whole, it appears that the curia is much more hostile to a questioning press than the pope.

READING BETWEEN THE LINES

An ordinary newspaper reader picking up an issue of *L'Osservatore Romano* one day in the autumn of 1979 would probably have skipped a long review of a book by an 88-year-old Italian cardinal on the philosophy of Saint Thomas Aquinas, as reflected in the teachings of modern popes. Yet to the special constituency of the austere Vatican daily the article, spread over five columns on an inside page, was close to sensational.

The author of the volume that *L'Osservatore Romano* had found to be exceptionally praiseworthy was Pietro Cardinal Parente, a retired member of the sacred college whose theology was so ultraorthodox that even conservative officials of the Roman Curia referred to him, smilingly, as "our ayatollah." That the pontifical newspaper had devoted so much space to Parente's work, "Thomist Therapy for Modern Problems from Leo XIII to Paul VI," was unmistakably a signal from high up. There was immediate speculation that the favorable book review heralded a new theological hard line promoted by John Paul II, who had been elected to the papacy just a year earlier.

The Polish pope was steeped in what Roman Catholic dogmatists call the "perennial philosophy" of Saint Thomas; the pontiff had, as will be recalled, engaged in postgraduate studies at the Dominican college in Rome that seeks to perpetuate the tradition of the thirteenth-century "Angelic Doctor," the Angelicum, now the Pontifical University of St. Thomas Aquinas. As pope, John Paul II left little doubt that he was worried about liberal scholars who propounded a "new theology" reinterpreting age-old tenets of the faith.

Thomism, based on the philosophy and logic of Aquinas, teaches that the existence of God and all other dogmas of the Roman Catholic faith can be proved and grasped by the rational mind. Rooted in a medieval way of thinking, the perennial philosophy leaves little room for a critical reappraisal of the sacred Scriptures and the doctrines of the church.

The new theology undertakes the reexamination of the Scriptures and the traditions of Christianity in the light of modern historical research and scientific knowledge. Conservatives in the church—including, to some extent, John Paul II—view the critical methods of liberal theologians as a danger to papal authority, the unity of the church, and faith itself.

With implied approval the article in the pontifical newspaper quoted the aged cardinal's criticism of one of the world's foremost Roman Catholic theologians, Karl Rahner. Father Rahner, a Jesuit, was a moderate liberal rather than an extremist of the new theology. Parente himself conceded that Rahner was a sincere believer and an original thinker, but asserted that the Jesuit, through theological ambiguity, "subverts the entire doctrine of faith." What was wrong with Rahner above all, the cardinal found, was that he was misrepresenting Thomism. The charge, in the Roman Catholic Church, is as serious as if a Kremlin ideologist in an article in *Pravda* accused a Communist theoretician of deviating from Marxism-Leninism.

Parente, however, in the book he'd written, had reserved his harshest attacks for Hans Küng, the Swiss theologian who was teaching at the University of Tübingen, West Germany, and who at the time was under investigation by the Sacred Congregation for the Doctrine of the Faith. The cardinal himself had once served in that supreme tribunal of orthodoxy when it was still officially called the Holy Office (the former Inquisition). In his volume, Parente said that Küng, a champion of the new theology, was guilty of "scandalous audacities"; *L'Osservatore Romano* quoted the cardinal's appraisal with apparent satisfaction. Those who knew how to read between the lines of the Vatican newspaper were by no means surprised when, only a few weeks later, the Sacred Congregation for the Doctrine of the Faith, with the express approval of John Paul II, declared that Küng was no longer to be recognized a "Catholic theologian." Küng remained a Roman Catholic priest and, holding a post in a secular institution, could not be deprived by the Vatican of his professorship. But, what he taught could be officially disavowed by Rome.

The signpost book review in the papal daily is a good example of the way *L'Osservatore Romano* must be read, if it is read at all. To outsiders the large-size newspaper that comes out in Vatican City at 3:00 P.M. every weekday seems about as informative and entertaining as the Bulgarian Communist party daily. The entire front page of *L'Osservatore Romano* is often filled with papal speeches in the languages in which they were delivered, or with pontifical documents in Latin (an Italian translation can be found in the inside pages). Under the heading "Our Information," indicating official material that reads like the court circular from Buckingham Palace, there will be lists of formal audiences with the pope (although many audiences go unreported), and appointments of new bishops. Also on page one, or inside, there may be a bland column or two of Italian and foreign news items, gleaned from the news agencies to which *L'Osservatore Romano* subscribes. The remainder of the six or eight pages of a normal issue is filled with features on missionary work in Upper Volta or Papua New Guinea, excerpts from lectures delivered in church institutions in Rome, reports on archeological discoveries, some cultural articles, and a few advertisements for insurance companies and ecclesiastical tailors.

Professional Vatican watchers scan *L'Osservatore Romano* the way their opposite numbers in Moscow peruse the Soviet press—looking for allusions, emphasis, and gaps, weighing what is published against what is not. Often it is frustrating and sterile business. However, ecclesiastics who are interested in the power plays in the Roman Curia—and many are—appear to find enough clues in *L'Osservatore Romano* to make daily reading of the newspaper eminently worthwhile.

A knowledge of various languages, in addition to fluency in Italian, is necessary if one wants to get out of *L'Osservatore Romano* all that it has to offer. A papal homily in Polish or Portuguese may contain a hint that is blurred in the Italian translation. For example, a new ambassador from a Latin American country presents his letters of credence to the pope, who in his welcoming address in Spanish seems to pay a prudent tribute to the law-and-order line of the military government that has dispatched the diplomat to the Holy See. The papal remarks will prompt ambassadors who note the discrepancies between the original version and the sanitized Italian translation to file reports to their home governments. A churchman may have private information that a friend or a superior has been received by the pontiff, but the Vatican newspaper fails to include his name in its daily list of papal audiences. Why?

Much of what appears in *L'Osservatore Romano,* and the way it is presented in print, originates in the Secretariat of State. Officials of that superagency of the curia also instruct the papal newspaper what to keep out of its pages. Occasionally, special wishes or instructions may come directly from the pope's entourage. For other material that goes into the newspaper, or doesn't, the small editorial staff—a dozen people including four or five priests—are on their own. Without guidance from above, they tend to practice self-censorship for fear of causing irritation in the Apostolic Palace, which towers over their small three-storey brick building in the northwest corner of Vatican City. Normally, the staff of *L'Osservatore Romano* does not submit galley proofs to any higher official; Vatican control of the newspaper is informal, though continual.

Before the pontifical state was established in 1939, *L'Osservatore Romano* was printed in various places in Rome outside the Vatican, and its ties to the curia, though never seriously questioned, seemed less obvious than they are now. A measure of ambiguity was built into the singular newspaper from its beginnings. It was founded as a "political-moral journal" (its self-definition on the original masthead) in 1861. Two laymen, Nicola Zanchini and Giuseppe Bastià, propapal political refugees from the territories in the north that the States of the Church had already lost to the nascent Kingdom of Italy, were the ostensible publishers. Actually they were a front for the Interior Department of the pontifical government, which from the start was the newspaper's real owner, exercising ideological control of all editorial matter. The formula whereby the Holy See began to operate a seemingly private daily was devised by Pope Pius IX's acting interior minister, Marcantonio Pacelli, the paternal grandfather of Pius XII.

To this day the Roman Curia makes a point of declaring from time to time that the Holy See's official publication is not *L'Osservatore Romano* but *Acta Apostolicae Sedis.* A monthly bulletin in Latin containing papal decrees and landmark sentences by church tribunals, *Acta Apostolicae Sedis* is indeed the official gazette of one of the world's most awesome bureaucratic systems, more filed than read. Its annual volumes, in somber bindings, adorn the libraries of cardinals and canon lawyers. As for *L'Osservatore Romano,* which now describes itself in its masthead as a "Political-Religious Daily Newspaper," the curia keeps insisting that it is neither official nor semiofficial, except for the texts of papal pronouncements that it prints verbatim and for the material appearing under Our Information.

Official or not, anyone who wants to keep up with developments in the Vatican must set aside some time for *L'Osservatore Romano.* It is not light reading, but the stately Italian style of the papal newspaper, with its faint nineteenth-century flavor, is much more tolerable than the cliché-ridden jargon of the contemporary Italian press. Since the election of the Polish pope even the annoying provincialism of *L'Osservatore Romano* seemed to become less pronounced. Earlier, the Vatican daily would petulantly carry on controversies with some newspaper in, say, Cremona or Genoa that had permitted itself an anticlerical remark or cartoon, while completely ignoring what the international press wrote about the papacy. In those days it was also indispensable to have read carefully Alessandro Manzoni's *The Betrothed* to understand the allusions in *L'Osservatore Romano.* Count Giuseppe Dalla Torre, an imperious layman who was editor-in-chief of the Vatican daily for 30 years and was known as "the Thunderer," apparently knew the great nineteenth-century novel by heart, and continually quoted from it or referred to its characters to make a point in his endless polemics whenever some obscure writer had not shown due veneration for the church.

In 1959 Pope John XXIII's secretary, Capovilla, brought in a friend, Raimondo Manzini, as new editor-in-chief of the Vatican daily when Dalla Torre went into retirement. Manzini had been a journalist in Bologna and a member of Parliament for the Christian Democratic party. A layman like his predecessor, he hardly made any impact on the way the Vatican newspaper was put together; however, during his nineteen years at *L'Osservatore Romano* it started weekly editions in six languages.

A new pope does not necessarily appoint a new editor-in-chief of *L'Osservatore Romano.* Manzini remained in his post under Paul VI until reaching retirement age, but the most influential member of the newspaper staff was a priest belonging to the Milan mafia, Father Levi. In 1978 another layman, Valerio Volpini, a friend of Cardinal Benelli's, became editor-in-chief at a time when staff morale was plummeting. At the beginning of

John Paul II's pontificate the Vatican newspaper was rarely selling more than 30,000 copies a day, including those mailed to long-term subscribers all over the world, while the deficit rose to $2 million a year. The circulation of *L'Osservatore Romano* had reached an all-time peak of 120,000 at the beginning of World War I, when it was the only daily available in Italy that printed the Allied military bulletins side by side with those issued by the armed forces of Nazi Germany. Later, when Italy joined the war, pressure from the Fascist government forced the Vatican newspaper to drop the Allied bulletins. Many Romans bought it nevertheless to read its daily roundups of international news because, despite obvious self-censorship, it managed to slip in items that the Fascist press would not print. The pontifical daily has never been able to recapture its wartime audience. For years its circulation hovered around 60,000, and started shrinking under Paul VI.

Also the priests and the laymen on the staff of *L'Osservatore Romano* didn't get on well with each other, more for personal reasons than because of disagreements on editorial policy. The printers of the papal newspaper demanded higher pay. As losses were piling up, John Paul II asked the prefect of the Apostolic Library, the Reverend Alfons Stickler, to make recommendations on what to do with the Vatican newspaper. Father Stickler, an Austrian member of the Salesian order and an expert on canon law, counseled economies, and said that *L'Osservatore Romano* should not try to expand its services at a time when newspapers everywhere were in trouble. There were rumors that a successor for Volpini was being sought.

For some time it seemed that Father Levi, who for years had been Volpini's antagonist on the staff, might be chosen as the new editor-in-chief. Then, at the end of the Polish pontiff's second journey to his homeland in June 1983, Father Levi, following events from Rome, wrote an editorial for the front page of *L'Osservatore Romano,* in which he gave to understand that Lech Walesa, the champion of the Solidarity labor movement, had decided to withdraw into private life. The obvious inference was that John Paul II had requested such a "sacrifice"—the word was used in Levi's article—when he granted a semisecret audience to the labor leader and Mrs. Walesa in the Polish mountain resort of Zakopane.

The pontiff apparently did tell Walesa that he must stand aside, at least for the time being, to reduce tensions in Poland. Nevertheless, John Paul II was upset that Father Levi should have hinted so in *L'Osservatore Romano*. At the pope's order, Cardinal Casaroli's deputy in the Secretariat of State, Archbishop Eduardo Martinez Somalo, summoned Levi and told him to resign from his post. He did. Friends of the priest-journalist said that before the pontiff's Polish journey Levi had asked Martinez Somalo in writing for guidance regarding editorial coverage in *L'Osservatore Romano* but had received no reply.

The pope himself picked a successor to Levi. The new deputy editor was Gianfranco Svidercoschi, an Italian layman of Polish ancestry—again the ethnic preference—who had been the Vatican specialist of the conservative newspaper *Il Tempo* of Rome.

One novelty struck readers of the Vatican daily under John Paul II. The newspaper's printing plant suddenly acquired type faces with all the diacritical signs of the Polish alphabet, the crossed *l*'s and the hooks under vowels indicating that an *n* must be pronounced. The many Polish texts published by *L'Osservatore Romano* were at last graphically correct.

While the importance of *L'Osservatore Romano* seemed to wane, and the Vatican's money men were worrying about its deficits, John Paul II was impressed by the worldwide power of the electronic media, and made use of them with a skill and expertise such as no pontiff before him had shown. The Holy See lacked video services of its own when the Polish pope was elected, and still does not have them, but Vatican Radio was instructed to give every assistance to Italian state television and other networks that wanted to relay papal appearances and ceremonies from St. Peter's Basilica or St. Peter's Square. Television crews enjoy privileged treatment whenever John Paul II goes on one of his frequent journeys. The photogenic pontiff, who was an amateur actor in his young years in Krakow, soon became one of the world's best-known video personalities. It is a foregone conclusion that as soon as the technology of direct transmission by satellite is advanced enough, the Holy See will operate its own television service to project the image of the head of the church all over the world.

Meanwhile Vatican Radio was beaming the church's message to all continents, and the polyglot pope was able to address listeners in many countries in their own languages. At the most solemn ceremonies he carried a microphone that looked like a gold-plated pencil over his pontifical vestments and over the pallium, and would painstakingly time his homily or the phrasing of the liturgy to satisfy the broadcasting technicians. Even passively John Paul II was an incomparable media star: when he was shot down in St. Peter's Square on May 13, 1981, Vatican Radio, which had routinely been covering his general audience, went right on reporting the attack, the pontiff being rushed to hospital, and the surgery. Networks in many countries took on the running broadcast from the Vatican in one of the greatest radio hookups ever achieved. Vatican Radio, which does not often have a chance to make money, later put out a recording of the dramatic May 13 broadcast as a cassette, which was widely sold.

John Paul II had regularly listened to Vatican Radio when he was archbishop of Krakow, as do members of the hierarchy, priests, nuns, and lay people on all continents, some clandestinely. The Jesuits, who are in charge of the pontifical broadcasting services, claim that they can reach every Roman Catholic on earth. Since the election of the Slavic pope Vatican Radio has stepped up its programs in the languages of Eastern Europe. Broadcasts are also beamed to Albania in the idiom of that country, which has officially outlawed all religions and closed all houses of worship. There are frequent programs in Mandarin Chinese, in Japanese, and in more than thirty other tongues—all by native speakers.

Many nationalities are represented among the 350 employees of Vatican Radio; the majority of them are lay people. The core, however, is made up of 35 Jesuits who live at the headquarters of their order in a separate unit along with the official historians of the Society of Jesus. There is no formal rule that all clerics who work at Vatican Radio must be Jesuits, and indeed some of them aren't. But up to now, the director general of Vatican Radio; the technical director; and the heads of the program, music, and news sections have always been Jesuits. This is something the pope could change at will if he so desired.

Some offices and studies of the papal broadcasting services are still in an old tower near the highest point of the Vatican gardens. Over the centuries the tower has been rebuilt several times, and it once housed the pope's astronomical observatory. Nearby is a small pavilion where Marconi activated the first radio transmission from the center of the church with a live address by Pius XI on February 12, 1931.

Antennas still provide spidery contrast to the dome of St. Peter's in the skyline of Vatican City. However, the most powerful signals from the pontifical broadcasting system surge into the ether from the steel towers of a vast transmission center at Santa Maria di Galeria, a 1,000-acre complex some ten miles northwest of Rome. The fenced-in area, near Lake Bracciano, is under Vatican jurisdiction on the basis of an accord between Italy and the Holy See. Most of the offices and studios of Vatican Radio are in the Palazzo Pio, a modern church-owned building on the Via della Conciliazione near the Tiber embankment.

The mainstay of the programs is daily mass in Latin, and a round of news broadcasts in various languages, each usually fifteen minutes long. The newscasts start with a report on the activities of the pope, followed by items on other Vatican and general church developments, and on international events. References to the Soviet Union, the People's Republic of China, and other Communist countries are restrained and factual; the crusading tone that sometimes marked Vatican Radio under Pius XII has been abandoned. Since Paul VI, and with his consent, the Jesuits of the Vatican broadcasting station have had some leeway in enriching the programs with interviews, topical reports, and music. Earlier, only liturgical chants and an occasional concert of sacred music had been heard on Vatican Radio. Since the late 1960s the station has won many new listeners, in Italy and in other countries, with programs featuring recordings of classical and modern music, including jazz. Hard rock is not heard from the papal station, but Ella Fitzgerald and Frank Sinatra records are permitted because, the Jesuits in charge of the music selections explain, "they are classics."

Reporters of Vatican Radio travel with the pope and provide extensive coverage of his trips. John Paul II appeared to be impressed by the competence of the Jesuit director general of the broadcasting services, Rev. Roberto Tucci, a frequent member of his party on his early journeys. When Archbishop Marcinkus found himself embroiled in the Banco Ambrosiano affair, and was unable or unwilling to leave Vatican City, John Paul II picked Father Tucci as his new tour manager. In this capacity the Jesuit proved to be much more cooperative with the press than either Marcinkus or Panciroli, the official Vatican spokesman, had ever been.

If there were rumors that Opus Dei might take over Vatican Radio, they were surely not caused by papal dissatisfaction with the 35 members of the Society of Jesus who were, in effect, running it. The speculation about the future of an instrument of the Holy See that speaks to all the world every day reflected, rather, the rivalry between the Jesuit order as a whole and the aggressive new church force that Monsignor Escrivá founded, as well as financial considerations.

270

CHAPTER 9

PRINCES, SWITZERS, LABOR ACTIVISTS

ECCLESIASTICS ARE IN command in the Vatican, but its sociology would be incomplete, and indeed faulty, if its varied lay personnel were ignored. High Roman nobility, armed security forces, women secretaries, sanitation men, financial analysts —about one thousand eight hundred persons who are not bound by clerical vows are at the pope's service.

In the parlance of the Roman Catholic Church the word *laity,* or "people," suggests a mass of uninitiated faithful who have to be guided and instructed by a priesthood versed in the "sacred mysteries." Modern theology, it is true, has sought to upgrade the status of laymen and laywomen in the community of believers; the phrase *people of God,* meaning clergy and laity together, has become current since the Second Vatican Council. The disparaging flavor of *lay,* in the sense of unlearned, or amateurish, nevertheless lingers in the church, and imperceptibly influences relations between priests and nuns on one side and the rest of the faithful on the other.

In the Vatican there is an invisible barrier between clerical and lay staff. In subtle, even unconscious, ways the priests in the pontifical offices often betray a feeling of superiority and apartness with regard to their nonordained colleagues. Lay employees of the Holy See occasionally repay such faint discrimination with mordant judgments, in private, about the clergy in general.

271

Savage observations about "the priests" can be found in the satires of Giuseppe Gioacchino Belli, the extraordinary Roman vernacular poet of the nineteenth century who held a badly paying job in the pontifical administration.

New variations on the age-old theme of antagonism between the "clerks" (the priests) and the laymen at the pontifical court were introduced recently by the emergence of a militant trade-union movement among the pope's civilian employees.

POMP AND CIRCUMSTANCE

When royalty or a republican head of state calls on the pope, or whenever a new ambassador to the Holy See presents his letters of credence, one of the first members of the pontifical household the visitor meets on arriving in the Courtyard of St. Damasus is a Roman nobleman in a dress coat. The nobleman bows, not too low, mumbling a welcome, while a picket of the Swiss Guard presents halberds, and a band plays snatches of the honored guest's own national anthem and of Gounod's "Pontifical March." The greeter is the prince assistant to the pontifical throne, the chief of either the Colonna or the Torlonia family, who both combine many resounding old titles with great wealth.

The prince, and some ecclesiastics wearing purple sashes and skullcaps, take the visitor to the second floor of the Apostolic Palace whence they proceed in a formal cortege through a succession of loggias, halls, and antechambers to the pope's private library. There the head of the church will talk alone with his caller for some time in front of a painting by Pinturicchio. Then the visitor's entourage, maybe a spouse and some aides, are called in for picture taking and a ceremonial exchange of gifts. The pope may receive a sculpture or a miniature, which he will turn over to the Vatican collections, and may present his guest with a book, produced by the Vatican's own Polyglot printing plant, and give the retinue commemorative medals of his pontificate or rosaries. Eventually the pope and his visitor walk to the Throne Hall or some larger room to exchange formal addresses that will be published in the original language by *L'Osservatore Romano* the same afternoon.

Then the masters of ceremonies will steer the pope to some other audience or religious rite on the day's schedule, and the prince assistant to the pontifical throne will escort the distinguished caller to the floor below the papal suite for the meeting with the cardinal secretary of state that protocol demands. If the visitor is a Roman Catholic, an appearance in St. Peter's Basilica for a stylized homage to the Prince of the Apostles is the last figure in the ballet of a solemn papal audience.

This choreography—in some periods enacted once, or even several times every week—takes up much time, effort, and Vatican manpower. It keeps the prefecture of the pontifical household and the ceremonial staff on their toes, helps perpetuate the atmosphere of a royal court in the Apostolic Palace, and breeds the smugness that prevails in its halls and corridors. Bishops and priests from other countries and cultures who happen to be visiting and witness the pageantry may be impressed by the majesty of the papal office. Or they may ask, as quite a number have been doing lately, whether all this is really necessary, or isn't it an embarrassing anachronism? Does the spiritual authority of the vicar on earth of Jesus Christ and successor to Saint Peter need halberds, Gounod's triumphant march, the medals and ribbons on the lapels of Vatican worthies, and the tips slipped into the greedy hands of flunkies in the antechambers?

Gratuities have been distributed among Vatican staff since time immemorial. The ancient, though hardly venerable, practice has become ritualized like a blessing for the faithful. After an official or private audience with the pope, an aide of the personage who has been received by the head of the church hands little envelopes with money to the doorkeepers, elevator attendants, lay receptionists, and a few low-ranking priests with vague jobs in the pontiff's entourage, whether they have actually rendered any services or not. Embassies in Rome exchange information as to what the correct amount is at a given time, and who is entitled to a handout; nobody wants to pay too little or too much. Higher-ranking ecclesiastics and the Swiss Guard are not tipped. Various prelates in Vatican jobs deign to accept contributions by visitors or favor-seekers for their "good works." This isn't considered bribery, just the Roman way of oiling the wheels of the papal bureaucracy. Some cardinals from the United States who have rich archdioceses to administer have developed the art of tipping to the degree of perfection that Paganini achieved on the violin.

With all the pomp surrounding the papacy today, it is a far cry from what was still routine long after the end of World War

273

II. When a potentate or statesman called on Pius XII, members of Roman aristocratic clans in hereditary Vatican posts were at hand in the costume of Spanish grandees of bygone days with white lace and ruffs, and shoes with silver buckles, carrying rapiers at their sides. Marquess Serlupi Crescenzi, chief equerry of His Holiness, would give the order for a Vatican motorcade to fetch the visiting king or president from his embassy or hotel; Prince Massimo, general superintendent of the Vatican posts, would ride in one of the cars; and Marquess Sacchetti, chief quartermaster of the Sacred Apostolic Palaces, would wait in the Courtyard of St. Damasus to open the door of the visitor's limousine as a detail of haughty Noble guardsmen, all officers and aristocrats, would languidly render military honors, and the prince assistant to the pontifical throne would get into the act.

During ceremonies in St. Peter's, the prince assistant would stand for hours at Pius XII's right side, ranking immediately after the cardinals in order of precedence; he would smell of incense when he finally got home and out of his black costume. At that time the two princes assistants to the pontifical throne were Don Aspreno Colonna and Don Filippo Napoleone Orsini. Both families have popes among their ancestors; throughout the Middle Ages the Colonnas, leaders of the pro-emperor Ghibelline faction, feuded with the Orsinis, chiefs of the Guelphs, the papal loyalists. Then and later their private armies fought pitched battles in the streets of Rome and laid siege to each other's fortified towers in the city and castles in the countryside while their cardinals were hatching cabals at the papal court.

Both aristocratic clans were so powerful in the late Middle Ages and in the Renaissance that they claimed, and obtained, a permanent presence at the pontifical court. Thus the office of the prince assistant was born under Julius II (1503–1513), the imperious Ligurian. The job was always purely ceremonial, symbolizing aristocratic influence in papal Rome, but individual incumbents have been able to use the prestige for political or financial leverage. With the Colonnas and Orsinis both entitled to a post as prince assistant, their rivalry was extended to the day-by-day routine in the Vatican.

Benedict XIII, a meek eighteenth-century pope, decreed that, to forestall further quarrels over precedence, the two incumbents should serve alternately, meaning that at one pontifical mass a Colonna was in attendance, and at the next papal ceremony an Orsini.

The system functioned until Pius XII, when one of the two Roman princes got into trouble. Orsini, who had cut a dashing, though often fidgety, figure at Vatican ceremonies, early in 1958 was found in his Roman apartment with slashed wrists. (The historic Palazzo Orsini had changed hands long ago, the family after which it was named had lost much of its former wealth, and Prince Filippo Napoleone had, not too successfully, been dabbling in business.) The local press gleefully linked the apparent suicide attempt with the case of the prince's friend, Belinda Lee, a British film actress, who had recently taken an overdose of sleeping drugs, but was saved. In the ensuing scandal the prince's wife came loyally to his defense, had him whisked into a psychiatric institution, and enlisted Vatican support for her story of a nervous breakdown. The J. Arthur Rank Organization, which had Miss Lee under contract, flew her to South Africa. But before long the papal nobleman and the movie starlet were together again, and the prince assistant appeared as a swashbuckling extra in a Lucrezia Borgia film made to order for Miss Lee. It was too much for the pope. Prince Orsini was banned from the Vatican; he also had to return the SCV (State of Vatican City) license plate of his car, which had often been conspicuous outside Roman night spots.

For some years Colonna remained the only prince assistant to the pontifical throne. His family traced its history back to the tenth century, and since the Middle Ages had been living on the same spot, on the slopes of the Quirinal hill. Martin V, the fifteenth-century pontiff who restored the papal state and power after the Great Schism, was a Colonna; he rebuilt the family palace. Vittoria Colonna, marquess of Pescara and a poetess, exchanged sonnets with her friend, Michelangelo. Marc Antonio Colonna commanded the papal galleys of the Christian fleet with which John of Austria routed the Turks in the Battle of Lepanto in 1571. When another Marcantonio Colonna married a Levantine heiress, Isabella Sursock of Beirut, in 1909, the Romans called the wedding a "revenge for Lepanto." Princess Isabella Colonna indeed conquered Rome with her refinement and ambition as a hostess; one of those who were fascinated by her was Count Ciano, Mussolini's son-in-law and foreign minister. The Ciano set met at the Colonna Palace ("the branch office of the Italian foreign ministry") and at the Acqua Santa Golf Club. During World War II Princess Isabella, because of her Vatican and international connections, was vilified by Fascists as the "Fifth Column," a pun on the Colonna name, which in Italian means "column." Her palace was eventually ransacked by the Nazis while she was in hiding.

In 1947 her husband died, and their only son, Don Aspreno, inherited his title and Vatican post. As a little boy he had been trained to stand motionless for hours. In St. Peter's the new prince assistant would resemble the column in his coat of arms; Pius XII, during an interminable pontifical mass, once whispered to him, "Patience, Aspreno, only one more hour!" and not a muscle in the prince's face moved.

Don Aspreno married Princess Maria Milagros Del Drago, whose father was commander of the Pontifical Noble Guard with the rank of lieutenant general. The match had been planned like a dynastic alliance, and was highly welcome to the Vatican. Prelates later talked about how the young Princess Colonna, Don Aspreno's wife, was striving to assert herself against an overweening mother-in-law in the museumlike Colonna Palace, where one of the halls contained a throne turned to the wall— waiting to be used by the pope.

The world of yesterday? It lingers on in the Vatican to an astonishing degree. Rome has a Communist-Socialist city administration, the papal state is beset by security and labor problems, the cardinals have elected a pontiff from Eastern Europe for the first time in history—yet the influence of the Roman nobility is still noticeable in the papal establishment. To relieve Don Aspreno Colonna and replace the disgraced Orsinis, a second prince assistant was chosen from the Torlonia family. The Torlonias are a branch of the vast Borghese clan whose name, in enormous letters, stares down from the facade of St. Peter's. It is a vainglorious memorial to the seventeenth-century Borghese Pope, Paul V, who commissioned the portico of the largest Christian church in the world and other buildings in Rome, and also permitted his relatives to amass extraordinary wealth during his pontificate.

Noblemen continue to play more than ceremonial roles at the Holy See. Under John Paul II, the 24-member Consultative Council of the State of Vatican City, a prestigious lay body, still includes the two princes assistants to the pontifical throne and a Prince Del Drago, together with other aristocrats and moneyed men; the chief executive of the papal state is a titled and wealthy landowner, Marquess Giulio Sacchetti. Titled personages still obtain papal audiences or Vatican favors with greater ease than other people.

As a recognized group, the papal nobility has nevertheless ceased to exist since the 1960s. There is no longer a Heraldic Commission of the Pontifical Court, which until then kept a roster of the "black" (papal) aristocracy, comprising between three hundred and four hundred families, and would every now and then strike off the rolls some playboy blueblood who had married a rich divorcee or otherwise strayed. The popes have stopped conferring new aristocratic titles on commoners, although, as sovereigns, they could do so again any time they wanted. The Roman nobility no longer presents its New Year's wishes to the pontiff in a group audience every January. On one of the last such occasions, in 1952, Pius XII told the princes, dukes, marquesses, counts, barons, and their relatives, who were assembled in a hall of the Apostolic Palace, that with the establishment of the Italian Republic "a page has been turned," and urged them to take the loss of their class privileges as *"beaux joueurs"* (elegant players, or good losers). Maybe it was a wry allusion to the gambling passion of many Roman nobles. Pius XII, himself a member of petty papal nobility and an uncle of three princes, also suggested that, rather than remain idle, the Roman aristocrats should try to make good in Italy's professional and political life. A few of them did, but others contented themselves with selling off their land holdings to real estate developers, and leading the sweet life.

While noblemen still count in the Vatican, they have almost completely disappeared from the Roman Catholic priesthood and the hierarchy. The old custom that Roman aristocratic families would encourage a younger son to enter a fashionable seminary, like the Capranica College, to take holy orders and reach high ecclesiastical office in due course is extinct. For noblemen, today, there is more money in a rich marriage than in the church. Almost all cardinals are now of middle-class and working-class origin, as was John Paul I and is John Paul II. The last nobleman to join the sacred college was Maximilien de Furstenberg, a Belgian-born church diplomat before he received the red hat in 1967 and became a conservative curia stalwart.

An ultimate holdout of old-world aristocracy connected with the Vatican is the Roman headquarters of the Sovereign Military Order of Malta. A group of noblemen and wealthy people, the Knights of Malta are decorative at church functions with their red tunics, flowing capes, and plumed hats. In their palace in the Via Condotti, the Italian capital's elegant shopping street, the knights pose as an independent power, sending ambassadors

277

and ministers to the Holy See and a number of countries—
mostly in Latin America and Africa—that recognize them. An
international network that presumes to keep alive the traditions
of the merciful hospitaler knights during the Crusades, the
Order of Malta donates medicines and ambulances to needy nations, and performs other humanitarian work. The order
stresses its loyalty to the Holy See but at the same time is leery
of excessive Vatican supervision. In the Roman Curia the order
has many critics who contend that whatever good works the
Knights of Malta are doing might be better done without their
aristocratic snobbery and diplomatic charades.

Under Pius XII the Vatican tried to bring the Knights of
Malta under its complete control and strip it of its old privileges, but failed. Since then the Holy See, rather uneasily, deals
with the knights on two levels. On one, the curia department in
charge of monks and nuns supervises the group of some thirty
knights who have vowed poverty (of sorts), obedience, and chastity, and who form the core of the organization. In a different
context the Vatican continues to recognize the Knights of Malta
as a sovereign entity and accepts their diplomatic representatives just as it does ambassadors from secular powers.

John Paul II has seemed better disposed toward the order
than his immediate predecessors, maybe because the Knights of
Malta have done much to ease material needs in Poland.

HALBERDS AND MACE

On May 6, 1981, Pope John Paul II gazed at the ranks of the
Pontifical Swiss Guard, some ninety officers and men drawn up
before him, and told them in German: "We must pray to the
Lord that He may keep violence and fanaticism away from the
walls of the Vatican." A week later a Turk fired at the head of
the church in St. Peter's Square as a pair of Swiss halberdiers,
posted nearby, stood as helpless and stunned as the plainclothesmen who had been escorting the pontiff in his slow tour of the
piazza during his weekly general audience.

Violence had again come to the Vatican as it had so often in
the past. The walls to which the Polish pontiff had referred in
his address to his Swiss Guard had risen to protect St. Peter's
and the adjoining palaces from attackers. The jagged remains of

the ninth-century fortifications that Pope Saint Leo IV had erected to keep the Saracen raiders of the Dark Ages away from the sanctuary, located on the right bank of the Tiber, can still be seen in the Vatican gardens. The older buildings clustering near St. Peter's, with their ramparts and battlements, and the Renaissance walls surrounding the papal state (some of them designed by Michelangelo) are a reminder that the Vatican functioned for centuries as a fortress, meant to withstand incursions and sieges.

The Swiss Guard parade before John Paul II was the annual commemoration of that desperate day in 1527 when the Swiss mercenaries saved Clement VII from being slain during the Sack of Rome. At that time, Swiss troops had been stationed permanently in the Vatican for barely twenty years; they had been hired by Julius II, the soldier pope who delighted in leading his own troops for the reconquest of the territories that the States of the Church had lost earlier. On that May 6, 1527, when Emperor Charles V's soldiers ran wild, 147 of 189 Switzers (including their commander, Kaspar Roust) died, but not before having slain at least eight hundred of their attackers. The bravery of the Swiss Guard gave Clement VII, the fickle Medici pope, enough time to flee to Castel Sant'Angelo by way of the catwalk that linked (and still links) the sacred palaces with the mausoleum of Emperor Hadrian. Medieval popes had transformed this building, overlooking the Tiber, into a prison and a conveniently close fortress. Paulus Jovius, an ecclesiastical historian, threw his purple cloak over the white-clad pope, and Clement VII, thus disguised, made it to safety in the castle. The Vatican has seen much trouble before and after 1527, but it has never forgotten the Sack of Rome and the loyalty of its Switzers.

It is a Roman truism that the papacy is ungrateful. (The same has been said and is being said of other great institutions. "Gratitude from the House of Hapsburg" was the stock comment in Austria-Hungary whenever a faithful servant of the emperor was forced into obscurity; the way modern business corporations treat devoted members of their staffs who are no longer needed is no better than the proverbial ingratitude of monarchs, dynasties, and popes.) However, the Holy See has shown that it is thankful to its sturdy Swiss, besides thinking that they might still be useful. Paul VI kept the Swiss Guard in service when, in 1970, he transformed the Pontifical Gendarmerie into a civilian force, and disbanded the Noble Guard and the Palatine Guard.

As an ostensibly military organization, the Pontifical Noble Guard was an oddity. Every member was at least a lieutenant—two of Pius XII's nephews were colonels—and everyone had an aristocratic title; the resplendent uniforms came with long cavalry sabers and clinking spurs, although there were no horses; and the guard never had any training or exercise. The Palatine Guard, a lowly branch of the papal armed forces, gave shopkeepers and artisans of the Borghi, the teeming neighborhood just outside the Vatican, and other Roman districts a chance to don gold-embroidered uniforms from time to time and to present unloaded rifles at papal ceremonies. The last time this formation served some useful purpose was toward the end of World War II, when the Vatican permitted hundreds of frightened young Romans to join the Palatine Guard as a stratagem to evade being pressed into Nazi work battalions or into Mussolini's last-ditch forces.

Despite its archaic military trappings, the Swiss Guard today is essentially a police force that shares duties inside the Vatican with the 120 men of the Vigilance Office. (It may be noted that Italy's security system also is based on a similar dualism; the Carabinieri, a paramilitary police corps, vie in law enforcement with the civilian state police.) Competition and rivalries are built into such a parallel setup. And ethnic tensions, too, are noticeable. The personnel of the Vigilance Office, in blue uniforms that resemble those of drivers or bank guards, or in plainclothes, are almost all Italians, many of them former papal gendarmes or Italian Carabinieri. If one talks to them for awhile, one will probably hear them describe their Helvetian colleagues as dim-witted and mulish.

The Swiss guardsmen, recruited from the Roman Catholic cantons of the Helvetian Confederation, and all Catholics themselves, usually learn Italian quickly enough, but most of them do not seem to care for Italians, especially Romans. Few of the Swiss reenlist when their two-year service term is over, and some of them have told me how impatient they were to go home again and take civilian jobs or go into police work. In the Vatican they keep to themselves, although they play basketball now and then against a team of Vatican firemen in front of a replica of the grotto of Lourdes (a gift of French Catholics to Leo XIII) in the Vatican gardens. The Swiss guardsmen have a tavern of their own in their barracks at the left of the Gate of St.

Anne, and can be seen also, in mufti, in the wine shops in the narrow streets of the Borghi, the ancient and somewhat seedy neighborhood between St. Peter's and the Tiber River. Whenever a Roman is blond and has blue eyes, his friends will joke, "Your grandfather must have been a Swiss guardsman." If so, the bloodline could perhaps be traced back to the Borghi.

For some years after World War II the Swiss Guard had trouble finding enough recruits, but better pay has resolved this problem. After deductions for mess-hall food, the ordinary Swiss guardsman now receives more than the equivalent of $100 in cash every week. Under an accord between the Confederation and the Holy See the men must have performed their military service at home before they can sign up for duty in the Vatican; while they are in the papal force they are exempt from the periodical reserve exercises in Switzerland. In Rome, the Swiss guardsmen go in small groups every week to an Italian police rifle range at Tor di Quinto, a neighborhood farther up the Tiber, to maintain their marksmanship.

The Swiss Guard has long been armed with pistols and submachine guns, but these weapons are kept in the guardsmen's barracks, to be oiled regularly and taken up only if an attack on the Vatican were imminent. The last time such a danger loomed was in 1943, after Italy had concluded its armistice with the Allies. The German army had occupied Rome, and paratrooper sentries had been posted by the Nazis at the dividing line between Italian and Holy See territory at the edge of St. Peter's Square. During the nine months that Rome was under direct Nazi rule there were repeated rumors that Hitler was planning to have the pope captured and held as a hostage somewhere in Germany, maybe in a convent near Lake Constance. It would not have been an unprecedented action. In 1809 Napoleon had Pius VII taken prisoner in Rome and moved to Fontainebleau, where the pontiff spent nearly six years in captivity. It is not known whether the Swiss in the Vatican had any specific orders to resist a Nazi invasion, and it can only be speculated what they would have done in keeping with their mandate to protect "the sacred person of the pontiff" even at the cost of their own lives. Mother Pasqualina told me that Pius XII was aware of the danger of being kidnaped by the Nazis, and that he had repeatedly said he would never leave the Vatican voluntarily but would only "yield to force."

During the Nazi occupation of Rome there was a military attack on the State of Vatican City, but it came from the air, and neither the Swiss Guard nor any other of the papal forces then in existence could do anything about it. In the evening of November 5, 1943, an aircraft that had been heard flying low over the northwestern districts of blacked-out Rome for some time dropped four bombs over the Vatican gardens, and disappeared. One of the bombs, later found to have been of British make, hit the papal mosaic workshop, causing considerable damage. Many windows of St. Peter's and of other Vatican buildings were shattered, but nobody was hurt.

Nazi and Fascist propaganda accused the Allies of having perpetrated the outrage, the first military action against papal territory since 1870, when the troops of unified Italy entered Rome. The Allies at once denied that any of their war planes had been over Rome on November 5, and recalled earlier warnings that the Nazi and Fascist forces might engineer a fake raid on the Vatican. The German ambassador to the Holy See gave formal assurances to the Secretariat of State that the German air force had had nothing to do with the bombing. A few days later Prince Carlo Pacelli, the nephew of Pius XII, and Count Galeazzi called on the German commander of Rome, Lieutenant General Kurt Mälzer, and demanded measures to protect the State of Vatican City from possible further attacks, wherever they might originate. The two Vatican officials even suggested that the papal state might consider having antiaircraft artillery positioned within its walls. Nothing came of this surprising idea.

Soon afterward the Vatican received new proof that Fascists had organized the air attack, using bombs from British stores that had been overrun earlier in the war by Axis forces in North Africa. One of the crew members of the mysterious aircraft gave an account of the enterprise to a priest in Viterbo, a city northwest of Rome, where its flight had started and ended. It confirmed information from other Italian sources that Roberto Farinacci, a leader of an anticlerical and extremely pro-Nazi faction in the Fascist party, had devised that operation both as an anti-Allied propaganda stunt and as a gesture to intimidate the pope and his advisers.

The true story of the bombs on the Vatican, about which various inaccurate versions have been published over the years, shows that the papal state, small though it is, may still become the target of warlike attacks.

In 1960 the United Nations Educational, Scientific, and Cultural Organization entered the entire State of Vatican City in its international register of cultural treasures that are entitled to special protection. Many nations, including the United States and the Soviet Union, committed themselves by this UNESCO act to refrain from any military operation against the papal state. Although there is no other formal international accord that would guarantee permanent inviolability to the State of Vatican City, its neutral status appears to be almost universally recognized. Yet the 1943 bombing and the attempt on the life of John Paul II in 1981 are examples of dangers that the pontifical state must nevertheless be prepared to face at all times: provocation, terrorism, and irrational behavior. This is the justification for the existence of papal security forces.

To come back to the Swiss Guard, its men now undergo karate training and carry not only halberds and swords but also containers of a Mace-type spray, concealed under their Renaissance costumes. Swiss guardsmen are near the pope around the clock, and at night keep watch outside his private apartment. They patrol the Apostolic Palace, and guard the main entrances to the Vatican. At the Bronze Doors they always wear the uniform with the blue, yellow, and red stripes that, according to tradition, was designed by either Michelangelo or Raphael. At the Gate of St. Anne the guardsmen are usually in dark blue fatigues, sixteenth-century fashion. When the pope repairs to Castel Gandolfo, a Swiss Guard detachment goes with him to the hills. A couple of Swiss in plainclothes, armed with revolvers, are in the pontiff's party when he travels.

The commander of the Swiss Guard has the rank of colonel and belongs to the official family of the supreme pontiff, which entitles him to walk with his officers behind the pope in solemn procession in St. Peter's. The commander's post customarily goes to a member of a handful of Swiss Roman Catholic families. Col. Franz Pfyffer von Altishofen, the guard's military chief from 1972 to 1982, was the eleventh Pfyffer von Altishofen to serve the pope in that capacity; the first was a Johann Rudolph from 1652 to 1657.

The civilian, or plainclothes, force of the Vatican's Office of Vigilance is a direct offshoot of a uniformed police organization that was set up in the declining years of the States of the Church in the nineteenth century, the Pontifical Gendarmerie. Some of the older Vigilance officers who today patrol the Vatican walls on the inside and check the credentials of visitors to curia offices have worn the black-blue uniforms and the bearskins of the papal gendarmerie until 1970; many members of the Vatican police formerly served with the Italian Carabinieri. All are Italians and all Roman Catholic laymen. The Vigilance Office keeps in close contact with Italy's law enforcement agencies.

The Vigilance men look unarmed, but they sometimes carry handguns in shoulder holsters. They can arrest suspected lawbreakers on Vatican soil, to turn them over to the judiciary arm of the papal government. Under the Lateran Treaties of 1929 the Holy See may itself try and punish lawbreakers for crimes committed in the Vatican; the Holy See has a penal court and an appeals court, as well as a rarely used jail. Under the 1929 accords, the Holy See may also request Italy to put lawbreakers on trial and carry out their sentences. Thus, when a Hungarian-born Australian attacked Michelangelo's *Pietà* with a hammer in 1972, gravely damaging the marble sculpture, the Vatican handed the vandal over to the Italian authorities for criminal proceedings (he was found to be mentally deranged). The Turkish man who fired at John Paul II was extradited to Italy; a Rome court tried him and sentenced him to life imprisonment, to be served in an Italian penitentiary.

During papal audiences and solemn Vatican ceremonies plainclothesmen of the Vigilance Office watch out for pickpockets, some of whom come from Naples and other cities for the occasion. There are also other shady types who are attracted by large crowds: in the crush of people during a canonization or other papal function that fills St. Peter's to overflowing some men will make passes at young women, preferably tourists, or even nuns or boys. Unless there is a complaint, it is hard to prove that an offense has been committed. "Sometimes we take one of those *pomicioni* aside and tell him sternly to get lost, never to show up again," a member of the Vigilance force said. "Usually he disappears for a while but, you wouldn't believe it, one or the other of them drifts back later, thinking we have forgotten him." *Pomicione,* which might be translated as "pumice-stone artist," is Roman vernacular for masher. Would-be suicides are another worry for the Vigilance personnel. Almost every year at least one visitor to St. Peter's will try to jump from the inner gallery of the dome of St. Peter's or seek to die in some other way near the tomb of the Prince of the Apostles in the—theologically untenable—belief of going to Heaven. If the attempt succeeds, the huge church is closed for an hour or so until it is reconsecrated by a prelate of its staff.

A special unit of the Vigilance Office does detective work in the Vatican, investigating thefts and burglaries—which do occur—and sometimes other crimes. It is widely believed that this group of Vigilance officers also monitors telephones in the papal state and carries out other covert activities aimed at suspect persons. The unit reports to the first deputy of the cardinal secretary of state.

Other handpicked Vigilance men help the Swiss Guard protect the pope. Such a plainclothes squad was organized in the 1970s when the Holy See's security officers realized that pontiffs might have to face physical violence of the kind their predecessors had often experienced. For more than a century no pope had seemed in danger of bodily harm. In 1848 Pius IX escaped from the Vatican to the papal fortress of Gaeta, disguised as a simple priest, when the Roman populace rose up in a rebellion that led to the proclamation of a (short-lived) republic. In 1870 the same pope had ample time to abandon the Quirinal Palace, taking the latchkey to its big portal with him, and withdrew to the Vatican without seeing any of the Italian soldiers who were conquering Rome. (But there was posthumous violence. Two years after Pius IX's death in 1878 as "prisoner in the Vatican," his body was transferred to the Basilica of St. Lawrence Outside the Walls which he had designated as his last resting place; an anticlerical mob snatched the casket as the cortege traversed downtown Rome at night, and would have thrown it into the Tiber if the royal police had not charged the rioters.)

It was Paul VI who, for the first time in the twentieth century, experienced violence aimed at a pontiff. In April 1970 during a visit to Cagliari, Sardinia, a crowd of left-wing extremists stoned the papal motorcade. A few months later a man hurled a rock at Paul VI, without hitting him, when the pope was addressing pilgrims in Castel Gandolfo. And toward the end of 1970 he narrowly escaped an assailant's knife in the Philippines.

Whenever Paul VI and, later, John Paul II were traveling, Bishop Marcinkus or Father Tucci, the papal tour managers, saw to it that the pontiff's bodyguards linked up with the local police officers in charge of security arrangements. After the attack on John Paul II in St. Peter's Square in 1981 the head of the Vatican's Vigilance Office, Camillo Cibin, was ordered to reorganize the unit responsible for the pontiff's physical safety. The group was beefed up, and its men were sent to a training center of the Italian Carabinieri to learn antiterrorism techniques. The fact that an ambulance had been standing by just inside the Vatican, and that plasma of John Paul II's blood group, A Rh-negative, had been available at once for copious transfusions were found to have been decisive in saving his life. (Whenever Marcinkus or Tucci were organizing one of John Paul II's journeys they made sure that an ambulance would be unobtrusively close to the pope and that the nearest hospital stored compatible plasma.)

The Mercedes-Benz Division of Daimler-Benz, the West German auto manufacturer, donated to John Paul II a prototype of what was quickly called the "Popemobile," a white-painted, sturdy vehicle that allowed the pontiff to stand up in a cage of bullet-proof glass to bless the crowds in St. Peter's Square or around the world. The engine and other vital parts of the car were protected with steel plate, and a special gearbox was designed for sudden fast forward and reverse movements. The Vatican had John Paul II's butler-driver, Angelo Gugel, and some men from the Vigilance Office trained to make full use of the model's special features, ordered three more Popemobiles, and had at least one of them shipped out in advance whenever the pontiff made a trip outside Rome.

New measures were also taken for the protection of the pope during his Vatican routines. The window on the third floor of the Apostolic Palace from which he addresses people in St. Peter's Square every Sunday was fitted with a bullet-proof transparent lectern. Bullet-proof glass panels were also installed on top of the Apostolic Palace all along the private terrace that Paul VI had had built. John Paul II liked to walk in tennis shoes up and down that aerie (the "hanging gardens," as it was called sarcastically) to read his breviary, but the Vatican security men worried that a sniper with a gunsight might fire at the pontiff from the Janiculum hill or from one of the tall residential buildings outside the pontifical state. As in the Middle Ages and in the Renaissance, the Vatican was again aware that it might become the target of violence at any hour.

"SOLIDARITY" AT THE HOLY SEE

Just as John Paul II was putting the full weight of the papacy behind the Solidarity independent workers' movement in his homeland in defiance of the Communist state, the Polish pontiff was himself, as an employer, confronted with labor unrest in the Vatican. A majority of the 1,800 lay persons, mostly men, among the personnel of the Holy See was pressing for higher pay and better job conditions. Many of the 2,500 priests, monks, friars, and nuns who also held posts in the central government of the church sympathized with the agitation of their civilian colleagues, obviously hoping that their own status might benefit from it.

For many centuries the Vatican has displayed a combination of sternness and paternalism in its dealings with its own work force. Statistics on the number of persons in the pope's employ do not go back very far, but all available evidence indicates that by the Middle Ages there were hundreds of them. The majority of the Vatican staff was regularly made up of ecclesiastics, who did not cost the pontiff much, as many of them were housed and fed by their own religious orders and communities; however, there were also laymen—courtiers, laborers, and eventually mercenary soldiers—who had to be paid out of the papal treasury.

Leo XIII in his encyclical "Rerum Novarum" (Of New Things) on social questions in 1891 expressly approved of trade unions, and Roman Catholic workers were encouraged by the church in many countries to join Christian labor movements. Yet the Vatican persisted in its authoritarian-paternalistic attitude toward those who were on its payroll; it took 90 years after "Rerum Novarum" for a Vatican labor union to win papal recognition.

One reason for the long absence of organized workers' militancy in the Vatican was that most of its wage earners, though they might grumble about low pay and alleged injustices, knew they had a good thing going. There might be less money than in a comparable job elsewhere in Rome, but there was a number of perquisites that made working for the pope attractive. For one thing, many Vatican employees were able to live in low-rent apartments in church-owned buildings. All Holy See personnel were, after 1929, exempt from Italian income tax on their Vatican earnings, and the pontifical state withheld only contributions for its pension system from the salaries and wages it paid. Whenever a pope died, the entire Vatican staff was entitled, under an old privilege, to a month's extra pay, and the election of a successor would bring another such largess. (The year of the three popes, 1978, was quite lucrative for Vatican personnel, and caused the Holy See acute cash-flow problems, although only

287

three, instead of four, extra salaries, without cost-of-living bonuses, were paid out.) Furthermore, at least a part of the gratuities that visiting cardinals and archbishops from wealthy sees outside Italy distribute would go to doorkeepers, drivers, and other lay staff. Another very important sweetener for working in the Vatican was access to the commissary where consumer goods are sold at prices notably lower than those in other Roman stores.

Then there is the job security, a powerful incentive in a country with chronically high unemployment. The Holy See almost never fires an employee (the case of a woman file clerk who was dismissed because she had become married to a former priest was exceptional). Some families have served the Vatican for generations. Pius XII's grandfather and father were both papal lay officials. The majordomo and driver of Pius XII was one Mario Stoppa, who was often bullied by Mother Pasqualina; under John Paul II three Stoppas of the next generation held civilian posts in the pontifical administration. In 1980 Cardinal Casaroli, the secretary of state, tried to introduce new regulations that would have virtually banned the old practice of some Vatican lay jobs being passed on from father to son. A strong group of civilian employees protested in a formal letter. "Your Eminence," it read, "we spend our entire lives in the Vatican. If our relatives do not find employment with those who know us, to whom should they turn?" In other words, the Vatican workers wanted hereditary jobs, a demand that even the most radical labor unions in Italy had never raised. The Secretariat of State answered evasively that no significant hiring of new personnel was foreseen in the near future.

Until recently the fringe benefits of working for the pope resulted in a relatively high productivity, compared with the low morale and languid performance of many other wage earners in the Italian capital. Up to this day, for instance, the men behind the counters of the Vatican mail service are markedly more efficient (and also more courteous) than the personnel of the average Italian post office. A mere fifteen gardeners manage to tend the Vatican's many flower beds, greenery, trees, and exotic plants, as well as the vast estate in Castel Gandolfo, much better than any park in Rome is tended. The Apostolic Library and the other Vatican collections function in a much more satisfying manner than do comparable institutions in Rome. Stepping into Vatican City is like crossing the border from Italy into Switzerland's Canton Ticino: the local language is still Italian, but everything looks neater and seems to be working better than on the other side of the frontier.

Since Italy's "hot autumn" of 1969, with its strikes and violence, workers' militancy has spilled over into the pontifical state. The Holy See had always refused to acknowledge that Italian labor laws should be applicable to its own staff. The Vatican, for instance, did grant its workers an escalator clause, linking pay rates to the Italian consumer price index, to enable them to cope with Italian inflation; however, the Vatican's cost-of-living bonuses were calculated every six months, whereas workers in Italy received such adjustments every three months. Other benefits that the powerful Italian labor unions had wrested from the nation's employers, like shorter working hours and automatic pay increases every two years, were not shared by Vatican employees. Inflation in Italy, which hovered around 20 percent a year, also hurt the Vatican's workers, although they could do some of their shopping at the papal commissary.

In 1970 Paul VI authorized across-the-board pay raises for most categories of pontifical personnel. However, soon there were new grievances—senior lay employees complained that they were being underpaid, married workers wanted substantial increases in their family bonuses, and nearly everyone demanded a shorter working week.

To allay the grumbling among the labor force, the Vatican established an Office for the Relations with the Personnel of the Holy See. A monsignor and a lay official of the pontifical administration were available from 5:00 to 7:00 P.M. Mondays through Fridays to listen to complaints by Vatican employees. The new office was opened in May 1971, and it was authoritatively pointed out that the innovation coincided with the 80th anniversary of Leo XIII's social encyclical. The institutional channel for the grievances of Vatican employees was actually another paternalistic experiment: disgruntled members of the papal labor force were expected to present their complaints and demands individually, as if group action were seditious. Employees who did turn to the Holy See's new labor relations branch soon found that it was powerless.

Toward the end of Paul VI's pontificate discontent was widespread among the Vatican personnel, and was echoed in left-wing Italian newspapers. Soon after the election of the Polish pope an anonymous group of Holy See staff sent a letter to John

Paul II setting forth its complaints about low pay, inadequate family bonuses, slow promotions, and lack of representation. When there was no reaction whatsoever, the text of the letter to the pontiff was sent to the Italian press by the promoters of the action, who signed as "Very many Vatican employees who are forced to remain incognito." Several newspapers published the letter, but again there was no response from the sacred palaces. In September 1979, after John Paul II's triumphant tour of Poland, and just before his journey to Ireland and the United States, the anonymous activists of the Holy See's labor force issued another "Open Letter to Our Pope." The tone this time was less respectful and more combative than it had been in the earlier messages. "We don't want privileges and advantages but a just salary," the text read. It referred sarcastically to the "volcanic dynamism" that had taken the Polish pope far and wide, "maybe too far from us who are so close to you." After listing again their demands, the letter writers concluded: "People already say that you are a great pope, but we are waiting for people to say that you are a just pope."

This time there was a quick acknowledgment, apparently because of the tough tone of the open letter. Father Panciroli, the Holy See's spokesman for the press, announced that John Paul II had instructed his aides to examine the demands of the Vatican employees "with every attention and goodwill." The pope had been "well aware of the situation" of the work force in the pontifical state ever since his election, the spokesman stated, and had expressed his concern to his closest aides several times. Panciroli added stolidly that, unfortunately, the financial resources of the Holy See were limited "despite what a certain press has asserted." Vatican finances and the demands of the personnel were, as will be remembered, topics in the week-long session behind closed doors that John Paul II held with the sacred college of cardinals in November 1979. At that time the salaries of the Vatican's lay employees ranged from the equivalent of $6,000 to that of $9,000 a year. Ecclesiastics in the curia were paid considerably less owing to the circumstance that they were all celibate and were usually enjoying free lodging and food.

In December 1979 each member of the Holy See's personnel received a Christmas gift package on behalf of the pope. "I thought somebody had played a practical joke on me when I opened my parcel and found a color photo of Pope Wojtyla, a keyring with his coat of arms, and a plastic rosary inside," a mechanic at the Vatican's electric power station told me. "But everybody got the same junk; not even a *panettone.*" A *panettone* is a Milanese Christmas cake that has long conquered all of Italy. Maybe John Paul II had intended to joke. Two days later, just before Christmas, the Holy See announced substantial pay increases for all of its employees. All basic salaries and wages went up by 50 percent, and pensions by 10 percent. The papal administration also promised to recalculate the cost-of-living adjustments every three months (as was being done in Italy), to raise all family bonuses, and to grant automatic 2 percent increases in take-home pay every two years. For instance, an assistant editor of *L'Osservatore Romano* whose monthly salary, including cost-of-living and family bonuses, had been the equivalent of $678 was to receive the equivalent of $1,062 monthly from January 1, 1980. The Vatican's budget managers figured that the pay raises would cost some $8 million in 1980.

The Vatican staff was generally pleased, and John Paul II received a big hand from groups of his employees during his public appearances in the following weeks. The Vatican labor activists, however, had one criticism: the long overdue pay raises had been granted by papal "benevolence," that is, unilaterally and paternalistically, without consulting workers' representatives. The authors of the anonymous letters to the pontiff, purporting to present the grievances of the Vatican personnel, had meanwhile come into the open, no longer afraid of disciplinary action against them, and were setting up something like a union.

The chief organizer was Mariano Cerullo, a wiry, mustachioed technician at the Vatican Radio transmission center at Santa Maria di Galeria, who had previously worked for the Italian air force and for Trans World Airlines. (Aviation personnel is among the most militant categories of organized labor in Italy.) On December 4, 1979, Cerullo and about a dozen colleagues formally founded an Association of Vatican Lay Employees as a group for the defense of their economic interests. The promoters avoided the word "union" for fear of unduly alarming conservatives in the curia, and stressed that the organization had no political character whatsoever. No attempt was made to induce ecclesiastical employees of the Holy See to join. (In 1982 the Vatican expressly forbade anything resembling a priests' union anywhere in the world on the grounds that an organization seeking to improve the material situation of clergy would be contrary to the very nature of the holy ministry.)

During the first few months of 1980 more than two-thirds of the Vatican's civilian employees signed up with the new group, and the membership elected Cerullo as its president. When, in the summer of 1980, an independent labor movement, Solidarity, coalesced in Poland under the leadership of Lech Walesa, Romans inevitably observed that "Pope Wojtyla has his own Walesa right in the Vatican." The Polish pope's forceful backing of the Solidarity movement in his homeland doubtless helped the workers' activists of the Holy See. Cardinal Casaroli told Cerullo that the pontiff favored labor representation in the Vatican; the secretary of state allowed the new association to hold meetings in a hall of *L'Osservatore Romano*'s building on Vatican soil.

In April 1981 Cerullo and 39 other Vatican labor delegates met for the first time with the pope to submit their grievances. "I perfectly understand your problems," John Paul II told them at the beginning of the unprecedented labor talks in the Apostolic Palace. "You know, I have been a worker myself." (Whenever the Polish pope spoke to workers anywhere he liked to recall his experiences as a laborer at the Solvay chemical plant in Krakow during World War II.) On hearing the complaints of the Vatican lay staff, the pope gave the impression that he had not known there were so many disparities, and outright injustices, in the treatment of the various categories of employees; he also seemed astonished to learn that because of Italy's high inflation rate the advantages of a Vatican job no longer outweighed the low pay. John Paul II discarded a prepared speech, remarking to an aide that "this no longer serves," and expressed the hope, at the end of the two-hour meeting, that the dialogue with the Holy See's personnel would continue in a constructive manner. For the workers the important thing was papal recognition of their organization.

One result of the debate between the pope and the employees' delegates was that the normal work week in the Vatican was cut from 42 to 39 hours. However, the appetite of the Holy See's personnel had been whetted, and they wanted what labor unions everywhere want—more. The elected delegates drew up a set of demands for, among other things, new pay raises, a better pension system, and a 36-hour week. The pontifical administration appointed a team of lay officials who were to negotiate for what in industry would be called the management side; it was led by a prelate, Archbishop Marcinkus.

The Chicagoan, acting in his capacity as head of the State of

Vatican City government, fired off a letter to the employees' association rejecting any claim based on Italian labor legislation, and insisting that "the possibilities of the Holy See and the objective situation of requirements" must always be kept in mind. Marcinkus's new role as the institutional antagonist of the wage earners' front in the Vatican did not help his popularity, and his enemies in the curia seemed glad that he had to play the heavy in the labor negotiations. Anonymous leaflets with such taunts as "Marcinkus, Return to the Middle West!" and "We Don't Want the Sheriff Marcinkus!" were found pasted on walls in the pontifical state; an anti-American note seemed to creep into the Holy See's Solidarity movement. Somebody even scrawled "Down With Marcinkus!" on the inside wall of the antiquated elevator that takes visitors from the Courtyard of St. Damasus up to the pontifical apartments and the Secretariat of State.

In May 1982 the agitation of the Holy See's employees escalated: 1,200 of them, three-quarters of their association's membership, marched silently from the staff mess hall to the building of *L'Osservatore Romano*. There were no slogans and no signs, but the 300-yard parade made the point that the vast majority of the lay staff was behind the activists, and it had the effect of mollifying Marcinkus a little. It was the first labor demonstration in the Vatican in modern times. In an old place like this, one must be careful about using words like "unprecedented." In the long history of the papacy the clerks, mercenaries, and laborers more than once have become turbulent when they weren't getting paid for too long a period. However, the Holy See had never had union trouble before.

This time the Swiss Guard did not participate in the labor movement because, as a military body, it has a special status with separate pay scales and service regulations. The labor agitation in the Vatican was almost exclusively Italian, and it seemed inevitable that the Italian propensity for strikes would sooner or later be felt in the papal state.

Pope John Paul II betrayed his worries about such a threat in a formal letter to his secretary of state, Cardinal Casaroli, in November 1982. In the document, which was published in *L'Osservatore Romano,* the pontiff conceded that such groups as the Association of Vatican Lay Employees represented "an initiative in harmony with the social doctrine of the church," but warned that they must never "slide" into seeking conflict or class struggle.

CHAPTER 10

THE VATICAN OF TOMORROW

SOME ROMAN CATHOLIC theologians, trying to imagine the future of their church, have projected a vision of scattered islands of believers in a vastly secularized or godless world. As many seminaries, monasteries, and convents are emptying, or have already been closed, there will likely be far fewer Roman Catholic clergy in, say, the year 2000 than there are now. Despite opposition from the Roman Curia, regional bishops' conferences and individual members of the hierarchy at large will in all probability have won much more autonomy by that time than they enjoy at present. The bishops' conferences may obtain the right to coopt new members and assign them to vacant posts in dioceses, possibly on recommendations from priests' groups and lay organizations, with only formal consent by the pope. The current rearguard action by Roman Catholic conservatives will probably fail to prevent the ecumenical movement from overcoming some of the differences between the Church of Rome and the other Christian denominations.

If these assumptions prove correct, the role of the Vatican will be different from what it is today. With fewer priests, monks, friars, and nuns to oversee, and with the bishops in the various countries managing a large part of their local affairs in a decentralized church, much of the administrative apparatus in Rome should become superfluous.

Bureaucrats naturally cling to their posts and privileges, and refuse to fade away even after their functions have become obsolete; however, the monetary contributions from Roman Catholics in rich countries may dry up or be diverted to the Third World, forcing the Holy See to cut expenses and streamline the curia.

With some, or much, of the bureaucratic structure dismantled, Rome will probably prove unable to prevent priests and lay groups in poor countries from joining revolutionary movements —as some of them have already done in Latin America and in the Philippines—or to keep Roman Catholics out of "peace" fronts in the industrialized nations. Jesuits, other priests and monks, and nuns who feel committed to radical change in their societies may eventually be able to act without much interference from the Vatican.

At the same time, conservative forces in Rome, and tradition-minded Roman Catholics everywhere, backed by right-wing parties and business interests, may be expected to flock to Opus Dei and similar groups. It is true that a successor to John Paul II may again clip the wings of Opus Dei—but if the reign of the Polish pope lasts long enough, the movement founded by Monsignor Escrivá may become so strong and well entrenched that one of its men might be elected the next pontiff.

If Opus Dei continues to be attracted by secret work, it will run the risk of being considered subversive by various governments, and of turning out an embarrassment to the church, although it might provide a new crop of martyrs for it. On the other hand, the new "personal prelacy" of Monsignor Escrivá's successors could become a scheming sect of true believers, like Ayatollah Khomeini's Shiites, and a disruptive force in Christianity.

The weakening of the Roman Curia that may be expected, and the new power that John Paul II has given Opus Dei, seem to portend a widening split between liberal and conservative Roman Catholics—increasing polarization within the church.

In a world that may have become largely indifferent to organized religion, and with a decentralized church, it will become inevitable for the Vatican to retrench, do without frills, and get rid of unneeded ecclesiastical and lay personnel. The inchoate labor movement in the pontifical state, and the dearth of pastors in many areas, including the "holy city" of Rome and its surroundings, have already raised the question whether the Vatican, financially and morally, can afford a staff of thousands.

295

Pressures from the church at large and from public opinion in Italy and in other countries may induce the papacy, at last, to revamp the entire system of Vatican finances, lift the cloak of mystery, and explain which sums are actually allotted to "works of religion," and of what nature these works are.

Rather than reign in a costly religious Disneyland, the papacy would be wise to focus on essentials. It should shun what the Italians sarcastically call *presentismo,* an itch for omnipresence and for speaking out on every event and issue that happens to be in the news, from wars to world sports championships.

Even in societies that stress material values, there will always be room, and maybe the need, for an authoritative voice calling for belief in the supernatural, and commitment to unchanging ethical standards. Such a function would immeasurably enhance the moral prestige of the papacy. Although the Vatican presently maintains formal relations with more nations than ever, and from time to time yet another government decides, for the first time, to send an ambassador to the Holy See, it is questionable whether in the long run the popes will be able to toy with the trappings of sovereignty. Vatican II revealed that many bishops regard the worldwide network of nuncios as unnecessary, and think it might be abolished without any harm to the faith, and with considerable savings to boot. Some future pontiff may find, at last, that it is not the Holy See's business to play diplomatic charades, mark every January 1 by sending a rhetorical papal peace appeal to all heads of state around the globe, or reiterate futile offers to mediate in international conflicts.

Technology is providing new possibilities. The importance of the Vatican as a religious communications and media center will undoubtedly grow. Roman Catholics and other Christians everywhere—in fact, everybody in the world who cares—will be able to see and hear the bishop of Rome, daily if they want, thanks to satellite television and other advanced devices. It may safely be predicted that Vatican Radio will soon develop a video arm; it has already contracted for satellite sharing. The temptation to raise money by selling advertising time may become irresistible. Program policy will be of prime concern to the pope and his advisers.

If the head of the Roman Catholic Church has something to say, many in the world will tune in and listen. If the pope were to recognize that his main mission is to proclaim the verities of Christianity, the bishop of Rome would be indeed a Holy Father.

INDEX

Abs, Hermann J., 202, 205
acclamation, 78
Acqua Santa golf links, 187
Acta Apostolicae Sedis, 265–266
Adrian VI, Pope, 38–39, 129
Adzhubei, Aleksei, 29
Agça, Mehmet Ali, 45
Agency of Viligance and Repression
  of Anti-Fascists (OVRA),
  256–257, 258
aggiornamento concept, 28, 29, 95
Alexander VI, Pope, 13, 18, 35–36,
  129, 147
Andreatta, Beniamino, 201
Angelicum, 213, 262
Annona supermarket, 117–118
Annuario Pontificio, 87–88, 185
ANSA news agency, 171, 243
Antonelli, Giacomo Cardinal, 62
Antoniutti, Ildebrando Cardinal,
  230, 238
apologetics, 244
apostolic constitution (1967), 98
Apostolic Delegation, 64–65
Apostolic Palace, 69, 85, 147
Apostolic Signature, Tribunal of, 173
Aquinas, Saint Thomas, 262
Arrupe y Gondra, Pedro, as superior
  general of Jesuits, 215–222, 223,
  224, 226, 228

Association of Vatican Lay
  Employees, 291–293
Avignon, France, Papal residency at,
  7, 9, 128

Baggio, Sebastiano Cardinal, 239,
  240
Banca Commerciale Italiana, 174
Banca d'Italia, 197, 198
Banco Ambrosiano Holdings, 200
Banco Ambrosiano Overseas, 196
Banco Ambrosiano scandal, 176, 186,
  195–207, 270
Banco di Roma, 176, 181
Banco di Roma per la Svizzera, 181
Banco di Santo Spirito, 185
Bartoloni, Giulio, 257
Basilica of St. John Lateran, 7, 9
Basilica of St. Lawrence Outside the
  Walls, 162
Bastià, Giuseppe, 265
Bastion of Nicholas V, 181, 184, 186
Baum, William Cardinal, 89
Bea, Augustin Cardinal, 92–93,
  139–140, 142
beatification, 85, 131–132
Belli, Giuseppe Gioacchino, 272
Benedict IX, Pope, 32
Benedict XIII, Pope, 32, 274
Benedict XV, Pope, 144

Benelli, Giovanni Cardinal, as chief
  of staff in Secretariat, 116–120,
  121, 122, 147, 148, 166, 202, 219,
  232
Berlinguer, Enrico, 136
Bernardin, Joseph Cardinal, 65–66
Berrigan, Daniel, 217
Bertoli, Paolo Cardinal, 118, 157
Betrothed, The (Manzoni), 266
birth control, 17, 30–31, 44, 99
Bishops, Sacred Congregation of,
  239, 241
bishops' conferences, 101, 114, 294
Bishops' Synod, 99–100, 101
Bismarck, Prince Otto von, 212
"black" (pontifical) nobility, 129,
  139, 277
"blessed," 85, 131
Boccaccio, Giovanni, 8–9
Borgia, Cesare, 36, 128–129
Borgia, Lucrezia, 13, 275
Borromeo, Saint Carlo, 129
Bracker, Milton, 256
Brandt, Willy, 28
Brennan, Joseph, 202, 205
bulls, papal, 129
Burckhardt, Jakob, 18

Calixtus III, Pope, 128
Calvi, Roberto, in Banco Ambrosiano
  scandal, 196–201, 203, 204, 206
Camino (Escrivá), 233
Camon, Ferdinando, 42
canonical age, 134
canonization, 131–132
canon law, 92, 134, 173, 235–236
  cardinals and, 66, 77, 80, 114
  pope and, 17, 32, 46–47
Canova, Antonio, 212
Capovilla, Loris, as secretary to
  Pope John XXIII, 140–145, 266
Caprio, Giuseppe, 39, 161–162, 167,
  193
Capucci, Hilarion, 247
Carabinieri, 280, 284, 285
Caraffa, Carlo, 129
cardinal camerlengo, 37, 68, 75
"Cardinalitial" sees, 55
"cardinal nephew," 129
cardinal prefect, 90, 92
cardinals, 49–81
  canon law and, 66, 77, 80, 114
  conclave of, 52, 55, 70, 72–81
  in consultations, 80–81, 100,
    165–167, 170, 204

dean of, 60–61
election of, 55–60, 67, 72–74, 80
John Paul II and, 65, 79, 80–81
plenum of, 66–67, 79
retirement of, 53, 72–74, 81, 82,
  86, 98
as sacred college, 51–55, 60–72,
  75–76
secretaries to, 70–71
Tisserant as dean of, 60–61, 68,
  73, 137, 138
see also individual cardinals
cardinal vicar, 97
Carli, Guido, 183
Carlini, Paolo, 151
Casaroli, Agostino Cardinal:
  labor policies of, 288, 292, 293
  as secretary of state, 29, 105,
    121–126, 178–179, 223, 251
  Vatican finances and, 166, 193,
    194, 201, 202
Castel Gandolfo, 5, 6, 24, 41–42, 213
Castro, Fidel, 103, 123
Catherine the Great, empress of
  Russia, 211
Catholic Education, Sacred
  Congregation for, 92
Causes of Saints, Sacred
  Congregation for the, 85, 118, 132,
  237
Ceauşescu, Nicolae, 47
Celestine V, Pope Saint, 31, 74
Central Intelligence Agency (CIA),
  246
Cerullo, Mariano, 291, 292
Cerutti, Carlo, 202, 205
Charles V, king of France, 279
Cheli, Giovanni, 105, 123
Chicago, archdiocese of, 64–66
Chicago Sun-Times, 64
China, People's Republic of, 125
Christian Democratic party, 191, 197
Christina, queen of Sweden, 13
Church of the Gesù, 225
Church of the Most Holy Apostles,
  212
Ciano, Count Galeazzo, 187, 275
Cibin, Camillo, 285
Cicognani, Amleto Giovanni
  Cardinal, 114
Cicognani, Gaetano Cardinal, 114
Cippico, Edoardo Prettner, 182–183
Cisalpine Overseas Bank, Ltd.,
  196–197
Civiltà Cattolica, 214

Clement VI, Pope, 128
Clement VII, Pope, 69, 279
Clement XI, Pope, 211
Clement XIV, Pope, 210, 211, 212
Cody, John Patrick Cardinal, 64–65,
 177, 178
Collection of Religious Modern Art,
 147
collegiality, principle of, 99
Colonna, Don Aspreno, 274, 276
Colonna, Marc Antonio (Duke of
 Paliano), 275
Colonna, Marcantonio, 275
Colonna, Marquess Vittoria, 275
Columbus, Christopher, 132
Communism, Vatican's attitude
 toward, 57, 58, 59, 122–124, 136,
 171, 217–218, 251
Confalonieri, Carlo Cardinal, 61, 71,
 159
Congregations, Palace of, 84
Consalvi, Ercole Cardinal, 62
consistory, of cardinals, 55–60, 67,
 72–74, 80
Constance, Council of (1414–18),
 32
Consultive Council of the State of
 Vatican City, 276
contraception, 17, 30–31, 44, 99
Cooke, Terence Cardinal, 146, 167,
 232
cooperators, in Opus Dei, 234, 235
Cordero di Montezemolo, Vittorio,
 248
Corriere della Sera, 197
Corrocher, Graziella Teresa, 199
"counter letter," 201
Counter-Reformation, 17, 18, 129,
 211, 240
Crescenzi, Marquess Serlupi, 274
Curia, Roman, 8–13, 82–126
 as bureaucracy, 11–12, 21,
  67–68, 84–94, 265
 diplomatic activity of, 97,
  100–108
 Italian influence in, 83, 88–89
 John Paul II and, 82, 95–96
 "new curia" of, 92–93, 170
 pastoral experience and, 96–98,
  100
 pope vs., 82–83, 93–94, 95
 reform of, 94–100
 Sacred Congregations in, 11, 53,
  90–91, 92, 93, 110
 see also specific departments

Daily American, 191
Dalla Torre, Count Giuseppe, 266
Daniélou, Jean Cardinal, 63–64
Dante Alighieri, 31
deacons, 62
Dearden, John Francis Cardinal, 65,
 156
de Bonis, Donato, 206
Decameron (Boccaccio), 8–9
Declaration on Religious Liberty, 260
Declaration on the Relation of the
 Church to Non-Christian Religions,
 260
de Furstenberg, Maximilien, 277
delegates, apostolic, 101, 102
del Portillo y Diez de Sollano,
 Alvaro, 237, 239, 241
de Lubac, Henri Cardinal, 56, 216, 221
de Maillardoz, Henri, 175
Deng Yiming, 125
De Propaganda Fide, Sacred
 Congregation, 243
Deskur, Andrzej Maria, 39, 155
de Strobel, Pellegrino, 203, 206
"devil's advocate," 132
de Weck, Philippe, 202, 205
Dezza, Paolo, 223, 225, 226, 227, 228
Diez-Alegria, José Maria, 219
"Dignitatis Humanae," 260
di Murrone, Pietro, see Celestine V,
 Pope Saint
Discipline of the Faith, Sacred
 Congregation for, 209
Divine Comedy (Dante), 31
Doctrine of the Faith, Sacred
 Congregation for the, 91–92, 94,
 252, 263
Dominicans, 208, 213, 231
Drinan, Robert, 212
Dulles, John Foster, 22
Dziwisz, Stanislaw "Stash," 153–154

Eastern Churches, Sacred
 Congregation for, 252
Eastern rites, 61, 62, 229
Ecclesiastical Academy, 96–97, 103
ecclesiastical counselor, 249
Economic Affairs of the Holy See,
 Prefecture for, 162, 167–168, 177,
 180
"epicureanism," 209
Escrivá de Balaguer y Albás, José
 Maria, as founder of Opus Dei,
 230, 232–233, 235, 236, 237–238,
 239

Estudio General of Pamplona, 236
Etchegaray, Roger Cardinal, 156
Études, 64
European American Bank and Trust
  Company, 192
Evangelization of the Peoples,
  Sacred Congregation for the, 93,
  170, 178, 243
Ewaldis, Sister, 134
excommunication, 89–90, 250
extreme unction, 36–37

Farinacci, Roberto, 282
Fatima (Portugal) shrine, 21
Faulhaber, Michael Cardinal von, 22
Federal Information Service (W.
  Germany), 251
Felici, Pericle Cardinal, 34, 100, 105,
  124, 154, 156, 173, 179
Fiat Motor Company, 181
Fleischman, Lawrence, 146
Fleming, Alexander, 24
"fourth vow," 219
France, Vatican relations with, 246
Franciscans, 208, 216, 231, 241
Francis Joseph, emperor of
  Austria-Hungary, 59, 78
Francis of Assisi, Saint, 241
Franco, Carmen, 230
Franco, Francisco, 230
Frankel, Marvin, 193
Franklin National Bank failure,
  191–192, 193
Freemasonry, 198
Friends of American Art in Religion,
  146

Galeazzi, Count Enrico, 23, 138, 175,
  282
Galeazzi Lisi, Riccardo, as personal
  physician to Pius XII, 22–27, 137,
  250
Gantin, Bernardin Cardinal, 93
Garrone, Gabriel-Marie Cardinal, 152
Gasparri, Pietro Cardinal, 110
Gemelli clinic, 45
Gendarmerie, Pontifical, 279–280,
  283–284
Germany, West, Vatican relations
  with, 246, 251
Giacomina, Sister, 150
Giscard d'Estaing, Valéry, 156
Glemp, Josef Cardinal, 157, 249
Goebbels, Joseph, 243
Goretti, Saint Maria, 118, 157

"gorilla," of pope, 186–195
Graham, Robert A., 214, 258
Grano, Carlo Cardinal, 141
gratuities, for Vatican staff, 273
Great Britain, Vatican relations
  with, 246
Great Schism (1378–1417), 32, 128,
  275
Greek-Melchite rite, 247
Gregory XII, Pope, 32
Gregory XIII, Pope, 213
Gregory XV, Pope, 243
Guerri, Sergio Cardinal, 193
Gugel, Angelo, 286
Guitton, Jean, 32

Hall of Paul VI, 6
Hebblethwaite, Peter, 219
Heckel, Roger, 221
Henry VIII, king of England, 240
Heraldic Commission of the
  Pontifical Court, 277
heretics, 91
Höffner, Joseph Cardinal, 168, 177,
  178, 206–207
Holy House of Loreto, 144
Holy Land, status of, 120–121, 150,
  209
Holy Office, 91–92, 94, 252, 263
Holy Spirit, 77–78
Holy Year (1950), 118, 119, 136
Holy Year (1983), 118
House Pastor Angelicus, 131
Hudal, Alois, 252
"Humanae Vitae" encyclical, 31
Hume, George Basil Cardinal,
  236–237

I Believe in Hope (Diez-Alegria), 219
Ignatius of Loyola, Saint, 210, 212,
  225
Illich, Ivan, 91
Imitation of Christ (Thomas à
  Kempis), 37
indulgences, selling of, 160
"inner forum," 90
Innocent XI, Blessed, 133
Innocent XII, Pope, 129
Inquisition, Holy, 18, 91, 209
  see also Holy Office
Institute for Marxist Studies, 213
International Theological
  Commission, 91
Israel, Vatican relations with,
  246–247

Istituto Farmacologico Serono, 177
Italy, Vatican relations with, 67, 83, 88–89, 102, 107, 248, 289, 293

Jansenists, 210
Janssens, Jan B., 217
J. Arthur Rank Organization, 275
Jerusalem, status of, 120–121, 150, 209
Jesuits, 24, 38, 135, 139, 210–229, 295
    Arrupe as superior general of, 215–222, 223, 224, 226, 228
    General Congregation of, 215, 224–225, 227, 228
    John Paul II and, 212, 214, 220–229, 244, 270
    Opus Dei vs., 209, 231, 237, 240, 242, 245, 248, 254, 270
    Paul VI and, 219, 220, 270
    personal delegate to, 223, 224, 226
Joan, Popess, 13
Joan of Arc, Saint, 132
John XV, Pope, 128, 132
John XXIII, Pope, 2, 5, 30, 31, 74, 88, 112, 132
    Capovilla as secretary to, 140–145, 266
    Ostpolitik policy of, 57, 58, 59, 122–123, 251
    pontificate of, 27–29, 40, 79, 92, 113–114
John Paul I, Pope, 27, 88, 220
    death of, 35–38, 151, 165
    election of, 79, 149, 245, 255
    pontificate of, 33–35, 114, 119, 120–121, 194
John Paul II, Pope, 5, 14, 19, 88, 129, 144
    assassination attempt on, 44–46, 61, 125–126, 167, 244–245, 254, 261, 269, 283, 284, 285, 286
    cardinals and, 65, 79, 80–81
    election of, 15–16, 74–75, 79–80, 245, 255
    foreign trips of, 43–44, 47–48, 63, 93, 105, 125, 156, 194, 245, 285–286
    Jesuits and, 212, 214, 220–229, 244, 270
    media coverage of, 261–262, 268–269
    Opus Dei and, 230–231, 238, 239, 240, 244

Poland's importance to, 152, 245–246, 267–268
    pontificate of, 27, 38–44, 56, 109, 118, 121–126, 262–263, 286–287, 289–293
    Roman Curia and, 82, 95–96
    Vatican finances under, 161, 162, 163, 165–168, 169, 170, 178–179, 205
Jovius, Paulus, 279
Juan Carlos, king of Spain, 230
Jubany Arnau, Narciso Cardinal, 168
Julius II, Pope, 41, 274, 279

Kabongo, Emery, 154
Kakol, Kazimierz, 42
Keys of Saint Peter, The (Peyrefitte), 151
Koenig, Franz Cardinal, 31, 58, 79
Kolbe, Blessed Maximilian, 157
Kolvenbach, Peter-Hans, 228
Konkret, 251
Kreuger, Ivar, 190
Krol, John Cardinal, 79, 167, 168
Küng, Hans, 91, 263

laity, role of, 271–272
Langemann, Hans, 251
Lateran Treaties (1929), 4, 17, 102, 110, 139, 174, 284
Latin, macaronic, 88
Lawrence, Saint, 162
Ledóchowski, Wladimir, 221
Lee, Belinda, 275
Lefebvre, Marcel, 124
Léger, Paul Emile Cardinal, 66
Lehnert, Josefine, see Pasqualina, Mother
Leiber, Robert, 140
Lekai, Laszlo, 59
Leo III, Pope Saint, 7
Leo IV, Pope Saint, 279
Leo X, Pope, 41
Leo XIII, Pope, 35, 47, 185, 214, 287, 289
Levi, Vergilio, 151, 266, 267–268
Lincoln, Agnes, 124
"living cell" cure, 24
Lolli, Cesidio, 19, 28
Loreto (Italy) shrine, 143–144
Louis XVI, king of France, 104
Luciani, Albino Cardinal, see John Paul I, Pope
Lustiger, Jean-Marie, 156
Luther, Martin, 39, 210

Macchi, Pasquale, 117, 119
  as secretary to Pope Paul VI,
    145–151, 159, 188, 193
Macharski, Franciszek Cardinal,
  157
Machiavelli, Niccolò, 128
Magee, John, 37, 151, 154
Maglione, Luigi Cardinal, 110
Malachy, Saint, prophesy of, 21, 131
Malta, Knights of, 277–278
Malula, Joseph Cardinal, 63
Mälzer, Kurt, 282
Manzini, Raimondo, 266
Manzoni, Alessandro, 266
Marcinkus, Paul Casimir, 145, 156,
  214, 292–293
    in Banco Ambrosiano scandal,
      197, 201, 202, 203, 204, 206,
      270
    as head of Vatican Bank,
      188–189, 194, 206
    as papal tour manager, 187–188,
      194–195, 203, 285, 286
    in Sindona scandal, 188, 191,
      193, 194
Marconi, Guglielmo, 214, 269
Maria Conrada, Sister, 134
Maritain, Jacques, 30
Maronites, 171
Martin, Graham A., 191
Martin V, Pope, 32, 275
Martini, Carlo Maria, 221
Marty, François Cardinal, 156
Mary, Virgin, 21, 136–137, 144
Masonic lodges, 198
Massimo, Prince, 274
"Mater et Magistra" encyclical, 28
Mennini, Luigi, 195, 203, 206
Merry del Val, Rafael Cardinal, 114
Messaggero, Il, 42, 117
Mezzofanti, Giuseppe Cardinal, 88
Milagros Del Drago, Princess Maria,
  276
"Milan mafia," 145–151, 188, 190,
  261
Mindszenty, Joseph Cardinal, 58–59,
  63, 123
Mitterand, François, 226
Mobutu Sese Seko, 63
Month, The, 219
Montini, Giovanni Battista Cardinal,
  see Paul VI, Pope
Montini, Ludovico, 111
Moro, Aldo, 47
"mortification," 234

Murray, John Courtney, 216
Mussolini, Benito, 138–139

Napoleon I, emperor of France, 281
National Conference of Catholic
  Bishops, 103
Navarre, University of, 236
Navon, Yitzhak, 120
Nazis, Rome occupied by, 252–253,
  258, 281–282
Nervi, Pier Luigi, 6
New York Times, 22, 104, 243, 250,
  256
Nicholas III, Pope, 7
Nicholas V, Pope, 180
Niehans, Paul, 24
Nikodim, Metropolitan, 35
Noble Guard, Pontifical, 280
Nogara, Bernardino, 174
Non-Christians, Secretariat for, 150
"Nostra Aetate," 260
Notiziario, 257–258
numeraries, in Opus Dei, 233–234
nuncios, apostolic, duties of, 97,
  100–108, 296
Nuovo Banco Ambrosiano, 200
Nuzzi, Oreste, 25, 26

obeisance, rite of, 60
Observer, The, 219
Oddi, Silvio Cardinal, 124, 231
O'Flaherty, Hugh, 252
Oggi, 42–43
O'Keefe, Vincent T., 222, 224
"On the Vacancy of the Holy See,"
  38
Operation Eva, 251
Opus Dei, 229–242, 295
    Escriva as founder of, 230,
      232–233, 235, 236, 237–238,
      239
    Jesuits vs., 209, 231, 237, 240,
      242, 245, 248, 254, 270
    John Paul II and, 230–231, 238,
      239, 240, 244
    personal prelacy of, 231, 239,
      240, 295
orders, religious, see specific orders
Orsini, Don Filippo Napoleone, 274,
  275
Osservatore Romano, L', 19, 21, 40,
  117, 151, 172, 173, 178, 202, 206,
  235, 257, 272
    operation of, 258–259, 262–270,
      291

Ottaviani, Alfredo Cardinal, 73, 91,
94

Pacelli, Eugenio Cardinal, *see* Pius
XII, Pope
Pacelli, Prince Carlo, 138, 282
Pacelli, Prince Francesco, 139
Pacelli, Prince Giulio, 138
Pacelli, Prince Marcantonio, 138,
181, 265
"Pacem in Terris" encyclical, 28
Paetz, Juliusz, 155
Pajetta, Giancarlo, 136
Palace of the Datary, 171
Palatine Administrations, 178
Palatine Guard, 280
Palazzini, Pietro Cardinal, 231
Palazzo Altemps, 171
Palestine Liberation Organization
(PLO), 247
Palestine National Council, 247
pallium, 34, 40
Palmas, Angelo, 101
Panciroli, Romeo, 130, 151, 261, 270,
290
panettone, 291
Pantanella, 177, 190
papabiles, 52, 75
Paraclete, 77–78
Parente, Pietro Cardinal, 262
Pasqualina, Mother, as aide to Pope
Pius XII, 13, 22, 24, 54, 61, 113,
127, 130–138, 143, 144, 159,
163–164, 215, 281
patriarchs, 55, 61–62
Patrimony of the Holy See,
Administration of the (APSA), 85,
162, 176, 178, 179
Paul IV, Pope, 129
Paul V, Pope, 185, 276
Paul VI, Pope, 2, 10, 14, 27, 29, 88,
110–113, 136
cardinals and, 57, 58, 59, 63, 64,
72–74, 75, 76–77, 79, 98
ecclesiastical reforms by, 72–74,
76–77, 79, 91–92, 99, 100
election of, 33, 74
entourage of, 145–151, 188, 190,
261
foreign trips of, 43, 45, 56, 72,
187–188, 189, 285
Jesuits and, 219, 220, 270
Macchi as secretary to, 145–151,
159, 188, 193
personality of, 31, 41, 47

pontificate of, 29–32, 38, 40, 47,
193, 247, 248, 251, 279–280,
289
Vatican finances under, 164–165,
169, 175–178, 190–194, 202
Paul VI Institute, 149
Peck, Gregory, 252
Pellegrino, Michele Cardinal, 66
people of God, 271
perennial philosophy, 262, 263
perinde ac cadaver, 211
Peter, Saint, 5, 50
Peter's Pence, 168–170, 178, 179,
185, 205
Peyrefitte, Roger, 151, 183
Pfyffer von Altishofen, Franz, 283
Piacenza (Italy) seminary, 122
piatto cardinalizio, 71–72
Pietà, attack on, 284
Pignatelli family, 129
Pignedoli, Sergio Cardinal, 149–150
Pironio, Eduardo Cardinal, 238,
239
Pittau, Giuseppe, 223, 225, 226, 227,
228
Pius II, Pope, 41
Pius IV, Pope, 129
Pius V, Pope Saint, 133
Pius VII, Pope, 211, 281
Pius VIII, Pope, 35
Pius IX, Pope, 45, 203, 285
Pius X, Pope Saint, 35, 59–60,
132–133
Pius XI, Pope, 35, 41, 110, 134, 253,
269
Vatican finances under, 174–175,
196
Pius XII, Pope, 10, 13, 18, 34, 88
death of, 24–27, 35, 38, 60–61,
63, 67, 137
entourage of, 138–140, 280
Galeazzi Lisi as personal
physician to, 22–27, 137, 250
Mother Pasqualina as aide to,
13, 22, 24, 54, 61, 113, 127,
130–138, 143, 144, 159,
163–164, 215, 281
personality of, 19–24, 31, 41,
116, 163–164
pontificate of, 27, 28, 76, 79, 118,
151, 215, 248, 270, 274–277
proposed beatification of, 85,
131, 132, 133
Vatican finances under, 163–164,
181, 182–183, 185

Poland, as important to John Paul
    II, 152, 245–246, 267–268
Poletti, Ugo Cardinal, 109
Polyglot Vatican Printing Press, 84
pomicione, 284
Pontifical Bible Institute, 213
Pontifical Gregorian University, 213,
    240
Pontifical North American College,
    138
Pontifical Oriental Institute, 213,
    229
Pontifical University of St. Thomas
    Aquinas, 213, 262
pope, 1–3, 15–48
    as bishop of Rome, 55, 97
    canon law and, 17, 32, 46–47
    coronation of, 33–34, 40
    demythologizing of, 19–27, 42, 45
    election of, 15, 16, 52, 70, 72–81
    entourage of, 127–159
    infallibility of, 17, 21, 31, 136,
        227
    resignation of, 31–32
    Roman Curia vs., 82–83, 93–94, 95
    spiritual vs. temporal power of,
        15–19, 33, 46, 99, 172, 227
    see also specific popes
"Popemobile," 286
"positions," 12
presentismo, 296
press coverage, of Vatican, 243, 244,
    245, 248, 254–262
Press Room of the Holy See, 255,
    260–261
"professed" Jesuits, 219
"promoter of the cause," 132
Promotion of Christian Unity,
    Secretariat for the, 216
pro-nuncios, 103
Properties of the Holy See,
    Administration of the, 175–176
"protectors," of religious orders, 70
P.2 Masonic brethren, 198
Public Affairs of the Church,
    Council for, 109–110
Pucci, Emilio, 256–257
Puzyna, Jan Cardinal, 59

"Queen of Heaven" jail, 28

Rahner, Karl, 224, 225, 263
Rampolla del Tindaro, Mariano
    Cardinal, 59, 78
Ratti, Franco, 196

Ratzinger, Joseph Cardinal, 79, 91
Re, Giovanni Battista, 120
Red Brigades, 47
Relations with the Personnel of the
    Holy See, Office for the, 289
Religious and Secular Institutes,
    Sacred Congregation for, 236
Religious Relations with Judaism,
    Commission for, 93
"Rerum Novarum" encyclical, 287, 289
Reverend Fabric of St. Peter's, 178
Ribeiro, Antonio Cardinal, 229–230
Rijk, Cornelius, 1
rites controversy, 211
Roche, John, 236
"Romanum decet Pontificem," 129
Rome, Nazi occupation of, 252–253,
    258, 281–282
Roncalli, Angelo Cardinal, *see* John
    XXIII, Pope
Roosevelt, Franklin D., 111
Roothaan, Johannes Philipp, 228–229
Rossi, Agnelo Cardinal, 63
Roust, Kaspar, 279
Rubin, Wladyslaw, 155
Rudolph, Johann, 283
Russian Orthodox Church, 58
Ryan, Thomas, 28

Sacchetti, Marquess Giulio, 274, 276
Sacerdotal Society of the Holy Cross,
    see Opus Dei
Sacraments and Divine Worship,
    Sacred Congregation of, 84
Sacred Rota, 86
St. Peter in Shackles church, 164
Saints John and Paul church, 54–55
Samoré, Antonio Cardinal, 21
Santoni, Mimi, 64
Sarto, Giuseppe, *see* Pius X, Pope
    Saint
Scarlet and the Black, The, 252
Scattolini, Virgilio, 257–258
Schillebeeckx, Edward, 91
Scriptures, interpretation of, 263
Secret Archives, 104
Secretariat of State, 108–126
    Benelli as chief of staff in,
        116–120, 121, 122, 147, 148,
        166, 202, 219, 232
    Casaroli as head of, 29, 105,
        121–126, 178–179, 223, 251
    duties of Secretary in, 85, 98,
        108, 116–126, 250, 253
    operation of, 86, 91, 92, 108–126

Villot as head of, 114–116, 117, 120, 121
Secret Documents of the Vatican Diplomacy (Scattolini), 258
secular institutes, 235–236
sedia gestatoria, 34
Seper, Franjo Cardinal, 70, 91
Sermons of a Parisian Pastor, The (Lustiger), 156
Servants of the Sacred Heart, 153
Sforza, Giovanni, 13
Sheen, Fulton J., 50
simony, 160
Sindona, Michele, 145, 165
    financial dealings of, 188, 190–194, 196, 198
Siri, Giuseppe Cardinal, 29, 78, 164
Sixtus II, Pope, 162
Slipyj, Josyf Cardinal, 57–58
Social Communications, Pontifical Commission for, 260–261
Società Generale Immobiliare, 176, 187, 190, 191
Society of Jesus, *see* Jesuits
Solidarity labor movement, 153, 286, 292
Somalo, Eduardo Martinez, 268
Spada, Massimo, 189, 195
Special Administration of the Holy See, 174–175, 185
Spellman, Francis Cardinal, 22, 175, 256
    influence of, 50, 57, 66, 67, 68, 137, 138
spies, in Vatican, 244–254
Spiritual Considerations (Escrivá), 233
Stavisky, Serge Alexandre, 190
Stern, 251
Stickler, Alfons, 267
Stoppa, Mario, 288
Stritch, Samuel Cardinal, 63
Sursock, Isabella, 275–276
Svidercoschi, Gianfranco, 268
Swiss Guard, 10, 53
    organization of, 278–286, 293
Szoka, Edmund C., 156

Tardini, Domenico Cardinal, as secretary of state, 25, 110–114, 141
Tatò, Antonio, 136
Teaching Sisters of the Holy Cross, 131
Tedeschini, Federico Cardinal, 21
Teilhard de Chardin, Pierre, 91, 212

telephones, bugging of, 253–254, 285
Tempo, Il, 124–25, 268
Tempo magazine, 151
Teodolina, Sister, 130
Teresa of Calcutta, Mother, 14, 98, 184
Third World, Catholic congregations in, 54, 72, 84–85, 101, 103, 170, 200, 217, 295
Thomas à Kempis, 37
Thomism, 262–263
"Thomist Therapy for Modern Problems from Leo XIII to Paul VI" (Parente), 262
tiara (triple crown), 33, 34, 40
Times (London), 236
Tisserant, Eugène Cardinal, as dean of cardinals, 60–61, 68, 73, 137, 138
titular churches, 54–55, 90, 96, 97
Tomko, Joseph, 155
Tondini, Amleto, 189
Torlonia family, 276
Tucci, Roberto, 203, 270, 285, 286

Ulric, Saint, 132
Union of Christians, Secretariat for, 92
United Nations, Vatican observer at, 85, 103–104, 105
United Nations Educational, Scientific, and Cultural Organization (UNESCO), 282–283

Vagnozzi, Egidio Cardinal, 166, 167, 177–178
Valerian, emperor of Rome, 162
Vallainc, Fausto, 261
Vatican I (1869–70), 17, 21
Vatican II (1962–65):
    curia reforms by, 90, 92–93, 95, 96, 98, 99, 296
    as liberal influence, 16, 17, 29, 46, 139, 227, 232, 235, 294
Vatican Bank, 180–186
    in Banco Ambrosiano scandal, 196, 197, 198–199, 201, 202, 203–204, 205, 206
    "letters of comfort" by, 198–199, 201, 203–204, 205
    Marcinkus as head of, 188–189, 194, 206
    operation of, 163, 166, 169, 177, 178, 179, 180–186, 205, 206–207

Vatican Bank (*cont.*)
  in Sindona affair, 190, 192,
    193–194, 195, 206
Vatican City, 3–8
  administration of, 3–8, 102, 185,
    282–283
  diplomatic relations of, 12, 52,
    106–107, 245, 254, 296
  finances of, 80–81, 160–207, 244,
    296
  labor unions in, 286–293
"Vatican Finances, The" (Caprio),
  161
Vaticanisti, 255–256, 257, 261
Vatican observatory, 213–214
Vaticanology, 243–270
  covert activities and, 244–254
  definition of, 245, 254, 255
  at *L'Osservatore Romano,* 262–270
  in news reporting, 243, 244, 245,
    248, 254–262
Vatican Radio:
  news coverage by, 24–25, 80,
    261, 268–269
  operation of, 214, 269–270, 296
Venice, Republic of, Vatican
  relations with, 249
Victor Emmanuel III, king of Italy,
  138–139

Vienna, Congress of (1814–15), 103
Vigilance Office, 254, 280, 283, 285
Villa Abamelek, 253
Villa Agnese, 124
Villa Cavalletti, 225–226
Villot, Jean Cardinal, as secretary of
  state, 114–116, 117, 120, 121
Voce di San Marco, La, 141
Volpini, Valerio, 266, 267

Wagner, Robert F., Jr., 107
Walesa, Lech, 267, 292
Weigel, Gustave, 216
Willebrands, Johannes Cardinal,
  93
Wilson, Helen Dolan, 64
Wilson, William, 107
Wojtyla, Karol Cardinal, *see* John
  Paul II, Pope
Works of Religion, Institute for, *see*
  Vatican Bank
Wyszynski, Stefan Cardinal, 68,
  249

Xavier, Saint Francis, 211, 225

Zacchi, Cesare, 103
Zanchini, Nicola, 265